# Test Bank

## For Kalat's

# BIOLOGICAL PSYCHOLOGY

## SEVENTH EDITION

# Test Bank

## For Kalat's

# BIOLOGICAL PSYCHOLOGY

## SEVENTH EDITION

**Maria Lavooy**
*University of Central Florida, Brevard Campus*

**James W. Kalat**
*North Carolina State University*

**WADSWORTH**
TM
**THOMSON LEARNING**

Australia • Canada • Mexico • Singapore • Spain • United Kingdom • United States

# Preface

To the Instructor:  The following test bank contains items for each of the textbook's fifteen chapters.  In addition to many new items, a number of items come the sixth edition test bank authored by Dr. Teri Rust. Some of the items have been retained from the previous test bank in original form, while others have been modified.  Additionally, there is a final set of questions, prepared by James Kalat, which may be used as a comprehensive final exam.

The order of the test items follows the text chapters, page by page.  This is for your convenience.  You may want to consider randomizing the order of the items so as not to provide clues to the students.  Often, there are a number of items provided, which measure the same material. Including these on the same test would reduce the variety of information covered and provide obvious clues to students for answering other questions.  There are over 3,000 questions in this test bank, an average of 185 per chapter.  Our goal was to supply you with enough multiple-choice test questions of varied focus and difficulty to allow you to tailor tests, or even quizzes, to meet the specific needs of your students and your class.

You will find an "answer-key" line at the end of each question.  It provides the correct answer, a page reference where the answer can be found, and notation indicating whether the item tests knowledge at a factual or conceptual level. The answers to the factual questions can be found directly in the text and require the student to *remember* information.  The conceptual items require the student to *understand* relationships and make connections between concepts not specifically connected for them in the text.

Ten items in each chapter have a notation preceding the correct answer in the answer-key line. The "WWW" notation indicates that this item has been placed at a study site on the Internet for students.  When choosing questions for your test, please keep in mind that these items will be made available to students who may wish to access them.

A final set of items is included that may be used as a Comprehensive Final Exam.  Many items in that set require students to combine information from more than one chapter. The others at least have distracters that come from more than one chapter.  A few items come from just one chapter but reflect critical information worth retesting on a final exam. Chapter and page references, again, have been provided for your convenience.  Of course, a final exam need not be limited to these items but we hope you find many of them useful.

Any suggestion for improvement, or feedback on any kind, is most welcome.

Maria J. Lavooy, Ph.D.
Psychology Department
University of Central Florida
Cocoa, FL  32922
mlavooy@pegasus.cc.ucf.edu

## About the Author

Maria J. Lavooy has been a full-time psychology instructor since 1986, and has been with the University of Central Florida since 1995. She earned an undergraduate degree in Biology, and a Masters and Ph.D. in Psychology from Miami University, Oxford, Ohio.

## Acknowledgements

To James Kalat for offering me the opportunity to work with such a knowledgeable and accomplished biopsychologist.

To Jennifer Wilkinson, Wadsworth Publishing Company, for offering editorial support.

To my colleague, Michael, for offering advice and moral support.

And, finally, to my husband, Robert, and sons, Ross, Vince and Kees, for offering their patience and understanding over the many months spent on this project.

# Table of Contents

## Test Items

# Test Bank

## For Kalat's

# BIOLOGICAL PSYCHOLOGY

## SEVENTH EDITION

**Module 1.1:  The Mind-Brain Relationship**

1.    Biological psychology is defined as the study of:

      A. brain functions.
      B. brain damage and recovery.
      C. the physiological, evolutionary, and developmental mechanisms
         of the brain.
      D. the physiological, evolutionary, and developmental mechanisms
         of behavior and experience.
      ("WWW" D, p. 2, factual)

**Biological Explanations of Behavior**

2.    A researcher is interested in describing a behavior by studying
      how the brain functions.  This explanation is classified as:

      A. ontogenetic.
      B. evolutionary.
      C. physiological.
      D. functional.
      (C, p. 3, factual)

3.    Which type of explanation describes how a structure or behavior
      develops?

      A. physiological
      B. ontogenetic
      C. evolutionary
      D. functional
      (B, p. 3 factual)

4.    In Tinbergen's (1951) terminology, which type of explanation
      describes a behavior in terms of the internal and external
      factors affecting its development?

      A. physiological
      B. ontogenetic
      C. evolutionary
      D. functional
      (B, p. 3, conceptual)

5.    Which type of explanation describes the advantages provided by a
      particular structure or behavior?

      A. physiological
      B. ontogenetic
      C. evolutionary
      D. functional
      (D, p. 4, factual)

6.  Which type of explanation would describe eating in terms of the hypothalamus affecting insulin production which affects the availability of glucose in cells?

    A. physiological
    B. ontogenetic
    C. evolutionary
    D. functional
    (A, p. 3, conceptual)

7.  Which type of explanation might describe the presence of a behavior in a particular species by showing how that behavior increased the reproductive success of the species?

    A. physiological
    B. ontogenetic
    C. evolutionary
    D. mating behavior
    (C, p. 3, factual)

8.  In most bird species, only the male sings and then only in his territory during the reproductive season. This is to attract females and to ward off other males, which serves to improve their chances of mating. This behavior demonstrates:

    A. that physiological explanations are preferred over other kinds of explanations.
    B. learning during a critical period.
    C. that physiological, ontogenetic, evolutionary, and functional explanations are mutually exclusive.
    D. how physiological, ontogenetic, evolutionary, and functional explanations can all be used to explain the same behavior.
    (D, p. 4, conceptual)

9.  In certain species of songbirds, development of the song requires the opportunity to hear the appropriate song during a sensitive period in life as well as the genes to prepare them to learn the song.  This is a/an _____ explanation of birdsong.

    A. physiological
    B. ontogenetic
    C. evolutionary
    D. functional
    ("WWW" B, p. 4, factual)

10. What most directly controls the size of the brain area that is responsible for singing in a songbird?

    A. the amount of protein in the diet
    B. hormone levels
    C. the bird's previous opportunity to practice singing
    D. the population density of the species
    (B, p. 4, conceptual)

11.  Which of the following would be a physiological explanation for
     why birds sing?

     A. Testosterone causes the growth of certain brain areas which
        control singing in certain birds.
     B. Birds sing due to instinct.
     B. Birds sing because they hear their song early in life and form
        a template which controls later singing.
     D. Birds sing to defend territories and attract mates.
     (A, p. 4, factual)

12.  Which of the following would be a functional explanation for why
     birds sing?

     A. Testosterone causes the growth of certain brain areas which
        control singing in certain birds.
     B. Birds sing due to instinct.
     B. Birds sing because they hear their song early in life and form
        a template which controls later singing.
     D. Birds sing to defend territories and attract mates.
     (D, p. 4, factual)

13.  Which type of explanation would describe the hibernation of
     squirrels in terms of conserving energy when the environment is
     hostile to survival?

     A. physiological
     B. ontogenetic
     C. evolutionary
     D. functional
     (D, p. 4, conceptual)

14.  An adult male sparrow sings its normal song:

     A. if he hears the song during a sensitive period early in his
        life.
     B. if he hears and practices the song during a sensitive period
        early in his life.
     C. if his own species' song is the first song he hears when
        young.
     D. regardless of whether or not he has ever heard his species'
        song from another bird.
     (A, p. 4, factual)

**The Brain and Conscious Experience**

15.  Dualism is the belief that:

     A. mind and body are one and the same.
     B. mind and body exist independently and do not interact.
     C. mind and body are different in substance, but interact.
     D. the mind does not exist.
     (C, p. 5, factual)

16.    A monist believed that mind and body were:

    A. the same thing.
    B. separate but overlapping.
    C. separate but interacted.
    D. two distinct entities, with no connection whatsoever.
    (A, p. 5, factual)

17.    The belief that everything that exists is physical is:

    A. dualism.
    B. materialism.
    C. mentalism.
    D. Descartism.
    (B, p. 5, factual)

18.    The reason nearly all neuroscientists reject dualism is that:

    A. it conflicts with the law of conservation of matter and
       energy.
    B. the mind and brain interact, but not in the ways that interest
       neuroscientists.
    C. the mind exists only in our imagination.
    D. no research supports this notion.
    (A, p. 5, factual)

19.    Professor A. suggests that the fright you experience when
     confronted by a burglar is the same thing as the pattern of
     activity in your brain at that time.  What form of monism is
     this?

    A. mentality
    B. mentalism
    C. identify position
    D. law of conservation
    (C, p. 6, conceptual)

20.    Your instructor asks you to support your belief in monism.  Which
     of the following could be used to support this belief:

    A. Scientists have shown that brain activity is directly related
       to what the mind thinks.
    B. Scientists have shown that the mind and brain do not exist
       independently.
    C. Stimulation of brain areas provoke changes in behavior and
       experience.
    D. Humans experience consciousness.
    ("WWW" c, p. 6, conceptual)

21.    Solipsism is the position that:

       A. people experience consciousness.
       B. it is difficult to know whether other people have conscious
          experiences.
       C. I alone have consciousness.
       D. neither dualism nor monism is correct.
       (C, p. 6, factual)

**Module 1.2:  Nature and Nurture**

**The Genetics of Behavior**

22.    Units of heredity that maintain their structural identity from
       one generation to another are:

       A. enzymes.
       B. mutations.
       C. nucleic acids.
       D. genes.
       ("WWW" D, p. 9, factual)

23.    A person with two recessive genes is considered to be _____ for
       that trait.

       A. homozygous
       B. heterozygous
       C. unitary
       D. marginal
       (A, p. 9, conceptual)

24.    Chromosomes consist of large, double-stranded molecules of:

       A. deoxyribonucleic acid.
       B. ribonucleic acid.
       C. autosomal genes.
       D. recombination genes.
       (A, p. 9, factual)

25.    What are chromosomes composed of?

       A. DNA
       B. RNA
       C. proteins
       D. carbohydrates
       (A, p. 9, factual)

26.    Chemically, what is the route from genes to their expression?

       A. DNA to proteins to RNA
       B. DNA to RNA to proteins
       C. proteins to DNA to RNA
       D. RNA to DNA to proteins
       (B, p. 9, factual)

27.   What is RNA?

      A. It is an exact copy of DNA.
      B. It is a complementary copy of one strand of a DNA molecule.
      C. It is an up-graded version of DNA.
      D. It is based on a DNA strand, but contains totally different
         Bases.
      (B, p. 9, factual)

28.   Recessive genes manifest their effects only when the individual
      is_____ for them.

      A. sex limited
      B. homosapien
      C. homozygous
      D. heterozygous
      (C, p. 9, factual)

29.   Suppose "A" is a dominant gene and "a" is a recessive gene.  One
      parent has genes Aa and the other parent has genes aa.  What
      genes will the children probably have?

      A. All will be AA.
      B. All will be aa.
      C. Three-fourths will be Aa, one-fourth aa.
      D. Half will be Aa, half aa.
      (D, p. 9, conceptual)

30.   Suppose "A" is a dominant gene for the ability to curl the tongue
      lengthwise, and "a" is a recessive gene for inability to do so.
      Which of the following couples can be certain that all their
      children will be able to curl their tongue lengthwise?

      A. father aa, mother AA
      B. father Aa, mother Aa
      C. father aa, mother aa
      D. father Aa, mother aa
      (A, p. 9, application)

31.   Suppose "A" is a dominant gene for the ability to taste
      phenylthiocarbamide and "a" is a recessive gene for inability to
      taste it.  Which of the following couples could possibly have
      both a child who tastes it and a child who does not?

      A. father AA, mother aa
      B. father Aa, mother AA
      C. father Aa, mother Aa
      D. father AA, mother AA
      (C, p. 9, application)

32. Suppose both the father and the mother are "heterozygous" for the gene that controls ability to curl the tongue lengthwise, and this gene is dominant.  What can we predict about their children?

    A. All will be heterozygous for the ability to curl.
    B. All will be homozygous for the ability to curl.
    C. All will be homozygous for the ability to curl.
    D. They may be homozygous or heterozygous for ability to curl, or homozygous for inability.
    (D, p. 9, conceptual)

33. In one family, all three children are homozygous for a recessive gene.  What can be concluded about the parents?

    A. Each parent is also homozygous for the recessive gene.
    B. Each parent is heterozygous.
    C. One parent is homozygous for the dominant gene; the other is homozygous for the recessive gene.
    D. Each parent is either homozygous for the recessive gene or heterozygous.
    (D, p. 9, conceptual)

34. A trait not expressed when combined with a dominant trait is called a/an _____ trait:

    A. nurture
    B. recessive
    C. dominant
    D. homozygous
    (B, p. 9, factual)

35. Almost all humans have 23 pairs of which of the following?

    A. RNA
    B. chromosomes
    C. genes
    D. corduroys
    (B, p. 9, factual)

36. Each of two parents has brown eyes, with recessive genes for blue eyes.  What percentage of their children will have blue eyes?

    A. All their children will have blue eyes.
    B. Half of their children will have blue eyes.
    C. None of their children will have blue eyes.
    D. Only 25% of their children will have blue eyes.
    ("WWW" D, p. 9, conceptual)

37.    A chromosome has a BC combination and the other chromosome
       has a bc combination.  If crossing over between the B locus and
       the C locus occurs, this will result in:

       A. no change.
       B. new chromosomes with the combination Bc and bC.
       C. new chromosomes with the combination Bb and Cc.
       D. a mutation which will likely lead to death.
       (B, pp. 9-10, conceptual)

38.    What is an autosomal gene?

       A. a gene on the X chromosome
       B. a gene on the Y chromosome
       C. a gene on any chromosome other than the X or Y chromosome
       D. a gene that shows no evidence of crossing over
       (C, p. 10, factual)

39.    Which of the following pairs of sex chromosomes would be found in
       a normal male mammal?

       A. XX
       B. XY
       C. YY
       D. YZ
       (B, p. 10, factual)

40.    A baby's chromosomal makeup indicates one pair as XX.  What is
       the gender of this baby?

       A. a male
       B. a female
       C. only a geneticist could determine the gender
       D. a female with a genetic disease
       ("WWW" B, p. 10, factual)

41.    In humans, which chromosome(s) contain(s) *few* genes?

       A. All human chromosomes contains few genes.
       B. Both the X and Y chromosomes contains few genes.
       C. The X chromosome contains few genes.
       D. The Y chromosome contains few genes.
       (D, p. 10, factual)

42.    In general, when biologists speak of sex-linked genes to what are
       they are referring?

       A. genes on autosomal chromosomes
       B. genes on more than one chromosome
       C. genes on the X chromosome
       D. genes on the Y chromosome
       (C, p. 10, factual)

43.   If a characteristic is controlled by an X-linked recessive gene,
      it produces its apparent effects:

      A. more often in males.
      B. more often in females.
      C. only in childhood.
      D. only after puberty.
      (A, p. 10, conceptual)

44.   An example of a sex-linked trait is:

      A. eye color.
      B. color blindness.
      C. temperament.
      D. intelligence.
      (B, p. 10, factual)

45.   Color-blindness is more common in males than in females because
      it is controlled by

      A. a sex-limited gene.
      B. a Y-linked gene.
      C. a dominant X-linked gene.
      D. a recessive X-linked gene.
      (D, p. 10, factual)

46.   If a recessive gene is on an autosomal chromosome, its effects
      will be found:

      A. equally often in males and females.
      B. more often in males.
      C. more often in females.
      D. only in the presence of certain other genes.
      (A, p. 10, conceptual)

47.   Sex-limited genes are found on:

      A. X chromosomes only.
      B. Y chromosomes only.
      C. X **AND** Y chromosomes.
      D. any chromosomes.
      (D, p. 10, factual)

48.   A gene is found that controls the age at which a man grows bald,
      if at all. That gene seldom affects women, even if they have the
      gene.  What kind of gene is this MOST likely to be?

      A. an X-linked gene
      B. a sex-limited gene
      C. a sex-linked dominant gene
      D. a sex-linked recessive gene
      (B, p. 10, conceptual)

49.    Suppose a genetically controlled characteristic is found in many
       men and almost never in women.  What would it mean to say that
       this is a sex-limited gene?

       A. It is an X-linked dominant gene.
       B. It is an X-linked recessive gene.
       C. It is a Y-linked recessive gene.
       D. Women can be homozygous for the gene and still show no effect.
       (D, p. 10, conceptual)

50.    Under what conditions are the effects of sex-limited genes
       demonstrated?

       A. when they are dominant
       B. when they are homozygous
       C. when particular hormones are present
       D. when they appear on the X chromosome
       (C, p. 10, conceptual)

51.    John's parents are both average in height and have dark skin.
       John, however, is very tall and light skinned.  This probably
       happened as a result of:

       A. recombination
       B. dominance
       C. crossing over
       D. heritability
       (A, p. 11, conceptual)

52.    The fact that three sisters in the same family have different
       appearances, personalities, and abilities from each other and
       from their parents is due primarily to which of the following?

       A. recombination of genes
       B. mutation of genes
       C. one parent contributing more than one copy of each chromosome
       D. sex-limited recessive genes
       (A, p. 11, conceptual)

53.    Which of the following is TRUE regarding mutations?

       A. Mutated genes tend to be dominant.
       B. Mutations are random events.
       C. Ten to twenty percent of anyone's genes are mutations.
       D. Mutations most often result in beneficial changes.
       ("WWW" B, p. 11, factual)

54.    Mutations:

       A. are a common occurrence in most single genes.
       B. are guided by the needs of the organism in its environment.
       C. are almost always beneficial to the organism.
       D. are changes in single genes.
       (D, p. 11, factual)

55.    Most mutations:

       A. produce dominant genes.
       B. produce recessive genes.
       C. produce sex-linked genes.
       D. produce sex-limited genes.
       (B, pg. 11, factual)

56.    What is measured by the mathematical construct of heritability?

       A. which is more important, heredity or environment, for a given
          species
       B. which is more important, heredity or environment, for a given
          behavior
       C. how differences among individuals are related to differences
          in heredity
       D. the overall importance of one's heredity versus environment
       (C, p.11, conceptual)

57.    A heritability of 1 (one) indicates that differences in heredity
       are responsible for what percent of the observed variations in
       some characteristic?

       A. 0
       B. 1
       C. 50
       D. 100
       (D, p. 11, factual)

58.    For a given trait, a stronger resemblance between monozygotic
       twins, as compared to dizygotic twins suggests that:

       A. heritability is low.
       B. heritability is high.
       C. heritability cannot be determined.
       D. the environment is more important than genetics.
       (B, p. 11, factual)

59.    If a group of individuals shares a highly similar environment,
       what effect does this have on the heritability estimate of a
       characteristic?

       A. Heritability will be low.
       B. Heritability will be high.
       C. Heritability estimates will be unaffected.
       D. It is determined by the power of the environmental factors.
       (B, p. 11, conceptual)

60.   For a group of individuals, the heritability score for a
      particular trait = .5.  What can be said about the heredity of
      this trait:

      A. Hereditary differences account for all of the observed
         differences for this group of individuals.
      B. Hereditary differences account for none of the observed
         differences for this group of individuals.
      C. Hereditary differences account for some of the observed
         differences for this group of individuals.
      D. The differences found within this group are mostly due to
         differences in the environment.
      (C, p. 11, factual)

61.   If monozygotic twins reared in distinctly different environments
      resemble each other on some characteristic, then this suggests
      that this characteristic is related to which of the following?

      A. heredity only
      B. heredity more than environment
      C. environment more than heredity
      D. environment only
      (B, p. 11, conceptual)

62.   What is the relationship between heritability estimates and
      environmental factors?

      A. High environmental consistency raises heritability estimates.
      B. High environmental consistency lowers heritability estimates.
      C. Environments have no effect on heritability estimates.
      D. The effects of the environment on heritability estimates are
         unpredictable.
      (A, p. 11, conceptual)

63.   If a trait has high heritability:

      A. hereditary differences account for none of the observed
         variations in that characteristic within that population.
      B. the environment cannot influence that trait.
      C. it is still possible for the environment to influence that
         trait.
      D. the trait is not influenced by heredity.
      (C, p. 11, conceptual)

64.   Heritability estimates for one population:

      A. can be generalized to many others.
      B. can be generalized across cultures but not over time.
      C. can be generalized across time but not across cultures.
      D. should not be generalized to other populations.
      (D, p. 11, conceptual)

65.    Who is at greatest risk for mental retardation due to PKU?

       A. people of African ancestry
       B. people of Asian or European ancestry
       C. people who live in cold climates
       D. people who live in tropical climates
       (B, p. 12, factual)

66.    Why do children with PKU become mentally retarded?

       A. Unmetabolized amino acids accumulate and affect the brain.
       B. Essential axons lack myelin sheaths.
       C. Dendrites and synapses fail to form in associative areas of
          the cortex.
       D. Their immune systems do not fight off brain infections.
       (A, p. 12, factual)

67.    Individuals afflicted with PKU need to avoid:

       A. foods high in phenylalanine.
       B. foods high in vitamin K.
       C. alcohol.
       D. sunlight.
       (A, p. 12, factual)

68.    When do concerns exist about the detrimental effects of PKU in a
       male?

       A. during any time when he may father a child
       B. until he is about 5 years old
       C. until brain development is essentially complete
       D. throughout his life
       (C, p. 12, conceptual)

69.    When do concerns exist about the detrimental effects of PKU in a
       female?

       A. throughout her life
       B. throughout her child-bearing years
       C. until she is about 5 years old
       D. until brain development is essentially complete as well as
          during pregnancy and nursing
       (D, p. 12, conceptual)

70.    What is TRUE about the mental abilities of a newborn baby with
       PKU?

       A. It is already, irreversibly mentally retarded.
       B. It is not mentally retarded, but inevitably will become
          mentally retarded.
       C. It can avoid becoming mentally retarded by special education.
       D. It can avoid becoming mentally retarded by following a strict
          diet.
       (D, p. 12, factual)

71.   How is it possible to prevent the mental retardation that is
      generally associated with PKU?

      A. through exercise
      B. through diet
      C. through drugs
      D. through exposure to bright light
      (B, p. 12, factual)

72.   Which of the following is an example of a genetically controlled
      condition that can be minimized by following a particular diet?

      A. Down syndrome
      B. color-blindness
      C. epilepsy
      D. phenylketonuria (PKU)
      (D, p. 12, factual)

73.   Someone claims that if genes control a condition, it can be
      controlled only by drugs or surgery, but not by changes in the
      environment. Which of the following is the strongest example to
      CONTRADICT that claim?

      A. color-blindness
      B. eye color
      C. phenylketonuria (PKU)
      D. Down syndrome
      (C, p. 12, conceptual)

74.   Which of the following sweeteners would be most detrimental to a
      child with PKU?

      A. sugar
      B. saccharin
      C. NutraSweet
      D. honey
      (C, p. 12, factual)

75.   A person on a diet for PKU should be most cautious of food
      packages that advertise which of the following?

      A. "low fat"
      B. "high fiber"
      C. "diet"
      D. "no artificial ingredients"
      (C, p. 12, application)

76.   For children with PKU on an ordinary diet, the heritability of
      PKU would be virtually:

      A. 0
      B. .5
      C. 1.0
      D. impossible to calculate
      (C, p. 12, factual)

77.    To say that there is a "gene for blue eyes":

       A. means that a gene directly produces blue eyes.
       B. suggests dominance, since you only need one gene to express
          the trait.
       C. is an oversimplification of a complex environmental process.
       D. means that a gene indirectly produces blue eyes through a
          complex process of protein synthesis and environmental input.
       (D, p. 12, conceptual)

78.    Which of the following best characterizes the effects that genes
       have on behavior?  The effects of genes on behavior are:

       A. direct.
       B. nonexistent.
       C. impossible to measure.
       D. indirect and interactive with the environment.
       (D, p. 13, conceptual)

**The Evolution of Behavior**

79.    For natural selection to generate evolutionary change in a
       population:

       A. there need not be any differences in the traits of individuals
          in that population.
       B. the change in gene frequencies must help the species in the
          long run.
       C. the differences must have a hereditary basis.
       D. the change in gene frequencies will probably be harmful to the
          species.
       ("WWW" C, p. 13, conceptual)

80.    Which of the following is necessarily included in the concept of
       evolution?

       A. species improvements from one generation to the next
       B. "If you don't use it, you lose it."
       C. generationally changing frequencies of various genes in the
          population
       D. improvements to the individual
       (C, p. 13, conceptual)

81.    Which of the following best describes the concept of evolution?

       A. "Survival of the fittest"
       B. "Reproduction of the fittest"
       C. "If you don't use it, you lose it."
       D. "Always look for ways to improve."
       (B, p. 13, conceptual)

82.   Which of the following is TRUE with respect to evolution?

A. "If you don't use it, you lose it."
B. Evolutionary success is assessed by the number of one's offspring surviving to reproduce.
C. Evolution benefits the species, in the long run.
D. Evolution benefits the individual.
(b, p. 13, conceptual)

83.   What is it called when some animals are selectively bred because they possess some desirable characteristic?

A. evolution
B. natural selection
C. artificial selection
D. artificial insemination
(C, p. 13, factual)

84.   When a dog is bred for a particular trait, this is called:

A. artificial selection.
B. evolution.
C. natural selection.
D. group selection.
(A, p. 13, factual)

85.   A dog is bred for its uncommon coat color through a process called:

A. natural selection.
B. evolution.
C. group selection.
D. artificial selection.
(D, p. 13, conceptual)

86.   Which of the following represents Lamarckian evolution?

A. "survival of the fittest"
B. "reproduction of the fittest"
C. "If you don't use it, you lose it"
D. "look out for #1"
(C, p. 14, conceptual)

87.   What "evidence" could you present to support the argument that humans have NOT stopped evolving?

A. Medicine and technology are keeping more people alive these days.
B. More mutations will occur because of increased use of pesticides.
C. Evolution is based on reproduction rates so as long as some people have more children than others do, their genes will spread.
D. Humans are no longer subject to "survival of the fittest."
(C, p. 15, conceptual)

88.   Evolution improves the *fitness* of the population, which is
      defined as:

      A. the number of copies of one's genes that endure in later
         generations.
      B. survival of the individual.
      C. how many children you have.
      D. how large your extended family is.
      (A, p. 15, factual)

89.   Who does altruistic behavior benefit?

      A. It benefits someone other than the individual doing the
         behavior.
      B. It indirectly benefits the individual doing the behavior.
      C. It benefits both the "doer" and the receiver.
      D. It benefits the receiver and is detrimental to the "doer."
      (A, pp. 15-16, factual)

90.   What is TRUE about altruistic behavior?

      A. It is evident in every animal species.
      B. It can be completely explained in terms of genetic
         contributions.
      C. It is difficult to explain from an evolutionary/genetic point
         of view.
      D. It has a genetic component only in humans.
      (C, p. 16, conceptual)

91.   Which of the following explanations for a genetic basis for
      altruism is most favored by the text?

      A. Altruism benefits the species.
      B. kin selection
      C. group selection
      D. Altruism involves little individual cost.
      (B, p. 16, conceptual)

92.   Why is a genetic explanation for altruism problematic?

      A. Only non-human animals exhibit altruistic behaviors.
      B. Altruistic behaviors rarely benefit the individual performing
         them.
      C. Altruistic behaviors can't benefit the individual performing
         them, so true altruism does not exist.
      D. No behavior has been linked to any genes.
      (B, p. 16, conceptual)

93.    When organisms help those they recognize as capable of returning
       the favor, this is termed:

       A. kin selection.
       B. group selection.
       C. reciprocal altruism.
       D. Sociobiology.
       (C, p. 16, factual)

94.    What explanation would sociobiologists give for the tendency for
       men to be more promiscuous than women?

       A. Men have a lower level of moral development.
       B. A dominant gene on the Y axis is responsible.
       C. It is simply a culturally learned behavior.
       D. This is an efficient method for men to spread their genes.
       (D, p. 17, conceptual)

**Module 1.3:   The Use of Animals in Research**

**Reasons for Animal Research**

95.    Which of the following is NOT a reason that biological
       psychologists study animals?

       A. Animal's brains and behavior are often similar to humans.
       B. Animals are often easier to study than humans.
       C. Biological psychologists are interested in the animals
          themselves.
       D. One does not have to consider ethical issues with animals.
       (D, p. 19, conceptual)

**The Ethical Debate**

96.    Minimalists believe that:

       A. some animals should be used for all types of research.
       B. some animal research is acceptable, but not all.
       C. no animal research should be conducted.
       D. we learn from animal research, but what is learned is not
          important enough.
       (B, p. 21, factual)

97.    Which of the following is NOT an argument a true abolitionist
       would use against animal research?

       A. Animal research is beneficial.
       B. Animals cannot give informed consent to participate.
       C. Animals have the same rights as humans.
       D. Killing animals for scientific gain is murder.
       (A, p. 21, conceptual)

98.   Which statement about most psychological experiments using
      nonhuman animals is correct?

      A. Animals are given intense, repeated, inescapable shocks in
         many experiments.
      B. Extreme pain and stress are inflicted in attempts to drive
         the animals insane.
      C. The research leads to no useful discoveries.
      D. The research is regulated by animal care committees.
      ("WWW" D, p. 22, conceptual)

99.   What is the function of an Institutional Animal Care and Use
      Committee?

      A. to evaluate veterinarians who provide care to laboratory
         animals
      B. to determine whether research is merely for the benefit of
         humans
      C. to evaluate proposed experiments to ensure that they minimize
         pain and discomfort
      D. to provide food and water for lab animals, and keep cages
         clean
      (C, p. 22, factual)

100.  How do most biological psychologists feel regarding the use of
      animals in research?

      A. They believe that any animal has the same rights as any human.
      B. They will avoid using painful procedures, unless they will
         directly benefit the animal.
      C. They are working to replace all animal experimentation with
         computer simulations.
      D. They use animals only if the potential benefits to humans
         outweigh the costs to the animals.
      (D, p. 22, conceptual)

**Module 1.4: Prospects for Further Study**

101.  A researcher is interested in how the nervous system responds
      when the organism is in a certain emotional situation.  This
      researcher might be identified as a/an:

      A. neuroscientist
      B. neurosurgeon
      C. sociobiologist
      D. comparative psychologist
      (A, p. 24, conceptual)

102.   Someone who investigates how the functioning of the brain and
       other organs influence behavior is called a:

       A. sociobiologist
       B. neuropsychologist
       C. behavioral neuroscientist
       D. comparative psychologist
       ("WWW" C, pp. 24, factual)

103.   Which of the following describes a neuropsychologist?

       A. has an M.D. and specializes in the treatment of brain damage
       B. conducts research on animal behavior (similar to an
          ethologist)
       C. is more often a teacher than a practitioner
       D. tests the abilities and disabilities of brain-damaged people
       (D, p. 24, factual)

104.   A comparative psychologist:

       A. compares the reactions different people have in similar
          situations.
       B. considers the evolutionary histories of different species and
          their behaviors.
       C. compares nervous system responses of different people.
       D. helps people with emotional distress.
       (B, p. 24, factual)

105.   Which of the following specialists is MOST likely to hold a
       medical degree?

       A. behavioral neuroscientist
       B. neurologist
       C. biopsychologist
       D. neuropsychologist
       (B, p. 24, factual)

106.   Which of the following specialists is MOST likely to work with
       people with brain damage?

       A. comparative psychologist
       B. biopsychologist
       C. neuropsychologist
       D. psychobiologist
       (C, p. 24, factual)

107.   A psychiatrist:

       A.  helps people with emotional distress.
       B.  performs brain surgery.
       C.  treats people with brain damage.
       D.  relates behaviors to the functions they have served in their
           evolutionary past.
       (A, p. 24, factual)

**Module 2.1: The Cells of the Nervous System**

1.   Who was the first researcher to demonstrate that neurons are
     separate from one another?

     A. Curt P. Richter
     B. Santiago Ramon y Cajal
     C. Charles S. Sherrington
     D. Jose Delgado
     (B, p. 30, factual)

2.   Prior to the work of Santiago Ramon y Cajal, what did many
     investigators believe?

     A. Nerves conducted impulses at the speed of light.
     B. Transmission across a synapse was just as fast as transmission
        along an axon.
     C. The tip of an axon physically merged with the next neuron.
     D. All neurons were of similar size and shape.
     (C, p. 30, factual)

3.   According to one estimate, the average adult human brain
     contains _____ neurons?

     A. 10,000
     B. B. 100,000
     C. 1 billion
     D. 100 billion
     (D, p. 30, factual)

**Neurons and Glia**

4.   The nervous system cell which receives and transmits
     information is called a:

     A. neuron.
     B. glial cell.
     C. mitochondria.
     D. ribosome.
     (A, p. 30, factual)

5.   What are the two kinds of cells in the nervous system?

     A. neurons and glia
     B. dendrites and axons
     C. ribosomes and lysosomes
     D. neurons and axons
     (A, p. 30, factual)

6.     A structure that contains the chromosomes is called a/an:

       A.  endoplasmic reticulum.
       B.  nucleus.
       C.  mitochondrion.
       D.  ribosome.
       (B, p. 31, factual)

7.     What is composed of two layers of fat molecules that are free to
       flow around one another?

       A. the endoplasmic reticulum
       B. a ribosome
       C. a mitochondrion
       D. the membrane
       (D, p. 30, factual)

8.     Which chemicals flow most freely across a cell membrane?

       A. proteins, fats, and carbohydrates
       B. positively charged ions
       C. water, oxygen, and carbon dioxide
       D. calcium and magnesium
       (C, p. 30, factual)

9.     How do chemicals than cannot flow freely across a cell membrane
       enter a neuron?

       A. through a Golgi complex
       B. through specialized protein channels
       C. through the endoplasmic reticulum
       D. through gaps in the myelin sheath
       (B, p. 30, factual)

10.    Where do the metabolic activities occur that provide energy for
       all of the other activities of the cell?

       A. mitochondria
       B. ribosomes
       C. lysosomes
       D. Golgi complexes
       (A, p. 31, factual)

11.    The sites at which the cell synthesizes new protein molecules are
       called:

       A. mitochondria.
       B. endoplasmic reticula.
       C. ribosomes.
       D. plasma membranes.
       (C, p. 31, factual)

12.    The endoplasmic reticulum is a:

       A. network of thin tubes that transport newly synthesized
          proteins.
       B. site where the cell synthesizes new protein molecules.
       C. structure that separates the inside of the cell from the
          outside.
       D. structure that contains the chromosomes.
       (A, p. 32, factual)

13.    What is the main feature that distinguishes a neuron from other
       animal cells?

       A. A neuron has a larger nucleus.
       B. A neuron has a distinctive shape.
       C. A neuron has the ability to metabolize a variety of fuels.
       D. A neuron has a high internal concentration of sodium ions.
       ("WWW" B, p. 32, factual)

14.    What receives excitation from other neurons and conducts impulses
       to muscle or gland cells?

       A. sensory neurons
       B. motor neurons
       C. dendrites
       D. dendritic spines
       (B, p. 32, factual)

15.    The branching fibers that form the information-receiving pole of
       the nerve cells are called:

       A. motor neurons
       B. dendrites
       C. sensory neurons
       D. axons
       (B, p. 32, factual)

16.    Sensory neurons:

       A. are specialized at one end to be highly sensitive to
          particular types of stimulation.
       B. receive excitation from other neurons and conduct impulses to
          muscle or gland cells.
       C. are covered with an insulating material.
       D. have branching fibers of constant diameter.
       (A, p. 32, factual)

17.    The surface of a dendrite is lined with specialized junctions
       through which the dendrite receives information from other
       neurons.  What are these junctions called?

       A. synaptic receptors
       B. axons
       C. synaptic hillocks
       D. glia
       (A, p. 32, factual)

18.    Which of the following is NOT a characteristic of a dendrite?

       A. It tapers as it gets further from the cell body.
       B. It is in contact with the dendrites of other neurons.
       C. Its surface may be lined with synaptic receptors.
       D. It receives information from other neurons or the environment.
       (B, p. 32, factual)

19.    Which of the following is a characteristic of a dendrite?

       A. It can be up to a meter long.
       B. It tapers as it gets further from the cell body.
       C. It may be covered with a myelin sheath.
       D. It carries information away from the cell body.
       (B, p. 32, factual)

20.    Some dendrites contain additional short outgrowths.  What are
       these outgrowths called?

       A. hillocks
       B. dendritic spines
       C. dendritic roots
       D. myelin sheaths
       (B, pp. 32-33, factual)

21.    Dendrites often contain additional short outgrowths.  These are
       believed to:

       A. increases the surface area available for synapses.
       B. increase the speed of transmission.
       C. eliminate cell waste products.
       D. help the cell maintain its shape.
       (A, p. 33, factual)

22.    Which part of a neuron contains the nucleus?

       A. the cell body
       B. the dendrite
       C. the axon
       D. the presynaptic terminal
       (A, p. 33, factual)

23.    Which part of the neuron contains the mitochondria?

       A. the axon
       B. the dendrites
       C. the soma
       D. the dendritic spines
       (C, p. 33, factual)

24.    The part of the neuron which contains the ribosomes is the:

       A. axon
       B. dendrite
       C. soma
       D. presynaptic terminal
       (C, p. 33, factual)

25.    The information sender of the neuron, conveying an impulse toward
       either other neurons or a gland or muscle is called the:

       A. axon
       B. dendrite
       C. soma
       D. myelin
       (A, p. 33, factual)

26.    The insulating material which covers many vertebrate axons is
       called the:

       A. dendrite
       B. myelin sheath
       C. cell body or soma
       D. presynaptic terminal
       (B, p. 33, factual)

27.    Neurons typically have one _____, but many _____.

       A. dendrite; axons
       B. axon; dendrites
       C. cell body; axons
       D. dendrite; cell bodies
       (B, p. 33, factual)

28.    Which of the following is a characteristic of an axon?

       A. It narrows as it gets further from the cell body.
       B. It physically touches the next neuron.
       C. It contains many ribosomes.
       D. It ends in multiple branches.
       (D, p. 33, factual)

29.   Which of the following is NOT a characteristic of an axon?

A. It can be up to a meter long.
B. It has a constant diameter.
C. It carries information toward the cell body.
D. It may be covered with a myelin sheath.
(C, p. 33, factual)

30.   What is one way to tell the difference between a dendrite and an axon?  Axons usually:

A. form the information-receiving pole of the neuron.
B. are shorter than the dendrites.
C. are covered with myelin.
D. taper in diameter toward their periphery.
(C, p. 33, factual)

31.   As a general rule, where do axons convey information?

A. toward dendrites of their own cell
B. toward their own cell body
C. away from their own the cell body
D. to surrounding glia
(B, p. 33, factual)

32.   Myelin covers:

A. vertebrate axons
B. invertebrate axons
C. vertebrate dendrites
D. invertebrate dendrites
(A, p. 33, factual)

33.   What does myelin cover?

A. all axons
B. most dendrites
C. some axons in vertebrates and none in invertebrates
D. all vertebrate axons and some invertebrate axons
(C, p. 33, factual)

34.   What is the insulating material that covers some axons?

A. a bouton
B. a myelin sheath
C. an axonic spine
D. an intrinsic neuron
(B, p. 33, factual)

35.   What is the point from which an axon releases chemicals into the synapse?

A. the myelin sheath
B. the presynaptic terminal
C. a dendritic spine
D. the endoplasmic reticulum
(B, p. 33, factual)

36.   An axon has many branches, each of which swells at its tip. These are known as:

A. presynaptic terminals.
B. efferent axons.
C. afferent axons.
D. intrinsic neurons.
(A, p. 33, factual)

37.   An axon releases chemicals:

A. into the presynaptic terminal.
B. into the junction between neurons.
C. through the efferent terminals.
D. to the mitochondria.
("WWW" B, p. 33, factual)

38.   Where are mitochondria found in high concentrations?

A. in the axon
B. in the dendrites
C. in the presynaptic terminals
D. throughout the neuron
(C, p. 33, factual)

39.   Presynaptic terminals have many mitochondria:

A. in order to provide the energy axons need to synthesize chemicals there.
B. in order to provide the energy dendrites need to synthesize chemicals there.
C. so they can attach to the endoplasmic reticulum.
D. in order to produce ribosomes.
(A, p. 33, conceptual)

40.   A local neuron:

A. has an axon approximately a meter long.
B. conveys information to other neurons across great distances.
C. is a small neuron with no axon or a very short one.
D. has an axon with many branches far from the cell body.
(C, p. 33, factual)

41.    A local neuron is a:

       A. large neuron with many axons.
       B. small neuron with many axons.
       C. small neuron with a very short axon.
       D. large neuron with no axon.
       (C, p. 33, factual)

42.    With respect to the hippocampus, a neuron that conveys
       information toward the hippocampus is considered to be which of
       the following?

       A. afferent
       B. efferent
       C. intrinsic
       D. presynaptic
       (A, p. 33, conceptual)

43.    With respect to the hippocampus, a neuron that conveys
       information away from the hippocampus is considered to be which
       of the following?

       A. afferent
       B. efferent
       C. intrinsic
       D. post-synaptic
       (B, p. 33, conceptual)

44.    What would a neuron in the pons be called that receives
       information only from other cells in the pons and sends
       information only to other cells in the pons?

       A. afferent
       B. efferent
       C. intrinsic
       D. inter-synaptic
       (C, p. 34, conceptual)

45.    The Purkinje cell of the cerebellum:

       A. has axons which branch widely.
       B. has dendrites which branch widely.
       C. integrates lots of outgoing information.
       D. maintains its shape through its lifetime.
       (B, p. 34, factual)

46.    The shape of a neuron:

       A. does not change in its lifetime.
       B. can be modified through new experiences.
       C. is not related to its function.
       D. determines whether it can regenerate or not.
       (B, p. 34, factual)

47.   What kind of cell has an axon and dendrites that branch
      diffusely, but extend only within a small radius?

      A. a glial cell
      B. a motor neuron in the spinal cord
      C. an interneuron
      D. a sensory neuron
      (C, p. 34, conceptual)

48.   Which of the following is TRUE about dendrites that branch
      extremely widely?

      A. They integrate information from many sources.
      B. They integrate information only from select sources.
      C. They conduct information more slowly.
      D. They conduct information more quickly.
      (A, p. 34, factual)

49.   A given neuron's shape:

      A. remains constant throughout its lifetime.
      B. depends mainly on the ratio of mitochondria to ribosomes.
      C. is modified by experience.
      D. is determined by its connection with an intrinsic neuron.
      (C, pp. 34-35, factual)

50.   Which of the following is a characteristic of glial cells in the
      human brain?

      A. They are larger than neurons.
      B. They are capable of transmitting impulses when neurons fail to
         do so.
      C. They are more numerous than neurons.
      D. They are like neurons, except that they lack axons.
      (C, p. 35, factual)

51.   The average glial cell:

      A. is about ten times larger than a neuron.
      B. is about one-tenth the size of a neuron.
      C. is about one-half the size of a neuron.
      D. is about the same size as any given neuron in the human brain.
      (B, p. 36, factual)

52.   Glial cells:

      A. are less numerous than neurons in the human brain.
      B. transmit information over long distances within the central
         nervous system.
      C. occupy about ten times more space in the brain than do
         neurons.
      D. occupy about the same total space as do neurons.
      ("WWW" D, p. 36, factual)

53.    Which function is NOT performed by glia?

       A. removing waste materials
       B. building myelin sheaths
       C. transmitting information
       D. guiding the growth of axons and dendrites
       (C, p. 36, factual)

54.    One type of glia helps synchronize the activity of axons.  They
       are called:

       A. oligodendrocytes
       B. astrocytes
       C. radial glia
       D. Schwann cells
       (B, p. 36, factual)

55.    Which type of glia builds myelin sheaths around axons in the
       periphery of the body?

       A. astrocytes
       B. Schwann cells
       C. oligodendrocytes
       D. radial glia
       (B, p. 36, factual)

56.    Which type of glia remove waste material in the nervous system?

       A. astrocytes
       B. Schwann cells
       C. oligodendrocytes
       D. radial glia
       (A, p. 36, factual)

57.    Radial glia:

       A. guide the migration of neurons during embryonic development.
       B. synchronize the activity of axons.
       C. wrap around the presynaptic terminals of several axons.
       D. build the myelin sheaths that surround and insulate certain
          axons.
       (A, p. 36, factual)

**The Blood-Brain Barrier**

58.    What is the mechanism that prevents or slows some chemicals from
       entering the brain, while allowing others to enter?

       A. a threshold
       B. a blood-brain barrier
       C. an endoplasmic wall
       D. a differential-drug inhibitor
       (B, p. 36, factual)

59.    Which would be MOST likely to cross the blood-brain barrier?

       A. small, uncharged molecules
       B. large, charged molecules
       C. molecules that are not fat soluble
       D. viruses
       (A, p. 37, factual)

60.    In the brain, an arrangement of endothelial cells:

       A. has gaps large enough to allow the passage of molecules.
       B. synthesizes neurotransmitters.
       C. does not allow most molecules to pass because the cells are so
          tightly packed.
       D. has gaps that are filled with enzymes that attack most blood
          chemicals.
       (C, p. 37, factual)

61.    What happens to a virus that manages to cross the blood-brain
       barrier and enter the brain?

       A. It is destroyed by natural killer cells.
       B. It gets trapped in a neuron, then both are destroyed by
          natural killer cells.
       C. It gets trapped in a glial cell, then both are destroyed by
          natural killer cells.
       D. It stays in the nervous system throughout the person's life.
       ("WWW" D, p. 36, factual)

62.    Molecules that can cross the blood-brain barrier are usually:

       A. large, uncharged molecules, such as lactose.
       B. large, charged molecules.
       C. neurotransmitters, such as dopamine.
       D. molecules which can dissolve in the fats of the capillary
          walls.
       (D, p. 37, factual)

63.    How does glucose enter the brain?

       A. It passes freely through the blood-brain barrier because it is
          fat-soluble.
       B. It is pumped in by an active transport system.
       C. It attaches to charged molecules in order to cross the blood
          brain barrier.
       D. It passes freely through the blood-brain barrier because it is
          water-soluble.
       (B, p. 37, factual)

64.     What is the main source of nutrition for vertebrate neurons?

        A. fats
        B. glucose
        C. sodium
        D. complex carbohydrates
        (B, p. 37, factual)

65.     Why do neurons rely so heavily on glucose as their source of
        nutrition?

        A. Neurons lack the enzymes necessary to metabolize other fuels.
        B. Glucose is the only fuel that can be used even in the absence
           of vitamins.
        C. Glucose is not used extensively by other parts of the body.
        D. Other fuels do not readily cross the blood-brain barrier.
        (D, p. 37, factual)

66.     Under what circumstances does the brain sometimes use fuels other
        than glucose?

        A. during sleep
        B. when glucose levels in the brain decline
        C. during infancy
        D. during times of increased stress
        (C, p. 37, factual)

67.     What are two requirements for the brain to metabolize glucose?

        A. thiamine and oxygen
        B. amino acids and enzymes
        C. oxygen and enzymes
        D. amino acids and oxygen
        (A, p. 37, factual)

68.     Under what circumstances is the brain likely to suffer from
        inadequate nutrition?

        A. a lack of thiamine in the diet
        B. a lack of glucose in the diet
        C. a lack of fats in the diet
        D. too many carbohydrates in the diet
        (A, p. 37, factual)

69.     Why does the brain need thiamine?

        A. to enable glucose to cross the blood-brain barrier
        B. as a source of fuel in case there is not enough glucose
        C. as a building block for making proteins
        D. to enable it to metabolize glucose
        (D, p. 37, factual)

70.    If the brain does not have enough thiamine, what is it unable to
       do?

       A. maintain its blood-brain barrier
       B. pump glucose across the blood-brain barrier
       C. produce certain neurotransmitters
       D. metabolize glucose
       (D, p. 37, factual)

71.    Who is most likely to suffer from a thiamine deficiency?

       A. alcoholics
       B. heroin addicts
       C. diabetics
       D. infants
       (A, p. 37, factual)

72.    What leads to Korsakoff's syndrome?

       A. thiamine deficiency resulting from alcoholism
       B. glucose deficiency resulting from alcoholism
       C. viruses that manage to cross the blood-brain barrier
       D. glial cells that over-reproduce and increase pressure in the
          brain
       (A, pp. 37-38, factual)

73.    Korsakoff's syndrome:

       A. is marked by severe memory impairments.
       B. results from too much thiamine.
       C. results from lack of oxygen to the brain.
       D. is due to a breakdown of the blood-brain barrier.
       (A, p. 38, factual)

**Module 2.2: The Nerve Impulse**

74.    How will a pinch on the shoulder be felt compared to a pinch, of
       equal intensity, on the foot?

       A. sooner
       B. later
       C. stronger
       D. weaker
       (A, p. 39, factual)

75.   An axon conveys an impulse:

   A. in such a way that a pinch on your shoulder feels stronger
      than a pinch on your toes.
   B. in such a way that a pinch on your shoulder feels weaker than
      a pinch on your toes.
   C. in such a way that a pinch on your shoulder will reach your
      brain sooner than a pinch on your toes.
   D. at a speed approximately equal to household electricity.
   (C, p. 39, factual)

76.   Some parts of the retina are slightly closer to your brain than
      other parts.  As a result:

   A. simultaneous flashes of light arriving at different parts of
      the retina reach the brain at different times.
   B. our perception of light is never accurate.
   C. more distant axons must transmit slightly faster than axons
      closer to the brain.
   D. axons closer to the brain will transmit faster than more
      distant axons.
   (C, p. 39, factual)

77.   How does the brain deal with messages coming from neurons with
      axons of differing lengths?

   A. All sensory neurons compensate so that information reaches the
      brain simultaneously.
   B. The brain reconstructs the chronology, taking axon lengths
      into account.
   C. The time differences are so slight that they are unimportant.
   D. It depends on the sensory system sending the information.
   (D, p. 39, conceptual)

**The Resting Potential of the Neuron**

78.   The membrane of a neuron is specialized:

   A. to keep all types of intercellular chemicals from moving out
      of the neuron.
   B. to keep all types of extracellular chemicals from moving into
      the neuron.
   C. to control the exchange of chemicals between the inside and
      outside of the cell.
   D. to produce chains of fatty acids and proteins.
   ("WWW" C, p. 39, factual)

79.    The membrane of a neuron is composed of _____ with _____ embedded in them.

      A. carbohydrates; purines
      B. fat molecules; proteins
      C. proteins; neurotransmitters
      D. benzene molecules; carbohydrates
      (B, p. 39, conceptual)

80.    The membrane of a neuron is composed of what kind of molecules?

      A. fat molecules
      B. proteins
      C. carbohydrates
      D. sodium ions
      (A, p. 39, factual)

81.    What kind of molecules is embedded in neural membranes?

      A. potassium ions
      B. carbohydrates
      C. fat molecules
      D. proteins
      (D, p. 39, factual)

82.    What is the difference in voltage called that typically exists between the inside and the outside of a neuron?

      A. concentration gradient
      B. generator potential
      C. resting potential
      D. shock value
      (C, p. 39, factual)

83.    When you state that the neuron's membrane is polarized, you are referring to a difference in electrical potential between:

      A. the axons and the dendrites.
      B. the axon hillock and the cell body.
      C. sodium ions and potassium ions.
      D. the inside and the outside of the membrane.
      (D, p. 39, factual)

84.    The concentration gradient refers to:

      A. the fact that the concentration of ions is greater on the inside of a neuron.
      B. the fact that the concentration of ions is greater on the outside of a neuron.
      C. the difference in distribution for various ions between the inside and outside of the membrane.
      D. the negatively charged proteins inside the cell.
      (C, p. 39, factual)

85.   Which of the following characterizes the "concentration gradient"
      in neurons?

      A. Sodium ions are more concentrated inside the cell and
         potassium ions are more concentrated outside.
      B. Potassium ions are more concentrated inside the cell and
         sodium ions are more concentrated outside.
      C. Sodium ions are more concentrated in the dendrites and
         potassium ions are more concentrated in the axon.
      D. Potassium ions are more concentrated in the dendrites and
         sodium ions are more concentrated in the axon.
      (B, p. 39, factual)

86.   What is meant by the term "concentration gradient" with respect
      to neurons?

      A. Sodium is more concentrated in the dendrites and potassium in
         the axon.
      B. Negative charges are more concentrated outside the cell.
      C. Sodium and potassium ions are more concentrated on opposite
         sides of the membrane.
      D. Potassium is more concentrated in the dendrites and sodium in
         the axon.
      (C, p. 39, conceptual)

87.   Concentration gradients lead to what kind of movements?

      A. the general movement of ions into the neuron
      B. the general movement of ions out of the neuron
      C. the movement of ions to areas of their highest concentrations
      D. the movement of ions to areas of their lowest concentrations
      (D, p. 39, conceptual)

88.   The resting potential of a neuron refers to:

      A. the net positive charge on the inside of the neuron.
      B. ions which rest in one place in the cell.
      C. the movement of ions to the outside of the neuron.
      D. the net negative charge on the inside of the neuron.
      ("WWW" D, p. 39, conceptual)

89.   Electrical gradients lead to what kind of movements?

      A. the general movement of ions into the neuron
      B. the general movement of ions out of the neuron
      C. the movement of ions to areas having the same electrical
         charges
      D. the movement of ions to areas having the opposite electrical
         charges
      (D, p. 39, conceptual)

90.   Which of the following phrases captures the essence of ion
      movement resulting from electrical gradients?

      A. "opposites attract"
      B. "Birds of a feather flock together."
      C. "spread out"
      D. "one for all and all for one"
      (A, pp. 39-40, conceptual)

91.   A microelectrode is typically:

      A. a fine glass tube.
      B. made of strands of wire.
      C. a single, thin wire.
      D. made of biological materials such as cell membranes.
      (A, p. 40, factual)

92.   A common electrode is a fine glass tube filled with:

      A. a salt solution.
      B. glucose.
      C. potassium.
      D. glass particles.
      (A, p. 40, factual

93.   What is the approximate resting potential of the inside of a
      neuron's membrane, relative to the outside?

      A. -30 to -90 millivolts
      B. -10 to +10 millivolts
      C. 0 to + 10 millivolts
      D. +30 to +90 millivolts
      (A, p. 40, factual)

94.   When a neuron's membrane is at rest, which of the following
      molecules crosses through it MOST slowly?

      A. potassium
      B. sodium
      C. water
      D. carbon dioxide
      (B, p. 40, factual)

95.   When a neuron's membrane is at rest, which of the following
      molecules crosses through it MOST easily?

      A. potassium
      B. sodium
      C. chloride
      D. water
      (D, p. 40, factual)

96.   When the neuronal membrane is at rest, the potassium channels:

      A. permit potassium ions to pass quickly and easily.
      B. permit potassium ions to pass slowly.
      C. prohibit any movement of potassium ions.
      D. help to open up the sodium channels.
      (B, p. 40, factual)

97.   When the neuronal membrane is at rest, the sodium channels:

      A. permit sodium ions to pass quickly and easily.
      B. permit potassium ions to cross instead of sodium.
      C. are closed.
      D. fluctuate rapidly between open and closed.
      (C, p. 40, factual)

98.   Which of the following describes selective permeability?

      A. Ions can only travel in certain directions across the
         membrane.
      B. Only certain molecules are allowed to cross the membrane
         freely.
      C. Only certain types of stimulation will result in an action
         potential.
      D. All molecules must pass through designated channels.
      (B, p. 40, factual)

99.   Which feature of a neuron does the sodium-potassium pump make
      possible?

      A. the refractory period
      B. the resting potential
      C. selective permeability
      D. saltatory conduction
      (B, p. 40, factual)

100.  Under which conditions would the sodium-potassium pump be far
      less effective in creating a concentration gradient?

      A. if dendrites were generally longer than axons
      B. if the glia-to-neuron ratio were higher
      C. if selective permeability of the membrane did not exist
      D. if it were an active transport system that required energy
      (C, p. 40, conceptual)

101.  What is one major cause for the resting potential of a neuron's
      membrane?

      A. a difference in size between axons and dendrites
      B. a high permeability of the membrane to water molecules
      C. the refractory period of the membrane
      D. the sodium-potassium pump
      (D, p. 40, factual)

102.    The sodium-potassium pump pumps sodium ions _____ and potassium ions _____.

        A. into the cell; into the cell
        B. into the cell; out of the cell
        C. out of the cell; out of the cell
        D. out of the cell; into the cell
        (D, p. 40, factual)

103.    Under normal conditions the sodium-potassium pump moves:

        A. two Na+ ions into a neuron for every three K+ ions it moves
           out.
        B. three Na+ ions into a neuron for every three K+ ions it moves
           out.
        C. three Na+ ions out of a neuron for every two K+ ions it moves
           in.
        D. two Na+ ions out of a neuron for every three K+ ions it moves
           in.
        (C, p. 40, factual)

104.    The concentration gradient for potassium tends to:

        A. draw potassium into the cell.
        B. push chloride out of the cell.
        C. push sodium out of the cell.
        D. push potassium out of the cell.
        (D. p. 40, factual)

105.    Which of the following is NOT true for sodium ions when the cell
        is at resting potential?

        A. Sodium ions remain outside the cell because the sodium-
           potassium pump drives them out.
        B. Sodium gates are tightly closed.
        C. Sodium tends to be driven into the neuron by the concentration
           gradient.
        D. Sodium tends to be driven out of the neuron by the electrical
           gradient.
        (D, p. 40, factual)

106.    When the neuron is at rest, what is responsible for moving
        potassium ions OUT of the cell?

        A. a concentration gradient
        B. an electrical gradient
        C. both a concentration gradient and an electrical gradient
        D. the sodium-potassium pump
        (A, p. 40, factual)

107.  When the neuron is at rest, what is responsible for moving
      potassium ions into the cell?

      A. concentration gradient
      B. an electrical gradient
      C. the sodium-potassium pump
      D. both the sodium-potassium pump and electrical gradient
      (D, p. 40, factual)

108.  What effect does the movement of potassium ions out of the cell
      have on the electrical gradient?

      A. increases it
      B. decreases it
      C. has no effect on it
      D. it depends on the type of neuron
      (A, pp. 40-41, conceptual)

109.  When a membrane is at rest, what attracts potassium ions to the
      inside of the cell?

      A. an electrical gradient
      B. a concentration gradient
      C. both an electrical gradient and a concentration gradient
      D. neither an electrical gradient nor a concentration gradient
      (A, p. 41, factual)

110.  When a membrane is at rest, what attracts sodium ions to the
      inside of the cell?

      A. an electrical gradient
      B. a concentration gradient
      C. both an electrical gradient and a concentration gradient
      D. neither an electrical gradient nor a concentration gradient
      (C, p. 41, factual)

111.  When the neuron is at rest, what is responsible for moving sodium
      ions out of the cell?

      A. a concentration gradient
      B. an electrical gradient
      C. both a concentration gradient and an electrical gradient
      D. the sodium-potassium pump
      (D, p. 41, factual)

112.  Which of the following is an advantage of having a resting
      potential?

      A. The toxic effects of sodium are minimized inside the cell.
      B. No energy is required to maintain it.
      C. The cell is prepared to respond quickly to a stimulus.
      D. All of the ions are maintained in equal concentrations
         throughout the cytoplasm.
      (C, p. 41, factual)

113.   An analogy relevant to the resting potential of a neuron is:

A. a poised bow and arrow.
B. a machine gun.
C. evolution.
D. juggling.
(A, p. 41, conceptual)

**The Action Potential**

114.   Stimulation of a neuron takes place:

A. through hyperpolarization.
B. at the synapse.
C. in the mitochondria.
D. in the endoplasmic reticulum.
(B, p. 42, factual)

115.   What is the result if a stimulus shifts the potential inside a
neuron from the resting potential to a more negative potential?

A. hyperpolarization
B. depolarization
C. an action potential
D. a threshold
(A, p. 42, factual)

116.   Hyperpolarization is:

A. increased polarization.
B. decreased polarization.
C. the threshold of the cell.
D. the resting potential of the cell.
(A, p. 42, factual)

117.   What is the result if a stimulus shifts the potential inside a
neuron from the resting potential to a potential slightly closer
to zero?

A. hyperpolarization
B. depolarization
C. selective permeability
D. a refractory period
("WWW" B, p. 42, factual)

118.   The neuron will produce an action potential only if the
depolarization exceeds what level?

A. the threshold
B. the resting potential
C. hyperpolarization
D. the refractory period
(A, p. 42, factual)

119.  A membrane produces an action potential whenever the potential across it reaches what level?

      A. the resting potential
      B. -90 mV
      C. the threshold
      D. the refractory period
      (C, p. 42, factual)

120.  If there is a depolarizing effect on a neuron, the result will be that:

      A. the neuron will fire, no matter how slight the effect.
      B. the neuron will be inhibited from firing.
      C. the neuron will fire, but only if it reaches threshold.
      D. the neuron will fire only if the cell is in its relative refractory period.
      (C, p. 42, conceptual)

121.  At what point do the sodium gates start to allow sodium into the neuron?

      A. only when the threshold is surpassed
      B. in response to any depolarization
      C. in response to any hyperpolarization
      D. sodium is always allowed in, the gates prevent it from going out
      (B, p. 42, factual)

122.  What tends to open the sodium gates across a neuron's membrane?

      A. hyperpolarization of the membrane
      B. depolarization of the membrane
      C. increase in the sodium concentration outside the neuron
      D. passing the peak of the action potential and entering the refractory period
      (B, p. 42, factual)

123.  What happens to the ion gates when the membrane of a neuron is depolarized?

      A. Potassium gates close.
      B. Chloride gates open.
      C. Sodium gates close.
      D. Sodium gates open.
      (D, p. 42, factual)

124.  Stimulus A depolarizes a neuron just barely above the threshold.
      Stimulus B depolarizes a neuron to 10 mV beyond threshold.  What
      can we expect to happen?

      A. Stimulus B will produce an action potential that is conducted
         at a faster speed than A.
      B. Stimulus B will produce an action potential of greater
         magnitude than stimulus A.
      C. Stimulus B will produce an action potential but stimulus A
         will not.
      D. Stimulus A and stimulus B will produce the same response in
         the neurons.
      (D, p. 42, conceptual)

125.  What is the result of a change in the potential across the
      membrane that reaches the threshold?

      A. a refractory period
      B. saltatory conduction
      C. hyperpolarization
      D. an action potential
      ("WWW" D, p. 42, factual)

126.  Voltage-activated channels are channels:

      A. whose permeability depends on the voltage difference across
         the membrane.
      B. which allow sodium ions to flow more freely.
      C. which close during an action potential.
      D. which open to allow sodium ions out of the cell.
      (B, p. 42, factual)

127.  If depolarization is less than the cell's threshold:

      A. sodium is prevented from crossing the membrane.
      B. potassium is prevented from crossing the membrane.
      C. sodium crosses the membrane only slightly more than usual.
      D. the cell will still produce an action potential.
      (C, p. 42, factual)

128.  The action potential of a neuron depends mostly on what movement
      of ions?

      A. sodium ions entering the cell
      B. sodium ions leaving the cell
      C. potassium ions entering the cell
      D. potassium ions leaving the cell
      (A, p. 42, factual)

129.  When the potential across a membrane reaches threshold:

      A. the sodium channels open to let sodium enter the cell rapidly.
      B. the sodium channels close to prevent sodium from entering the
         cell.
      C. the sodium channels open to let sodium exit the cell rapidly.
      D. the sodium channels close to prevent sodium from exiting the
         cell.
      (A, p. 42, factual)

130.  Which movement of ions would depolarize the membrane of a neuron?

      A. sodium ions into the cell
      B. sodium ions out of the cell
      C. potassium ions out of the cell
      D. chloride ions into the cell
      (A, p. 42, conceptual)

131.  Suppose we applied a drug to a neuron that caused its sodium
      gates to suddenly open wide.  What would happen?

      A. hyperpolarization of the membrane
      B. an increase in the threshold
      C. an action potential
      D. nothing, because potassium gates would compensate
      (C, p. 42, conceptual)

132.  During the entire course of events from the start of an action
      potential until the membrane returns to its resting potential,
      what is the net movement of ions?

      A. sodium in, potassium in
      B. sodium out, potassium out
      C. sodium in, potassium out
      D. sodium out, potassium in
      ("WWW" C, p. 42, factual)

133.  What is the result of a drug that blocks the sodium gates of a
      neuron's membrane?

      A. It decreases the threshold.
      B. It blocks the action potential.
      C. It causes repeated action potentials.
      D. It eliminates the refractory period.
      (B, p. 42, factual)

134.  Which of the following movements of ions would hyperpolarize the
      membrane of a neuron?

      A. potassium ions into the cell
      B. sodium ions into the cell
      C. chloride ions out of the cell
      D. potassium ions out of the cell
      (D, p. 42, conceptual)

135.  At the peak of the action potential:

      A. sodium gates snap wide open.
      B. potassium gates snap shut.
      C. sodium gates begin to slowly close.
      D. sodium gates snap shut.
      (D, p. 43, factual)

136.  During an action potential:

      A. sodium concentration outside of a neuron increases by about
         50%.
      B. sodium concentration outside of a neuron increases by about
         1%.
      C. sodium concentration inside of a neuron increases by about 1%.
         sodium concentration inside of a neuron increases by about
         50%.
      (C, p. 43, factual)

137.  After the peak of an action potential, what prevents sodium ions
      from continuing to enter the cell?

      A. There is no longer a concentration gradient for sodium.
      B. The sodium-potassium pump greatly increases its rate of
         activity.
      C. All the available sodium ions have already entered the cell.
      D. The sodium gates in the membrane close.
      (D, p. 43, factual)

138.  Why do sodium ions enter a neuron more rapidly during an action
      potential than during the resting potential?

      A. decreased activity by the sodium-potassium pump
      B. opening of the sodium gates in the membrane
      C. increased concentration gradient during an action potential
      D. increased electrical gradient during an action potential
      (B, p. 43, factual)

139.  At what point do the sodium gates begin to close, shutting out
      further entry of sodium into the cell?

      A. at the peak of the action potential
      B. when the threshold is reached
      C. at the end of the relative refractory period
      D. when the concentration gradient for sodium is eliminated
      (A, p. 43, factual)

140. Just after the peak of the action potential, what movement of ions restores the membrane to approximately the resting potential?

A. Sodium ions enter the cell.
B. Potassium ions enter the cell.
C. Potassium ions leave the cell.
D. Sodium ions travel down the axon.
(C, p. 43 factual)

141. What causes potassium ions to leave the axon just after the peak of the action potential?

A. a continuing concentration gradient and the opening of the potassium gates
B. an increase in the concentration gradient across the membrane
C. increased tendency of the sodium-potassium pump to pump potassium out
D. binding of potassium ions to proteins that leave at this time
(A, p. 43, factual)

142. What would be the probable effect of a drug that decreases the flow of potassium through the potassium gates of the membrane?

A. It would block action potentials.
B. It would increase the threshold of the membrane.
C. It would slow the return of the membrane to its resting potential.
D. It would cause the membrane to be hyperpolarized.
(C, p. 43, conceptual)

143. What will happen after an extreme hyperpolarization of a neuron?

A. a normal action potential
B. an action potential resulting from rebounding ions
C. a refractory period
D. a return to resting potential
(D, p. 43, conceptual)

144. How do local anesthetic drugs, such as Novocain, work?

A. They open the potassium gates.
B. They block the sodium gates.
C. They inactivate the sodium-potassium pump.
D. They decrease blood flow to certain areas of the brain.
(B, p. 43, factual)

145.   What kind of drug would prevent an action potential?

   A. a drug that lowers the threshold of the membrane
   B. a drug that blocks the movement of potassium across the
      membrane
   C. a drug that blocks the movement of sodium across the membrane
   D. a drug that increases the movement of sodium across the
      membrane
   (C, p. 43, conceptual)

146.   How do general anesthetic drugs, such as ether, work?

   A. They open potassium gates.
   B. They block the sodium gates.
   C. They inactivate the sodium-potassium pump.
   D. They decrease blood flow to certain areas of the brain.
   (A, p. 43, factual)

147.   Which of the following represents the all-or-none law?

   A. Every depolarization produces an action potential.
   B. Every hyperpolarization produces an action potential.
   C. The size of the action potential is independent of the
      strength of the stimulus that initiated it.
   D. Every depolarization reaches the threshold, even if it fails
      to produce an action potential.
   (C, p. 44, factual)

148.   The all-or-none law states that:

   A. a neuron produces an action potential of maximal strength, or
      none at all.
   B. all neurons fire or none at all.
   C. all neurons in a pathway fire at the same time, or none do.
   D. all ions move in the same direction, or none do.
   (A, p. 44, factual)

149.   What characterizes the refractory period of a neuron?

   A. The sodium gates of the membrane are open.
   B. The sodium-potassium pump is active.
   C. A normally adequate stimulus cannot produce an action
      potential.
   D. Both the sodium gates and the potassium gates are fully
      closed.
   (C, p. 44, factual)

150.  Under what conditions is it impossible for a stimulus to produce
      an action potential?

      A. if the membrane is in its absolute refractory period
      B. if it occurs at the same time as a hyperpolarizing stimulus
      C. if sodium ions are more concentrated outside the cell than
         inside
      D. if the potassium gates have been blocked
      (A, p. 44, factual)

151.  Which feature of a neuron limits the number of action potentials
      it can produce per second?

      A. the threshold
      B. the refractory period
      C. saltatory conduction
      D. the length of the axon
      (B, p. 44, factual)

152.  A neuron's sodium gates are firmly closed and the membrane cannot
      produce an action potential during:

      A. the absolute refractory period.
      B. the relative refractory period.
      C. depolarization.
      D. saltatory conduction
      (A, p. 44, factual)

153.  During the relative refractory period:

      A. the sodium gates are firmly closed.
      B. the sodium gates are reverting to their usual state.
      C. the sodium gates are wide open.
      D. the potassium gates are firmly closed.
      (B, p. 44, factual)

154.  Where do most action potentials begin?

      A. in the dendrites
      B. in the cell body
      C. at the axon hillock
      D. at the tip of the axon
      (C, p. 44, factual)

155.  What happens once an action potential starts?

      A. It is conducted the rest of the way as an electrical current.
      B. It needs additional stimulation to keep it going along the
         axon.
      C. It increases in speed as it goes.
      D. It is regenerated at other points along the axon.
      (D, p. 44, factual)

156.   What will affect the speed of an action potential?

    A. the strength of the stimulus
    B. the time since the last action potential
    C. the length of the axon
    D. the resistance of the membrane
    (D, p. 44, factual)

157.   What will NOT affect the speed of an action potential?

    A. the presence of myelin
    B. the diameter of the axon
    C. the length of the axon
    D. the number of sodium gates
    (C, p. 44, conceptual)

158.   How effective is the axon as a conductor of electricity?

    A. All axons are very effective conductors of electricity.
    B. Myelinated axons are the least effective conductors of
       electricity.
    C. Axons conduct the impulse faster than electricity normally
       travels.
    D. Axons are poor conductors of electricity.
    (D, p. 44, factual)

159.   What is known about the velocity of an action potential?

    A. It is the same as the velocity of electricity.
    B. It is approximately the speed of sound.
    C. It is 1-100 m/sec.
    D. It is impossible to measure.
    (C, p. 44, factual)

160.   Which of the following BEST describes the velocity of an action
      potential?

    A. much faster than the velocity of electricity
    B. approximately the same as the velocity of electricity
    C. much slower than the speed of electricity
    D. impossible to measure
    (C, p. 44, factual)

161.   How is the speed of an action potential down an unmyelinated axon
      BEST described?

    A. the speed of electricity, regardless of the size of the axon
    B. less than 1 meter per second, regardless of the size of the
       axon
    C. faster in thin axons than in thick ones
    D. faster in thick axons than in thin ones
    (D, p. 44, factual)

162.    What is to prevent an action potential from exciting the area
        behind it and starting a "rebound" action potential traveling the
        opposite direction?

        A. the refractory period
        B. the absence of sodium ions in the area behind it
        C. the membrane can conduct action potentials in only one
           direction
        D. nothing; such rebound action potentials occur routinely
        (A, p. 44, factual)

163.    Suppose we artificially start one action potential at the axon
        hillock and another half-way down the axon. In general, what will
        happen?

        A. Each will travel in only one direction, toward the presynaptic
           terminals.
        B. Each will travel both directions, exciting neurons on both
           sides.
        C. The middle one will travel in both directions, stimulating an
           action potential on one side, and canceling the action
           potential on the other side.
        D. They will cross and continue in the opposite directions.
        (C, p. 45, conceptual)

164.    Suppose we artificially start one action potential at the axon
        hillock and another half-way down the axon. What will happen to
        the one at the middle?

        A. It will travel in only one direction, toward the presynaptic
           terminals.
        B. It will travel in both directions, resulting in two action
           potentials
        C. It will travel in both directions, but will be stopped by the
           other action potential.
        D. Nothing, it is not possible to generate an action potential in
           the middle of the axon.
        (C, p. 45, conceptual)

165.    Suppose we artificially start one action potential at the axon
        hillock and another half-way down the axon. What will happen to
        the one starting at the axon hillock?

        A. It will travel normally to the presynaptic terminals.
        B. It will cross over the one started half-way down the axon and
           continue in that direction.
        C. It will be canceled when it encounters the other traveling
           towards it.
        D. Nothing, it is not possible to generate an action potential at
           the axon hillock.
        (C, p. 45, conceptual)

166. Which two factors will affect the speed of an action potential?

    A. the strength and frequency of the stimulus
    B. the location of the cell body and the length of the axon
    C. the length and diameter of the axon
    D. the presence of myelin and the diameter of the axon
    (D, p. 45, factual)

167. On which type of axon would action potentials travel the slowest?

    A. a thin, myelinated axon
    B. a thin, unmyelinated axon
    C. a thick, myelinated axon
    D. a thick, unmyelinated axon
    (B, p. 45, conceptual)

168. What is the function of a myelin sheath?

    A. It prevents action potentials from traveling in the wrong
       direction.
    B. It increases the velocity of transmission along an axon.
    C. It increases the magnitude of an action potential.
    D. It provides a store of nutrients for the neuron.
    ("WWW" B, p. 45, factual)

169. Why is it necessary for some neurons to be able to convey
     messages much more quickly than others?

    A. to be able to coordinate actions
    B. so we do not talk faster than we can think
    C. allow predators to move faster than their prey
    D. allow prey to think faster than their predators
    (A, p. 45, conceptual)

170. What are the nodes of Ranvier?

    A. gates in the membrane that admit all ions freely
    B. gaps in the myelin sheath
    C. branching points in an axon
    D. places where dendrites join the cell body
    (B, p. 45, factual)

171. In a myelinated axon, where are sodium gates abundant?

    A. in the areas covered by myelin
    B. at the nodes of Ranvier
    C. throughout the axon
    D. only in the axon hillock
    (B, p. 45, factual)

172.   To what does saltatory conduction refer?

A. the production of an action potential by the movement of
   sodium ions
B. the transmission of an impulse along a myelinated axon
C. the transmission of impulses along dendrites
D. the transmission of an impulse between one neuron and another
(B, pp. 45-46, factual)

173.   Saltatory conduction _____ the velocity of action potentials, and
_____ the amount of energy used by the neuron.

A. decreases; decreases
B. decreases; increases
C. increases; decreases
D. increases; increases
(C, p. 46, factual)

174.   How does saltatory conduction affect energy use in a neuron?

A. It eliminates the need for action potentials.
B. It increases the duration of the refractory period.
C. It reduces the frequency of action potentials.
D. It reduces the work load for the sodium-potassium pump.
(D, p. 46, conceptual)

175.   What disease is related to the destruction of myelin sheaths?

A. multiple sclerosis
B. cystic fibrosis
C. myasthenia gravis
D. Parkinson's disease
(A, p. 46, factual)

176.   In what way is a myelinated axon that has lost its myelin
(through disease) different from an axon that was never
myelinated?

A. It has a smaller diameter.
B. It lacks sodium gates along parts of its surface.
C. It has a longer refractory period.
D. It has a much higher threshold.
(B, p. 46, factual)

**Signaling Without Action Potentials**

177.   Which of the following is missing in a small local neuron?

A. dendrites
B. cell body
C. action potentials
D. an electrical gradient across its membrane
(C, p. 46, factual)

178.  Which of the following is NOT governed by the all-or-none law?

      A. axons
      B. myelinated neurons
      C. motor neurons
      D. local neurons
      (D, p. 46, factual)

179.  Which of the following is(are) NOT governed by the all-or-none
      law?

      A. somata and dendrites
      B. axons and dendrites
      C. axons and somata
      D. axons
      (A, p. 46, factual)

180.  Which of the following is governed by the all-or-none law?

      A. axons
      B. dendrites
      C. cell bodies
      D. local neurons
      (A, p. 46, factual)

181.  In what direction does a local neuron transmit information?

      A. through its dendrites to cell body to axon
      B. through its axon to cell body to dendrites
      C. only toward the cell body
      D. equally well in any direction
      (D, p. 46, factual)

182.  Which of the following describes the transmission of information
      in a local neuron?

      A. The signal decreases in strength as it travels.
      B. The signal increases in strength as it travels.
      C. The signal strength remains constant as it travels.
      D. Local neurons do not transmit any information.
      (A, p. 46, factual)

183.  Why are local neurons more difficult to study?

      A. There are so few of them, they are difficult to find.
      B. They are so small.
      C. They exist only in humans, so there are ethical
         considerations.
      D. They die if separated from other neurons.
      (B, p. 46, factual)

**Module 3.1: Concept of the Synapse**

1.    Who first suggested that the synapse was capable of a specialized
      type of communication?

      A. Curt P. Richter
      B. Paul MacLean
      C. Santiago Ramon y Cajal
      D. Charles S. Sherrington
      (D, p. 52, factual)

2.    Charles S. Sherrington was the first to infer the properties of
      which of the following?

      A. synapses
      B. the refractory period
      C. the sodium-potassium pump
      D. dendrites and axons
      (A, p. 52, factual)

3.    On the basis of what evidence were the properties of synapses
      first inferred?

      A. the electron microscope
      B. single-neuron recordings
      C. behavioral observations
      D. PET scans
      (C, p. 52, factual)

**The Properties of Synapses**

4.    Sherrington deduced that transmission at a synapse must be slower
      than conduction along an axon.  This was based on what kind of
      evidence?

      A. temporal summation
      B. drugs that increase or inhibit activity at synapses
      C. the speed of reflexive responses
      D. differences in diameter between axons and dendrites
      (C, p. 52, factual)

5.    An automatic response to a stimulus:

      A. only occurs in the leg.
      B. occurs in the gap between two neurons.
      C. is a definition of reflex.
      D. represents a circuit from the spinal cord to the brain and
         back again.
      (C, p. 52, factual)

6.    The circuit from sensory neuron to muscle response is called:

      A. a reflex arc.
      B. a synapse.
      C. flexion.
      D. extension.
      ("WWW" A, p. 52, factual)

7.    Sherrington suggested that the brain:

      A. was not necessary for the occurrence of reflexive movements.
      B. was an integral part of the reflex arc.
      C. could not modify reflexive movements.
      D. was a necessary part of reflexive movements in animals other
         than humans.
      (A, p. 52, factual)

8.    The speed of conduction through a reflex arc is _____ the speed
      of conduction of an action potential.

      A. equal to
      B. faster than
      C. slower than
      D. modified by
      (C, p. 52, factual)

9.    Why is the speed of conduction through a reflex arc slower than
      the speed of conduction of an action potential along an axon?

      A. Transmission between neurons at synapses is slower than along
         axons.
      B. The longer an axon, the slower its velocity.
      C. Interneurons have thicker axons than other neurons.
      D. There are greater amounts of myelin involved in the reflex
         arc.
      (A, p. 52, factual)

10.   A certain weak stimulus produces no reflexive response, but a
      rapid repetition of that stimulus may produce such a response.
      What is this phenomenon called?

      A. spatial summation
      B. temporal summation
      C. saltatory conduction
      D. synaptic combination
      (B, p. 52, factual)

11.   Which of the following would produce temporal summation?

      A. Present two or more weak stimuli at the same time.
      B. Present an excitatory and an inhibitory stimulus at the same
         time.
      C. Do not allow a flexor muscle to relax before stimulating it
         again.
      D. Present a rapid sequence of weak stimuli.
      (D, pp. 52, factual)

12.   Sherrington proposed that subthreshold excitation:

      A.   increases over time since stimulation.
      B.   decays rapidly.
      C.   gradually changes into an inhibition.
      D.   produces a constant, permanent change in the membrane.
      (B, p. 53, factual)

13.   The neuron which delivers synaptic transmission is called the:

      A. postsynaptic neuron.
      B. presynaptic neuron.
      C. EPSP.
      D. temporal summator.
      ("WWW" B, p. 53, factual)

14.   The neuron which receives synaptic transmission is called the:

      A. postsynaptic neuron.
      B. presynaptic neuron.
      C. EPSP.
      D. temporal summator.
      (A, p. 53, factual)

15.   To measure temporal summation in single cells, researchers:

      A. attach electrodes to the scalp.
      B. insert an microelectrode into the scalp.
      C. collect sodium and potassium ions from nearby glial cells.
      D. record depolarizations of the presynaptic neuron.
      (D, p. 53, factual)

16.   What does the abbreviation EPSP stand for?

      A. excitatory presynaptic potential
      B. excitatory partial synaptic process
      C. extended presynaptic potential
      D. excitatory postsynaptic potential
      (D, p. 53, factual)

17.    What is an EPSP?

       A. a graded depolarization
       B. a depolarization with a rebounding hyperpolarization
       C. a graded hyperpolarization
       D. an action potential in a reflex arc
       (A, p. 53, factual)

18.    Which of the following is true about EPSPs?

       A. It takes two to produce an action potential.
       B. They decay over time and space.
       C. They can be either excitatory or inhibitory.
       D. They occur because potassium gates open.
       (B, pp. 53, factual)

19.    Which of the following is NOT true about EPSPs?

       A. They decay over time.
       B. Their strength decreases with distance.
       C. They operate on an all-or-none principle.
       D. They are depolarizations.
       (C, pp. 53, factual)

20.    Depolarization is to _____ as hyperpolarization is to _____.

       A. excitation; inhibition
       B. inhibition; excitation
       C. increasing the threshold; decreasing the threshold
       D. decreasing the threshold; increasing the threshold
       ("WWW" A, p. 53, factual)

21.    If an EPSP adds to what is left from a previous EPSP, what has
       occurred?

       A. spatial summation
       B. temporal summation
       C. saltatory conduction
       D. inhibitory synaptic transmission
       (B, p. 53, factual)

22.    Like an action potential, an EPSP results from:

       A. sodium ions entering the cell.
       B. potassium ions entering the cell.
       C. sodium ions exiting the cell.
       D. potassium ions exiting the cell.
       (A, p. 53, factual)

23.    An EPSP is UNLIKE an action potential in that:

    A. it is a subthreshold event that decays over time.
    B. it does not decay over time.
    C. the summation of two action potentials might not be enough to
       exceed threshold but you always need three EPSPs.
    D. it does not involve sodium ions.
    (A, p. 53, factual)

24.    What causes an EPSP?

    A. the deactivation of cytoplasmic enzymes
    B. the opening of sodium channels
    C. the opening of potassium channels
    D. inherited paranormal psychic abilities
    (B, p. 53, factual)

25.    How does an EPSP differ from an action potential?

    A. One involves hyperpolarization and the other involves
       depolarization.
    B. One is due to the opening of sodium channels, while the other
       is due to the opening of potassium channels.
    C. They differ in how many sodium channels are opened.
    D. They differ in how many potassium channels are opened.
    (C, p. 53, factual)

26.    Which decays as it travels along the membrane of a neuron?

    A. an action potential, but not an EPSP
    B. an EPSP, but not an action potential
    C. both an action potential and an EPSP
    D. neither an action potential nor an EPSP
    (B, p. 53, factual)

27.    Which of the following is NOT an inference that Sherrington made
    about neural transmission?

    A. temporal summation
    B. delayed transmission at the synapse
    C. complementary excitation and inhibition of opposing muscles
    D. Synaptic transmission involves chemical transmission.
    (D, p. 53, conceptual)

28.    Which of the following would produce spatial summation?

    A. Present two or more weak stimuli at the same time.
    B. Start action potentials at both ends of one axon at the same
       time.
    C. Do not allow a flexor muscle to relax before stimulating it
       again.
    D. Present a rapid sequence of weak stimuli.
    (A, p. 54, factual)

29.     Spatial summation refers to:

        A. multiple weak stimulations that occur in rapid succession.
        B. a decrease in responsiveness after repeated stimulation.
        C. multiple weak stimulations that occur at the same time.
        D. an increase in the strength of action potentials after
           repeated stimulation.
        (C, p. 54, factual)

30.     What is the primary difference between temporal summation and
        spatial summation?

        A. Only spatial summation can produce an action potential.
        B. Spatial summation depends on contributions from more than one
           sensory neuron.
        C. Temporal summation produces a hyperpolarization instead of a
           depolarization.
        D. Spatial summation alters the response of more than one
           postsynaptic cell.
        (B, p. 54, conceptual)

31.     Simultaneous weak stimuli at different locations produce a
        greater reflexive response than one of the stimuli by itself.
        What is this phenomenon called?

        A. Sherrington's law
        B. temporal summation
        C. spatial summation
        D. the all-or-none law
        (C, p. 54, factual)

32.     What do temporal summation and spatial summation have in common?

        A. Both involve the activity of only two neurons.
        B. Both require a response from the brain.
        C. Both depend on a combination of visual and auditory stimuli.
        D. Both enable a reflex to occur in response to weak stimuli.
        (D, p. 54, conceptual)

33.     Eccles' work, using microelectrodes, _____ Sherrington's earlier
        inferences about temporal summation, and _____ Sherrington's
        inferences about spatial summation.

        A. confirmed; refuted
        B. refuted; confirmed
        C. confirmed; confirmed
        D. refuted; refuted
        (C, p. 54, factual)

34.  When a vertebrate animal contracts the flexor muscles of a leg,
     it relaxes the extensor muscles of the same leg. Sherrington
     considered this evidence for the existence of:

     A. spatial summation.
     B. temporal summation.
     C. inhibitory messages.
     D. the delay in transmission at synapses.
     (C, pp. 55, factual)

35.  What ordinarily prevents extensor muscles from contracting at the
     same time as flexor muscles?

     A. the ligaments and tendons that bind them together
     B. learned patterns of coordination in the cerebral cortex
     C. inhibitory synapses in the spinal cord
     D. Both muscles are controlled by different branches of the same
        Axon.
     (C, p. 55, conceptual)

36.  A normal, healthy animal never contracts the flexor muscles and
     the extensor muscles of the same leg at the same time.  Why not?

     A. When the interneuron sends excitatory messages to one,
        inhibitory messages go to the other.
     B. They are mechanically connected in a way that makes it
        impossible for both to contract at the same time.
     C. Such coordination is learned through prenatal movement.
     D. Both muscles are controlled by branches of the same axon.
     (A, p. 55, conceptual)

37.  Inhibitory synapses on a neuron:

     A. hyperpolarize the postsynaptic cell.
     B. decrease the cell's negative charge.
     C. increase the probability of an action potential.
     D. move the potential closer to the cell's threshold.
     ("WWW" A, p. 55, factual)

38.  What does the abbreviation IPSP stand for?

     A. inhibitory presynaptic process
     B. interior postsensory process
     C. interior presynaptic potential
     D. inhibitory postsynaptic potential
     (D, p. 55, factual)

39.  An IPSP represents:

     A. the location where a dendrite branches.
     B. a gap in a myelin sheath.
     C. a subthreshold depolarization.
     D. a temporary hyperpolarization.
     (D, p. 55, factual)

40.    An IPSP occurs when:

       A. potassium gates open and ions enter the cell.
       B. sodium gates open and ions enter the cell.
       C. potassium gates open and ions leave the cell.
       D. sodium gates open and ions leave the cell.
       (C, p. 55, factual)

41.    An IPSP occurs when synaptic input selectively:

       A. opens the gates for chloride ions to leave the cell.
       B. opens the gates for chloride ions to enter the cell.
       C. closes chloride gates.
       D. closes potassium gates.
       (B, p. 55, factual)

42.    An EPSP is to _____ as an IPSP is to _____.

       A. hyperpolarization; depolarization
       B. depolarization; hyperpolarization
       C. spatial summation; temporal summation
       D. temporal summation; spatial summation
       (B, p. 56, factual)

**Relationship Among EPSP, IPSP, and Action Potential**

43.    Which of the following combinations would be most likely to
       summate to produce an action potential?

       A. two IPSPs
       B. two EPSPs
       C. an IPSP plus an EPSP
       D. Any of these combinations would be equally likely to produce
          an action potential.
       (B, p. 56, conceptual)

44.    The greater the number of EPSPs affecting a neuron at any given
       time, the _____ the probability of an action potential; the
       greater the number of IPSPs, the _____ the probability of an
       action potential.

       A. greater; greater
       B. lower; lower
       C. lower; greater
       D. greater; lower
       (D, p. 56, factual)

45.    What effect do EPSPs and IPSPs have on the probability of
       triggering an action potential?

       A. The probability is increased by EPSPs and decreased by IPSPs.
       B. The probability is increased by EPSPs and increased by IPSPs.
       C. The probability is decreased by EPSPs and decreased by IPSPs.
       D. The probability is decreased by EPSPs and increased by IPSPs.
       (A, p. 56, conceptual)

46.   What determines whether a neuron has an action potential?

        A. only the number of EPSPs impinging on an axon
        B. only the number of IPSPs impinging on the dendrites
        C. the combined effects of EPSPs and IPSPs
        D. summation effects of IPSPs
        (C, p. 56, conceptual)

47.   Some synapses are located near the far end of a dendrite. These
      synapses:

        A. have stronger effects on the cell.
        B. have weaker effects on the cell.
        C. affect the cell no differently than synapses on the closer end
           of a dendrite.
        D. compensate for their distance.
        (B, p. 56, factual)

48.   Why do graded potentials have different effects depending upon
      where they synapse on the neuron?

        A. They decay with distance, but only distance.
        B. They decay with time, but only time.
        C. They decay with time and distance.
        D. They decay with time if they synapse on the far end of a
           dendrite, but with distance if they synapse on the near end of
           a dendrite.
        (C, p. 56, conceptual)

49.   What are the effects of IPSPs and EPSPs, respectively, on the
      electrical potential across the membrane?

        A. IPSPs = more negative; EPSPs = less negative
        B. IPSPs = less negative; EPSPs = more negative
        C. IPSPs increase the threshold; EPSPs decrease the threshold.
        D. IPSPs decrease the threshold; EPSPs increase the threshold.
        (A, p. 56, conceptual)

50.   The "spontaneous firing rate" of a neuron refers to:

        A. its resting potential.
        B. its rate of energy consumption.
        C. its rate of producing action potentials even when it is not
           stimulated.
        D. the velocity of its action potentials under normal conditions.
        (C, p. 56, factual)

51.    Which of the following is true about the spontaneous firing rates
       of neurons?

       A. EPSPs increase the frequency.
       B. EPSPs decrease the frequency.
       C. IPSPs increase the frequency.
       D. One EPSP equals the effect of two IPSPs.
       (A, p. 56, factual)

52.    Which of the following would increase the spontaneous firing
       rates in neurons?

       A. IPSPs
       B. EPSPs
       C. both EPSPs and IPSPs
       D. neither EPSPs nor IPSPs
       (B, p. 56, factual)

53.    EPSPs and IPSPs reaching a neuron at a given moment:

       A. will always result in an action potential.
       B. will help determine whether or not a presynaptic cell will
          fire.
       C. will help determine whether or not a postsynaptic cell will
          fire.
       D. almost always cancel each other out, thereby inhibiting a
          neuron from firing.
       (C, p. 56, conceptual)

54.    Which of the following is TRUE about inhibitory synapses?

       A. They always result in suppressing behavior.
       B. They always result in stimulating behavior.
       C. They may result in either suppression or expression of
          behavior.
       D. They affect cells at the presynaptic level, but not
          at the postsynaptic level.
       (C, p. 56, conceptual)

**Module 3.2: Chemical Events at the Synapse**

55.    Which one of Sherrington's inferences about the synapse was
       WRONG?

       A. Transmission at a synapse is slower than transmission of
          impulses along an axon.
       B. Transmission at the synapse is primarily an electrical
          process.
       C. Synapses can be either excitatory or inhibitory.
       D. Synapses make spatial summation and temporal summation
          possible.
       (B, p. 58, factual)

### The Discovery that Most Synaptic Transmission is Chemical

56. What was the first evidence reported by T. R. Elliott suggesting that synapses operate chemically?

    A. Adrenaline mimics the effects of the parasympathetic nervous system.
    B. Adrenaline decreases heart rate.
    C. Adrenaline produces a hormone which decreases heart rate.
    D. Adrenaline mimics the effects of the sympathetic nervous system.
    (D, p. 58, factual)

57. Loewi demonstrated that synapses operate by the release of chemicals. He did this by:

    A. applying adrenaline directly to the heart muscle.
    B. collecting fluid from a stimulated frog's heart, transferring it to another frog's heart and measuring that heart rate.
    C. measuring the speed of a dog's reflexes while the dog was under the influence of various drugs.
    D. applying an extract of marijuana in eye drops and discovering that it dilated the pupils.
    (B, p. 58, factual)

58. After one frog's heart has been stimulated, an extract of fluid from that heart can make a second frog's heart beat faster. What conclusion did Otto Loewi draw from these results?

    A. Transmission at synapses is a chemical event.
    B. The sympathetic and parasympathetic nervous systems are antagonistic.
    C. Transmission at heart muscle synapses is electrical.
    D. Hormones facilitate the actions of the nervous system.
    (A, p. 58, factual)

### The Sequence of Chemical Events at a Synapse

59. How many different chemicals do neuroscientists believe function as neurotransmitters?

    A. 2 (one excitatory and the other inhibitory)
    B. 5-10
    C. dozens
    D. thousands
    (C, p. 59, factual)

60. What is NOT one of the major categories of neurotransmitters?

    A. steroids
    B. amino acids
    C. gases
    D. purines
    (A, pp. 59, factual)

61.     Peptides are:

        A. chemicals similar to amino acids.
        B. chains of amino acids.
        C. also known as purines.
        D. a category of chemicals including adenosine.
        (B, pp. 59, factual)

62.     What is the most unusual thing about the neurotransmitter nitric
        oxide (NO)?

        A. It is found only in sensory neurons.
        B. It is both excitatory and inhibitory.
        C. It is normally a poisonous gas.
        D. It is also known as "laughing gas."
        (C, p. 60, factual)

63.     Which neurotransmitter is ordinarily a poisonous gas?

        A. acetylcholine
        B. serotonin
        C. nitric oxide
        D. GABA
        (C, p. 60, factual)

64.     Nitric oxide's value is that it:

        A. increases blood flow to certain areas of the brain.
        B. restricts blood flow to certain areas of the brain.
        C. increases growth of microglia.
        D. decreases growth of microglia.
        (A, p. 60, factual)

65.     What provides the building blocks for synthesizing all
        neurotransmitters?

        A. substances found in the diet
        B. breakdown products of DNA
        C. breakdown products formed from other transmitters
        D. methane and ethanol
        (A, p. 60, conceptual)

66.     Which of the following is NOT a catecholamine?

        A. dopamine
        B. epinephrine
        C. norepinephrine
        D. serotonin
        (D, p. 60, factual)

67.    Acetylcholine is synthesized from choline, which is abundant in:

       A. all carbohydrates.
       B. all proteins.
       C. cauliflower and milk.
       D. onions and peppers.
       (C, p. 60, factual)

68.    Which amino acid is a precursor to serotonin in the brain?

       A. phenylalanine
       B. aspartate
       C. tryptophan
       D. glutamate
       (C, p. 60, factual)

69.    Given that protein contains tryptophan, why might little
       tryptophan reach the brain after a high protein meal?

       A. The meal contained carbohydrates also.
       B. The meal contained fats also.
       C. The meal also contained certain other amino acids.
       D. The meal contained inadequate levels of thiamine.
       (C, pp. 60, factual)

70.    If you eat a food containing tryptophan, what can you consume
       with it to increase its entry to the brain?

       A. phenylalanine
       B. carbohydrates
       C. fats
       D. thiamine
       (B, p. 60, factual)

71.    Insulin increases the entry of tryptophan into the brain by:

       A. weakening the blood-brain barrier.
       B. converting tryptophan into a compound that more easily enters
          the brain.
       C. increasing metabolic activity only in those areas of the
          brain that use tryptophan.
       D. causing certain competing amino acids to enter other cells,
          outside the brain.
       (D, p. 60, factual)

72.    How do carbohydrates in the diet lead to increased tryptophan in
       the brain?

       A. Carbohydrates contain the amino acid tryptophan.
       B. Carbohydrates are necessary to transport tryptophan.
       C. Carbohydrates weaken the blood-brain barrier.
       D. Carbohydrates stimulate insulin secretion.
       (D, p. 61, factual)

73.    Acetylcholine is synthesized in the:

A. postsynaptic terminal.
B. presynaptic terminal.
C. cell body.
D. dendrites.
(B, p. 61, factual)

74.    Large neurotransmitters are synthesized in the:

A. postsynaptic terminal.
B. presynaptic terminal.
C. cell body.
D. dendrites.
(C, p. 61, factual)

75.    What is true about neurons that release peptide
       neurotransmitters?

A. They take a long time to replenish their supply of
   transmitters.
B. They are exclusively inhibitory.
C. They are able to reabsorb peptides after their release.
D. They synthesize the peptides at the presynaptic terminals.
(A, p. 61, factual)

76.    Neurons reabsorb and recycle:

A. all neurotransmitters.
B. only the peptide neurotransmitters.
C. many of the nonpeptide transmitters.
D. acetylcholine, only.
(C, p. 61, factual)

77.    What is contained within a vesicle?

A. sodium ions
B. potassium ions
C. neurotransmitter molecules
D. calcium ions
(C, p. 62, factual)

78.    Vesicles are located:

A. in postsynaptic terminals.
B. in spherical packets in the postsynaptic terminals.
C. in presynaptic terminals.
D. only outside of the neuron in the extracellular fluid.
(C, p. 62, factual)

79.   Within the presynaptic terminals, where are neurotransmitters
      stored?

      A. in the calcium gates
      B. in the Nodes of Ranvier
      C. in vesicles
      D. in clefts
      (C, p. 62, factual)

80.   High concentrations of all neurotransmitters, except for NO, are
      stored in the:

      A. presynaptic terminals.
      B. postsynaptic terminals.
      C. axon.
      D. cell body.
      (A, p. 62, factual)

81.   When an action potential reaches the end of an axon, the
      depolarization causes what ionic movement in the presynaptic
      cell?

      A. sodium out of the cell
      B. lithium out of the cell
      C. iron into the cell
      D. calcium into the cell
      (D, p. 62, factual)

82.   How does an action potential cause the release of
      neurotransmitters?

      A. It blocks potassium pores in the membrane.
      B. It opens chloride pores in the membrane.
      C. It blocks iron pores in the membrane.
      D. It opens calcium pores in the membrane.
      (D, p. 62, factual)

83.   The neuron excretes neurotransmitter through its membrane by a
      process called:

      A. Dale's principle.
      B. exocytosis.
      C. endocytosis.
      D. voltage-dependent flow.
      (B, p. 62, factual)

84.   Exocytosis is the process by which neurotransmitters are:

      A. excreted into the synaptic cleft.
      B. synthesized.
      C. destroyed.
      D. secreted into synaptic vesicles.
      (A, p. 62, factual)

85.    Given a repetitive series of action potentials in a given neuron,
        we can expect that:

        A. each action potential will release the same amount of
            neurotransmitter.
        B. later action potentials in a series will release more
            neurotransmitter than the first.
        C. many action potentials will fail to release any
            neurotransmitters at all.
        D. some action potentials will release one chemical as the
            neurotransmitter, and others will release other chemicals.
        (C, p. 62, factual)

86.    What is the synaptic cleft?

        A. the gap between the presynaptic neuron and the postsynaptic
            neuron
        B. a packet that stores neurotransmitter molecules
        C. a subthreshold depolarization
        D. the storage location for calcium ions
        (A, p. 62, conceptual)

87.    What happens when neurotransmitter is released by a presynaptic
        cell?

        A. It causes calcium to rush into the presynaptic neuron.
        B. It causes calcium to rush into the postsynaptic neuron.
        C. The neurotransmitter passively spreads across the synaptic
            cleft.
        D. The neurotransmitter is actively transported across the
            synaptic cleft.
        (C, p. 62, conceptual)

88.    The process of neurotransmission takes:

        A. about 0.5 to 2 seconds.
        B. about 0.5 to 2 milliseconds.
        C. about 1 second.
        D. just over .05 of a second.
        (B, p. 62, factual)

89.    In most cases, how many neurotransmitters does a single neuron
        release?

        A. only one neurotransmitter
        B. dozens of neurotransmitters
        C. several neurotransmitters, with each axon branch releasing a
            different one
        D. several neurotransmitters, with each axon branch releasing the
            same combination
        (D, p. 62, factual)

90.    Investigators believed that each neuron released just one
       neurotransmitter.  This generalization is known as:

       A. Dale's principle.
       B. the James-Lange theory.
       C. the Young-Helmholtz theory.
       D. the Cannon-Bard theory.
       (A, p. 62, factual)

91.    What is Dale's principle?

       A. Each neuron responds to every neurotransmitter in some way.
       B. Each neuron releases only one neurotransmitter.
       C. Each axon terminal releases a different neurotransmitter.
       D. Each neuron responds to only one neurotransmitter.
       (B, p. 62, factual)

92.    In general, a single neuron releases _____ neurotransmitter(s),
       and can respond to _____ neurotransmitter(s).

       A. one; many
       B. dozens of; only one
       C. several; only one
       D. several; many
       (D, p. 62, factual)

93.    What is the relationship between the number of neurotransmitters
       a neuron can respond to and the number of neurotransmitters it
       releases?

       A. A neuron responds to more neurotransmitters than it releases.
       B. A neuron responds to fewer neurotransmitter than it releases.
       C. A neuron responds to and releases the exact same
          neurotransmitters.
       D. Each neuron either releases neurotransmitters or responds
          to them, but it cannot do both.
       (A, p. 62, conceptual)

94.    In most cases, how many neurotransmitters can activate a
       postsynaptic neuron?

       A. only one neurotransmitter
       B. any neurotransmitter
       C. several transmitters, with different synapses responding to
          different transmitters
       D. several transmitters, which must be received simultaneously
       (C, p. 62, factual)

95.   What is the main advantage of a neuron releasing more than one
      neurotransmitter?

      A. If it runs out of one, it has others.
      B. It can release different transmitters on different occasions.
      C. It can send more complex messages.
      D. It can release one from the axon's terminal and one from
         another location along the axon.
      (C, p. 62, factual)

96.   A neuron releases a limited number of neurotransmitters and
      receives and responds to:

      A. only one neurotransmitter.
      B. the same neurotransmitters it releases.
      C. a number of different neurotransmitters at various synapses.
      D. all neurotransmitters available in the brain.
      (C, p. 62, factual)

97.   What determines the effect that a neurotransmitter has on the
      postsynaptic neuron?

      A. the speed the action potential traveled down the axon
      B. the number of branches of the presynaptic axon
      C. the receptors on the postsynaptic membrane
      D. the number of synaptic vesicles present
      (C, p. 62, conceptual)

98.   A neurotransmitter receptor is:

      A. a protein embedded in the membrane.
      B. a channel in the membrane.
      C. found only on the soma.
      D. activated similarly for all neurotransmitters.
      (A, p. 62, factual)

99.   What does it mean to say that acetylcholine exerts ionotropic
      effects?

      A. It opens gates for a particular ion.
      B. It alters the permeability of the presynaptic neuron.
      C. It increases the concentration of ions within the vesicles.
      D. It causes a change in the electrical charge of sodium ions
         from positive to negative.
      (A, p. 63, factual)

100.  Glutamate opens sodium gates, enabling sodium ions to enter the
      postsynaptic cell.  What is this effect called?

      A. metabotropic
      B. ionotropic
      C. modulatory
      D. orthodromic
      (B, p. 62, conceptual)

101.  The neurotransmitter GABA exerts _____ effects, and its effects
      are almost always _____.

      A. ionotropic; excitatory
      B. ionotropic; inhibitory
      C. metabotropic; excitatory
      D. metabotropic; inhibitory
      (B, p. 63, factual)

102.  Which of the following is true about ionotropic effects?

      A. They depolarize the postsynaptic membrane.
      B. They hyperpolarize the postsynaptic membrane.
      C. They may depolarize or hyperpolarize the postsynaptic
         membrane.
      D. They enhance the reabsorption of neurotransmitters.
      (C, p. 63, conceptual)

103.  Which of the following characterizes ionotropic effects?

      A. rapid, short-lived effects
      B. rapid, long lasting effects
      C. excitatory only
      D. inhibitory only
      (A, p. 63, factual)

104.  Acetylcholine exerts ionotropic effects at _____ synapses.

      A. isomorphic
      B. nicotinic
      C. adrenergic
      D. inhibitory
      (B, p. 63, factual)

105.  Acetylcholine stimulates the same receptors as does:

      A. nicotine
      B. LSD
      C. marijuana
      D. cocaine
      ("WWW" A, p. 63, factual)

106.  Few pianists can play quickly enough to play the Minute Waltz in
      a minute.  The finger movements that are required are likely to
      involve which type of neurotransmitter effects?

      A. ionotropic effects
      B. metabotropic effects
      C. second messenger effects
      D. neuromodulator effects
      (A, p. 63, conceptual)

107. Compared to ionotropic effects, metabolic effects have:

     A. more rapid onset and briefer effects.
     B. slower onset and briefer effects.
     C. more rapid onset and longer lasting effects.
     D. slower onset and longer lasting effects.
     (D, p. 63, factual)

108. Ionotropic effects typically begin about _____ after release of
     the neurotransmitter, while metabotropic effects begin about
     _____ after the neurotransmitter is released.

     A. 10 msec; 10 msec
     B. 10 msec; 30 msec
     C. 10 sec; 30 sec
     D. 30 msec; 10 msec
     (B, p. 63, factual)

109. How do ionotropic effects compare to metabotropic effects?

     A. They are slower in onset, and briefer.
     B. They are slower in onset, and more long lasting.
     C. They are faster in onset, and briefer.
     D. They are faster in onset, and more long lasting.
     (C, p. 63, factual)

110. Which of the following is more typical of a metabotropic effect
     than an ionotropic effect?

     A. produces inhibitory effects on the postsynaptic cell
     B. influences the speed of conduction by the postsynaptic cell
     C. produces long-lasting effects on the post-synaptic cell
     D. controls sensory processes
     (C, p. 63, factual)

111. Which effect is consistently associated with a "second
     messenger"?

     A. ionotropic
     B. metabotropic
     C. inhibitory
     D. excitatory
     (B, p. 63, conceptual)

112. Receptor molecules for neurotransmitters that exert metabotropic
     effects are proteins that bind to _____ outside the membrane, and
     bind to _____ inside the membrane.

     A. calcium; potassium
     B. neurotransmitters; nicotine
     C. neurotransmitters; G-proteins
     D. adenosine; nitric oxide
     (C, p. 63, factual)

113. Guanosine triphosphate is:

     A. a major category of neurotransmitters.
     B. an important excitatory neurotransmitter.
     C. an important inhibitory neurotransmitter.
     D. an energy storing molecule.
     (D, p. 63, factual)

114. Which of the following characterizes a "second messenger"?

     A. It is released by the presynaptic cell at the same time as
        another transmitter.
     B. It is released by the presynaptic cell slightly after another
        transmitter.
     C. It is released by the postsynaptic cell and received by the
        presynaptic cell.
     D. It is released inside the postsynaptic cell, where it
        initiates chemical reactions.
     (D, pp. 63, conceptual)

115. Where do "second messengers" carry their messages?

     A. to the presynaptic membrane
     B. to areas within the postsynaptic cell
     C. to areas within the presynaptic cell
     D. to the surrounding glia
     (B, p. 63, factual)

116. The effect of the second messenger:

     A. is almost always excitatory.
     B. is almost always inhibitory.
     C. results in opening or closing channels.
     D. results in increasing or decreasing the velocity of an action
        potential.
     (C, p. 63, factual)

117. A metabotropic synapse, by way of its second messenger:

     A. has effects localized to one point on the membrane.
     B. can influence activity in much of the presynaptic cell.
     C. can influence activity in much or all of the postsynaptic
        cell.
     D. has minimal effect on the postsynaptic cell.
     (C, p. 63, factual)

118. How do the effects of neuromodulators compare to hormones?

     A. Neuromodulators are slower.
     B. Neuromodulators affect only the closest receptors.
     C. Neuromodulators are excitatory, whereas hormones are
        inhibitory.
     D. Neuromodulators are inhibitory, whereas hormones are
        excitatory.
     (B, p. 64, conceptual)

119.   What is the relationship between neuromodulators and
       neurotransmitters?  Neuromodulators usually work

       A. independently of neurotransmitters.
       B. by mimicking neurotransmitters.
       C. in combination with neurotransmitters.
       D. by blocking receptors for neurotransmitters.
       (C, p. 64, conceptual)

120.   Neuromodulators:

       A. can prolong or limit the effect of a neurotransmitter.
       B. change the chemical composition of neurotransmitters.
       C. alter the membranes of the cell to allow more or fewer
          neurotransmitter to move into the cell.
       D. produce their effect in the absence of neurotransmitters.
       (A, p. 64, factual)

121.   What is the function of the enzyme acetylcholinesterase?

       A. It synthesizes acetylcholine from the diet.
       B. It increases the sensitivity of the postsynaptic cell to
          acetylcholine.
       C. It blocks further release of the transmitter acetylcholine.
       D. It breaks acetylcholine down into components for recycling.
       (D, p. 65, factual)

122.   What happens to acetylcholine after it attaches to a receptor on
       the postsynaptic cell?

       A. It is broken down into two components.
       B. It is reabsorbed intact by the presynaptic cell.
       C. The postsynaptic cell metabolizes it as a source of energy.
       D. It continues to stimulate the postsynaptic neuron until
           replaced by another neurotransmitter.
       (A, p. 65, factual)

123.   What would be the effect of a drug that inhibits the action of
       the enzyme acetylcholinesterase?

       A. It would prolong the action of acetylcholine at its synapses.
       B. It would decrease the duration of action of acetylcholine at
          its synapses
       C. It would decrease the synthesis of acetylcholine by the
          presynaptic cell.
       D. It would increase the synthesis of acetylcholine by the
          presynaptic cell
       (A, p. 65, factual)

124.  What is one way to prolong the effects of the neurotransmitter
      acetylcholine?  Give a drug that:

      A. decreases production of monoamine oxidase.
      B. increases production of monoamine oxidase.
      C. mimics the effects of the enzyme acetylcholinesterase.
      D. inhibits the effects of the enzyme acetylcholinesterase.
      (D, p. 65, factual)

125.  What condition is improved by increasing the presence of
      acetylcholine in the synapse?

      A. alcohol abuse
      B. Parkinson's disease
      C. myasthenia gravis
      D. multiple sclerosis
      (C, p. 65, factual)

126.  Myasthenia gravis is a condition associated with:

      A. an inhibition of acetylcholinesterase.
      B. a deficit of transmission of acetylcholine.
      C. prolonged activity of acetylcholine.
      D. too little acetylcholinesterase in the synaptic gap.
      (B, p. 65, factual)

127.  What common function is served by acetylcholinesterase, MAO, and
      COMT?

      A. exciting certain synapses
      B. inhibiting certain synapses
      C. breaking neurotransmitters down into inactive chemicals
      D. increasing the presence of certain neurotransmitters in the
         synapse
      (C, p. 66, conceptual)

128.  After serotonin or one of the catecholamine transmitters
      stimulates the postsynaptic receptor, what happens to most of the
      transmitter molecules?

      A. They remain on the receptor until other neurotransmitters
         replace them.
      B. They are broken into components while still attached to the
         postsynaptic cell.
      C. They are metabolized by the postsynaptic cell as a source of
         energy.
      D. The presynaptic cell reabsorbs most of them intact.
      (D, p. 66, factual)

129.   What is reuptake?

   A. the absorption of neurotransmitters by the postsynaptic neuron
   B. the absorption of neurotransmitters by the presynaptic neuron
   C. the absorption of nutrients and waste products by glial cells
   D. the absorption of neurotransmitters by glial cells
   (B, p. 66, conceptual)

130.   Reuptake is an alternative to which other process?

   A. recycling of neurotransmitters
   B. enzymatic breakdown of neurotransmitters
   C. absorption of neurotransmitter by the postsynaptic neuron
   D. re-release of neurotransmitters from postsynaptic neurons
   (B, p. 66, conceptual)

131.   What is the function of "transporter" proteins?

   A. They allow neurotransmitters back into the presynaptic neuron.
   B. They ferry neurotransmitters across the synapse to the
      postsynaptic neuron.
   C. They ferry neurotransmitters across the synapse back to the
      presynaptic neuron.
   D. They help neurotransmitters find the appropriate receptor
      sites.
   (A, p. 66, conceptual)

132.   Transporters:

   A. are special membrane proteins.
   B. transport neurotransmitters to the postsynaptic membrane.
   C. transport much needed glucose to the brain.
   D. are enzymes that convert neurotransmitters into inactive
      chemicals.
   (A, p. 66, factual)

133.   COMT and MAO are:

   A. enzymes that convert catecholamines into inactive chemicals.
   B. enzymes that make catecholamines.
   C. neurotransmitters in the same group as serotonin.
   D. the inactive fragments of catecholamines.
   (A, p. 66, factual)

134. Why do the effects of certain transmitters, such as serotonin, vary from one synapse to another?

    A. The brain releases different forms of serotonin at different synapses.
    B. It depends if it is an original serotonin molecule or one that has been recycled.
    C. The width of the synaptic cleft varies from one synapse to another.
    D. There are several kinds of postsynaptic receptors for serotonin.
    (D, p. 66, conceptual)

**Module 3.3: Synapses, Abused Drugs, and Behavior**

135. Nearly all of the commonly abused drugs:

    A. share certain effects on dopamine synapses.
    B. are detrimental to humans.
    C. increase schizophrenic symptoms.
    D. are produced from everyday plants.
    (A, p. 68, factual)

136. The chemicals used as neurotransmitters in humans are found in:

    A. no other species.
    B. other mammals also, but not in nonmammals.
    C. other vertebrates, but not in invertebrates.
    D. apparently all other species, including plants.
    (D, p. 68, factual)

137. Our brains respond to plant chemicals because:

    A. plants use chemicals similar to neurotransmitters.
    B. animals evolved from plants.
    C. plants have evolved neuron-like cells.
    D. those are the only chemicals that are stable at common environmental temperatures.
    (A, p. 68, conceptual)

    **How Drugs Affect Synapses**

138. A drug that mimics or increases the effects of a neurotransmitter is called:

    A. an agonist.
    B. an antagonist.
    C. a stimulant.
    D. a protagonist.
    (A, p. 68, factual)

139.  A drug that blocks the effects of a neurotransmitter is called:

      A. an agonist
      B. an antagonist
      C. a depressant
      D. a protagonist
      (B, p. 68, factual)

140.  A drug that blocks the effects of a neurotransmitter is a(n)
      _____; a drug that mimics or increases the effects is a(n) _____.

      A. neuromodulator; synergist
      B. agonist; antagonist
      C. depressant; stimulant
      D. antagonist; agonist
      (D, p. 68, factual)

141.  "Increases the effects" is to _____ as "blocks the effects"
      is to _____.

      A. an agonist; an antagonist
      B. a protagonist; an agonist
      C. a stimulant; a depressant
      D. an antagonist; a protagonist
      (A, p. 68, conceptual)

142.  Which effect would be considered to be antagonistic?

      A. blocking the synthesis of neurotransmitters
      B. stimulating the release of neurotransmitters
      C. blocking the reuptake of neurotransmitters
      D. interfering with the breakdown of neurotransmitters
      (A, p. 68, conceptual)

143.  Which effect would be considered to be agonistic?

      A. blocking the synthesis of neurotransmitters
      B. stimulating the release of neurotransmitters
      C. blocking the postsynaptic receptors
      D. mimicking enzymes that breakdown neurotransmitters
      (B, p. 68, conceptual)

144.  To say that a drug has an affinity for a particular type of
      receptor is to imply that:

      A. the drug breaks down neurotransmitter chemicals at that
         receptor site.
      B. the drug will always excite the postsynaptic receptor.
      C. the drug will always inhibit the postsynaptic receptor.
      D. the drug binds to that receptor.
      (D, p. 68, factual)

145.  If a drug binds to a particular receptor, it is said to:

      A. increase the synthesis of the neurotransmitter used at that
         receptor.
      B. decrease the synthesis of the neurotransmitter used at that
         receptor.
      C. stimulate breakdown at that receptor.
      D. have an affinity for that type of receptor.
      (D, p. 68, factual)

146.  What does it mean to say that a drug has an affinity for a
      particular receptor?

      A. The drug damages the receptor.
      B. The drug readily binds with the receptor.
      C. The drug has an excitatory effect when attached to that
         receptor.
      D. The drug has beneficial behavioral effects at that receptor.
      (B, p. 68, factual)

147.  What does "efficacy" mean with respect to drug effects?

      A. the tendency of a drug to have inhibitory effects
      B. the tendency of a drug to have excitatory effects
      C. the tendency for a drug to attach to a receptor
      D. the tendency for a drug to activate a receptor
      (D, p. 68, factual)

148.  Efficacy is to _____ as affinity is to _____.

      A. proliferation; activation
      B. activation; attachment
      C. destruction; proliferation
      D. attachment; proliferation
      (B, p. 68, conceptual)

149.  If a drug has high affinity and low efficacy, what effect does it
      have on the postsynaptic neuron?

      A. antagonistic
      B. agonistic
      C. proactive
      D. destructive
      (A, p. 68, factual)

150.  If a drug has high affinity and high efficacy, what effect does
      it have on the postsynaptic neuron?

      A. antagonistic
      B. agonistic
      C. proactive
      D. destructive
      (B, p. 68, conceptual)

151. What is one factor in determining whether a drug that readily attaches to a receptor will have agonistic or antagonistic effects?

    A. its affinity for the receptor
    B. its efficacy
    C. the neurotransmitter than normally attaches to that receptor
    D. its electrical charge
    (B, p. 68, conceptual)

152. The effectiveness and side-effects of a drug vary from one person to the next.  One reason for this is that:

    A. most drugs are chemically unstable, resulting in unpredictable effects.
    B. most drugs interact with the diet to produce variable effects.
    C. each drug tends to affect more than one kind of synapse.
    D. drugs will break down neurotransmitters into different component parts in different people.
    (C, p. 68, factual)

**Synapses, Reinforcement, and Drug Use**

153. Which neurotransmitter has been repeatedly connected with addictive drugs?

    A. epinephrine
    B. acetylcholine
    C. serotonin
    D. dopamine
    (D, p. 69, factual)

154. Addictive drugs have been found to:

    A. increase dopamine effects.
    B. decrease dopamine effects.
    C. increase acetylcholine effects.
    D. decrease serotonin effects.
    (A, p. 69, factual)

155. Most habit-forming drugs activate which type of synapse?

    A. acetylcholine
    B. opiate
    C. GABA
    D. dopamine
    (D, p. 69, factual)

156.  Which type of subjects were first used in studies on self
      stimulation of the brain?

      A. rats
      B. monkeys
      C. college student volunteers
      D. drug addicts
      (A, p. 69, factual)

157.  What was a basic finding from early studies on self-stimulation
      of the brain?

      A. Humans would self-stimulate, but other species would not.
      B. Humans would not self-stimulate, but other species would.
      C. Self-stimulation findings were difficult to replicate.
      D. Animals would self-stimulate to exhaustion.
      (D, p. 69, conceptual)

158.  Which areas of the brain are most likely to lead to repeated
      self-stimulation?

      A. areas where dopamine is released
      B. areas where serotonin is released
      C. areas where epinephrine is released
      D. throughout the brain, independent of particular
         neurotransmitters
      (A, p. 69, factual)

159.  What brain area has been linked to drug addiction?

      A. the nucleus accumbens
      B. the whole limbic system
      C. the frontal lobes
      D. the brain stem
      (A, p. 69, factual)

160.  A small, subcortical area rich in dopamine is the:

      A. frontal lobe
      B. nucleus accumbens
      C. brain stem
      D. pituitary gland
      (B, p. 69, factual)

161.  In the nucleus accumbens, dopamine:

      A. is an excitatory transmitter.
      B. is an inhibitory transmitter.
      C. increases the activity of glutamate.
      D. affects glutamate, an inhibitory transmitter here.
      (B, p. 69, factual)

162. What general effect does dopamine have on postsynaptic cells?

    A. excitatory
    B. inhibitory
    C. increases action potential velocity
    D. decreases action potential velocity
    (B, p. 70, factual)

163. Food presented to a rat during the early stages of training evokes dopamine release.  The same amount of food to a well-trained rat evokes:

    A. very little dopamine release.
    B. even greater release of dopamine.
    C. a release of dopamine equal to that released during the early stages of training.
    D. GABA release instead.
    (A, p. 70, factual)

164. Currently, the role of dopamine and the nucleus accumbens is:

    A. hypothesized to be associated with pleasant events only.
    B. believed to relate to the attention-getting value of an event.
    C. believed to relate to the aggression-arousing tendency of the situation.
    D. hypothesized to be associated with unpleasant events only.
    (B, p. 70, factual)

165. A drug which produces excitement, alertness, elevated mood, and decreased fatigue is referred to as:

    A. a stimulant drug.
    B. a depressant.
    C. ADD
    D. a dopamine transporter.
    (A, p. 70, factual)

166. What effect does an amphetamine have at the synapse?

    A. It blocks the breakdown of dopamine.
    B. It increases the release of dopamine from the presynaptic terminal.
    C. It increases the sensitivity of dopamine receptors.
    D. It decreases the sensitivity of dopamine receptors.
    (B, p. 70, factual)

167. Why do cocaine and amphetamine produce similar effects?

    A. Both increase the activity of the sodium-potassium pump.
    B. Both increase the presence of dopamine in the synapses.
    C. Both cause a weakening of the blood-brain barrier.
    D. The brain converts both of them into acetylcholine.
    (B, p. 70, conceptual)

168.  What effect does cocaine have at the synapse?

      A. It increases the synthesis of dopamine.
      B. It blocks the breakdown of dopamine.
      C. It blocks the reuptake of dopamine.
      D. It accelerates the breakdown of dopamine.
      (C, p. 70, factual)

169.  Amphetamine and cocaine:

      A. decrease dopamine activity.
      B. increase dopamine activity.
      C. have effects which are intense and long-lived.
      D. decrease the accumulation of dopamine in the synaptic cleft.
      (B, p. 70, factual)

170.  The "crash" associated with amphetamine or cocaine abuse can be
      attributed to what effect of the drugs?

      A. They deplete normal levels of acetylcholine.
      B. They prevent the normal recycling of dopamine by the
         presynaptic neuron.
      C. They reduce blood flow to the brain.
      D. They interfere with the synthesis of norepinephrine.
      (B, p. 71, conceptual)

171.  Amphetamines and cocaine result in an excess of dopamine in the
      synaptic cleft.  The result a few hours later is a(n):

      A. increase in the release of dopamine from the presynaptic cell.
      B. absorption of dopamine into the postsynaptic cell.
      C. depressed state by the user.
      D. acceleration of the circadian rhythm.
      (C, p. 71, factual)

172.  What effect does an excess of a neurotransmitter in the synapse
      have on the presynaptic neuron?

      A. It stimulates synthesis.
      B. It encourages the release of more transmitter.
      C. It encourages the release of enzymes to break down the
         transmitter.
      D. It indicates adequate supplies and reduces release of more
         transmitter.
      (D, p. 71, conceptual)

173.  After repeated use of cocaine:

      A. the drug causes a release of more and more dopamine.
      B. the drug stimulates the release of a transmitter which adds to
         the reinforcing properties of the drug.
      C. the user becomes more sensitive to its effects.
      D. the drug causes a release of the transmitter, dynorphin.
      (D, p. 71, factual)

174. The synaptic effects of methylphenidate (Ritalin) are similar to what other drug?

    A. cocaine
    B. alcohol
    C. nicotine
    D. morphine
    (A, p. 71, factual)

175. Ritalin's benefits for people with ADD probably include:

    A. improved attention due to increased serotonin release.
    B. calming of activity due to dopamine effects.
    C. calming of activity due to serotonin effects.
    D. improved attention due to decreased serotonin release.
    (C, p. 71, factual)

176. One explanation of how an inhibitory neurotransmitter can act as a stimulant and increase arousal, activity, and sometimes even concentration is that:

    A. arousal and activity depend on hormones, not neurons.
    B. some neurons are stimulated by inhibitory transmitters.
    C. it decreases "background noise" in the brain.
    D. it inhibits the sympathetic nervous system.
    (C, p. 71, factual)

177. At high doses, MDMA:

    A. destroys axons that release acetylcholine.
    B. destroys axons that release dopamine and serotonin.
    C. stimulates axons that release acetylcholine.
    D. destroys axons in humans, but not in laboratory rats.
    (B, p. 71, factual)

178. Nicotine directly stimulates receptors in the central nervous system and at nerve-muscle junctions. These nicotinic receptors are also receptors for which neurotransmitter?

    A. glutamate
    B. dopamine
    C. serotonin
    D. acetylcholine
    (D, p. 72, factual)

179. Which would NOT be classified as an opiate?

    A. morphine
    B. marijuana
    C. heroin
    D. methadone
    (B, p. 72, factual)

180. Pert and Snyder's discovery that opiates bind with certain
     receptors led to what other discovery?

     A. the functions of inhibitory synpases
     B. the neurotransmitters that also bind with those receptors
     C. other classes of receptors with which opiates will bind
     D. more effective ways of manufacturing the drugs
     (B, pp. 72-73, conceptual)

181. Pert and Snyder (1973) found that opiate drugs bind with specific
     receptors in the brain.  These receptors normally respond to
     which naturally occurring neurotransmitters?

     A. endorphins
     B. catecholamines
     C. indolamines
     D. monoamines
     (A, p. 73, factual)

182. Opiates affect endorphin synapses, which in turn affect release
     of:

     A. acetylcholine
     B. serotonin
     C. dopamine
     D. GABA
     (D, p. 73, factual)

183. Endorphin synapses:

     A. excite neurons that release serotonin.
     B. excite neurons that release GABA.
     C. inhibit neurons that release GABA.
     D. inhibit neurons that release glutamate.
     (C, p. 73, factual)

184. What effect do opiate drugs have on dopamine?

     A. They increase the synthesis of dopamine.
     B. They increase the release of dopamine.
     C. They block transmitters that normally block dopamine.
     D. They mimic dopamine.
     (C, p. 73, conceptual)

185. Which drug has no effect on dopamine synapses?

     A. cocaine
     B. PCP (angel dust)
     C. nicotine
     D. morphine
     (B, p. 73, factual)

186.    What is the effect of PCP in the nucleus accumbens?

        A. reinforcing
        B. punishing
        C. increases dopamine
        D. decreases dopamine
        (A, p. 73, factual)

187.    What are the effects of phencyclidine (PCP or "angel dust")
        on synapses?

        A. increases synthesis of acetylcholine
        B. blocks reuptake of serotonin
        C. stimulation of dopamine synapses
        D. inhibition of glutamate synapses
        (D, p. 73, factual)

188.    Which of the following drugs is occasionally used to aid in the
        treatment of glaucoma (an eye disorder)?

        A. LSD
        B. cocaine
        C. nicotine
        D. marijuana
        (D, p. 74, factual)

189.    Cannabinoids are associated with which drug?

        A. nicotine
        B. cocaine
        C. morphine
        D. marijuana
        (D, p. 74, factual)

190.    A certain drug user experiences intensified sensations and the
        illusion that time is passing slowly.  He also experiences
        problems with attention and memory.  These symptoms are most
        characteristic of the use of which drug?

        A. LSD
        B. cocaine
        C. nicotine
        D. marijuana
        (D, p. 74, factual)

191.    Which is MORE characteristic of marijuana users than of cocaine
        users?

        A. sudden "crash" several hours after taking the drug
        B. impairments of attention and memory
        C. increased sensitivity to the drug's effects
        D. high risk of overdose on the drug
        (B, p. 74, conceptual)

192. Why are the withdrawal effects of marijuana usually less intense than other drugs?

    A. Marijuana affects only the brain stem.
    B. Marijuana leaves the body slowly.
    C. Marijuana affects only presynaptic neurons.
    D. The body compensates by producing more dopamine.
    (B, p. 74, conceptual)

193. Why is marijuana unlikely to interfere with breathing or heart rate?

    A. Marijuana cannot cross the blood-brain barrier.
    B. It is so slow acting that the brain can compensate
    C. Receptors for marijuana in those brain areas are absent.
    D. Marijuana dissolves quickly and leaves the body quickly.
    (C, p. 74, factual)

194. Of the following, which is most responsible for the effects of marijuana on behavior?

    A. a decrease in blood flow to the brain
    B. an increase in blood flow to the brain
    C. The drug binds with receptors in the hippocampus, basal ganglia, and cerebellum.
    D. The drug binds with receptors in the medulla and brain Stem.
    (C, p. 74, factual)

195. Which area of the brain contains the FEWEST specific receptors for marijuana?

    A. cerebellum
    B. basal ganglia
    C. hippocampus
    D. brain stem
    (D, p. 74, factual)

196. Anandamide and 2-AG are believed to be the naturally occurring neurotransmitters that bind to the same receptors as which drug?

    A. heroin
    B. cocaine
    C. alcohol
    D. marijuana
    (D, p. 74, factual)

197. 2-AG is believed to be a chemical that:

    A. binds to cannabinoid receptors.
    B. produces serotonin.
    C. is produced in very small quantities.
    D. is responsible for producing nausea.
    (A, p. 74, factual)

198.  What is the name given to drugs that grossly distort perception?

    A. hallucinogens
    B. cannabinoids
    C. opiates
    D. stimulants
    (A, p. 74, factual)

199.  Which drugs most closely resemble the neurotransmitter serotonin?

    A. hallucinogens
    B. cannabinoids
    C. opiates
    D. stimulants
    (A, p. 74, factual)

200.  LSD and other hallucinogenic drugs resemble which neurotransmitter?

    A. norepinephrine
    B. dopamine
    C. serotonin
    D. acetylcholine
    ("WWW" C, p. 74, factual)

201.  How is LSD related to serotonin?

    A. LSD has an affinity, but not efficacy, for serotonin
       receptors.
    B. LSD has an affinity and efficacy for serotonin receptors.
    C. LSD is a serotonin antagonist.
    D. LSD is an antagonist at low does and an agonist at high doses.
    (B, p. 74, conceptual)

202.  What happens if presynaptic neurons that release serotonin are destroyed?

    A. LSD becomes completely ineffective.
    B. LSD is effective, but somewhat less than before.
    C. LSD is as effective or more effective.
    D. LSD starts affecting other neurotransmitters.
    (C, p. 74, conceptual)

203.  LSD and other hallucinogenic drugs probably exert their effects most directly on what part of the neuron?

    A. axons terminals
    B. the postsynaptic receptors
    C. the reuptake protein channels
    D. the sodium-potassium pump
    (B, p. 74, conceptual)

204. Which neurotransmitter is most directly affected by caffeine?

    A. dopamine
    B. serotonin
    C. acetylcholine
    D. adenosine
    (D, p. 75, factual)

205. What is a common characteristic of caffeine withdrawal?

    A. headaches
    B. chills
    C. hand tremors
    D. dizziness
    (A, p. 75, factual)

206. Caffeine affects brain functioning by;

    A. dilating blood vessels in the brain.
    B. increasing release of pituitary hormones.
    C. interfering with the effects of adenosine.
    D. decreasing the release of dopamine and acetylcholine.
    ("WWW" C, p. 75, factual)

**Synapses, Reinforcement, And Personality**

207. Researchers have identified the gene that controls the
    development of the dopamine type D2 receptor in humans.  People
    with the less common form of this gene were:

    A. somewhat less likely than others to develop severe alcoholism.
    B. somewhat more likely than others to engage in a variety of
       pleasure-seeking behaviors.
    C. somewhat less likely than others to engage in a variety of
       pleasure-seeking behaviors.
    D. frequently introverts.
    (B, pp. 75-76, factual)

208. A handful of studies have found that novelty seeking:

    A. is associated with the gene that controls personality.
    B. is associated with the gene that controls the D4 receptor.
    C. is associated with schizophrenia.
    D. seems to be purely environmental in origin.
    (B, p. 76, factual)

**MODULE 3.4:  Hormones and Behavior**

209. Endocrine glands:

    A. release substances out of the body.
    B. release hormones into the circulatory system.
    C. absorb waste products from the blood.
    D. are also known as sweat glands.
    (B, p. 78, conceptual)

210.   A hormone is a chemical that is:

   A. secreted by a gland to the outside world.
   B. conveyed by the blood to other organs, whose activity it
      influences.
   C. capable of activating or inhibiting muscle fibers.
   D. a feedback message from the postsynaptic neuron to the
      presynaptic neuron.
   ("WWW" B, p. 78, factual)

**Mechanisms of Hormone Actions**

211.   Hormones exert their effects:

   A. similarly to metabotropic neurotransmitters.
   B. similarly to ionotropic neurotransmitters.
   C. by attaching to special receptors on muscle fibers.
   D. by being metabolized by presynaptic cells and thus converted
      into neurotransmitters.
   (A, p. 78, factual)

212.   A chemical is called a(n) _____ when it is released in small
   quantities close to its target cells.

   A. hormone
   B. neurotransmitter
   C. steroid
   D. peptide
   (B, p. 80, factual)

213.   A chemical is called a(n)_____ when it flows through the blood
   to targets throughout the body.

   A. hormone
   B. neurotransmitter
   C. neuromodulator
   D. endocrine
   (A, p. 80, factual)

214.   The major class of hormones which contains four carbon rings is:

   A. protein hormones
   B. peptide hormones
   C. steroid hormones
   D. leptin hormones
   (C, p. 80, factual)

215.   Insulin is a _____ hormone.

   A. protein
   B. peptide
   C. steroid
   D. leptin
   (A, p. 80, factual)

216. Steroids are derived from:

    A. fats.
    B. cholesterol.
    C. oxytocin.
    D. insulin.
    (B, p. 80, factual)

217. Cortisol is an important:

    A. steroid.
    B. thyroid hormone.
    C. protein.
    D. sex hormone.
    (A, p. 80, factual)

218. Two major classes of gonadal hormones are:

    A. luteinizing hormone and follicle-stimulating hormone.
    B. dopamine and serotonin.
    C. steroids and thyroid hormones
    D. androgens and estrogens
    ("WWW" D, pp. 81, factual)

219. The hormone which prepares the uterus for pregnancy is:

    A. testosterone
    B. androgen
    C. progesterone
    D. estradiol
    (C, p. 81, factual)

220. Sex-limited genes:

    A. are found only on the X chromosome.
    B. determine the sex of the fetus.
    C. have effects that are stronger in one sex than in the other.
    D. have effects only during pregnancy.
    (C, p. 81, factual)

221. Anabolic steroids tend to:

    A. affect females more than males.
    B. build up muscles.
    C. diminish the size and strength of muscles.
    D. activate ionotropic synapses in the thalamus.
    (B, p. 81, factual)

222. Catabolic steroids tend to:

    A. affect females more than males.
    B. affect males more than females.
    C. build up muscles.
    D. break down muscles.
    (D, p. 81, factual)

223.  High levels of steroids:

A.  improve attention and concentration.
B.  usually increase testis size, as well as build muscle.
C.  have been associated with depression.
D.  produce positive feedback on the anterior pituitary.
(C, p. 81, factual)

**Control of Hormone Release**

224.  The pituitary gland;

A.  modifies the activity of the hypothalamus.
B.  is not really a gland.
C.  has influence over many other glands.
D.  is actually composed of many distinct glands.
("WWW"C, p. 81, factual)

225.  The posterior pituitary:

A.  is composed of glandular tissue
B.  synthesizes many hormones, although the hypothalamus controls
    their release.
C.  can be considered an extension of the hypothalamus.
D.  releases TSH.
(C, p. 81, factual)

226.  The anterior pituitary:

A.  is composed of glandular tissue.
B.  releases oxytocin.
C.  releases vasopressin.
D.  controls the activity of the hypothalamus.
(A, p. 81 , factual)

227.  "Releasing hormones," secreted by the hypothalamus:

A.  flow through the blood to the anterior pituitary.
B.  flow through the blood to the posterior pituitary.
C.  synthesize oxytocin and vasopressin.
D.  directly control the secretions of all other endocrine organs.
(A, p. 82, factual)

228.  Luteinizing hormone (LH):

A.  controls secretions of the thyroid gland.
B.  controls secretions of the liver and kidneys.
C.  controls secretions of the gonads.
D.  promotes growth throughout the body.
(C, p. 82, factual)

229.  Gonadotropins:

    A. control secretions from the thyroid gland.
    B. stimulate the gonads to release their hormones.
    C. control secretions from the pineal gland.
    D. inhibit the gonads from releasing their hormones.
    (B, p. 82, factual)

**Module 4.1: The Divisions of the Vertebrate Nervous System**

1.    What are the two parts of the central nervous system?

      A. autonomic nervous system and somatic nervous system
      B. cerebrum and cerebellum
      C. sympathetic division and parasympathetic division
      D. brain and spinal cord
      (D, p. 88, factual)

2.    The central nervous system is composed of:

      A. the brain and spinal cord.
      B. all the nerves outside the brain and spinal cord.
      C. the sympathetic and parasympathetic nervous systems.
      D. the somatic and autonomic nervous systems.
      (A, p. 88, factual)

3.    Which division of the nervous system consists of neurons that
      control the heart, intestines, and other organs?

      A. internal
      B. parasomatic
      C. somatic
      D. autonomic
      (D, p. 88, factual)

4.    Which division of the nervous system consists of neurons bringing
      messages from the senses to the central nervous system?

      A. autonomic
      B. sympathetic
      C. somatic
      D. parasympathetic
      (C, p. 88, factual)

5.    Nerves from the central nervous system convey information to the
      muscles and glands by way of the:

      A. autonomic nervous system.
      B. somatic nervous system.
      C. sympathetic nervous system.
      D. parasympathetic nervous system.
      (B, p. 88, factual)

6.    Which division of the nervous system is composed of the autonomic
      and somatic nervous systems?

      A. central
      B. parasympathetic
      C. peripheral
      D. sympathetic
      (C, p. 88, factual)

7.  Sensory and motor neurons both belong to which division of the nervous system?

    A. somatic
    B. central
    C. autonomic
    D. sympathetic
    (A, p. 88, factual)

8.  An axon in your hand causes contraction of a muscle fiber in your finger as you write.  This neuron belongs to which nervous system?

    A. central
    B. somatic
    C. sympathetic
    D. parasympathetic
    (B, p. 88, conceptual)

    **Some Terminology**

9.  The dorsal part of the spinal cord:

    A. is that part closest to the stomach.
    B. is positioned toward the back.
    C. describes the top part of the cord.
    D. describes the bottom half of the cord.
    (B, p. 89, factual)

10. Which plane shows brain structures as they would be seen from above?

    A. coronal
    B. sagittal
    C. horizontal
    D. commuter
    (C, p. 89, factual)

11. Which plane shows brain structures as they would be seen from the side?

    A. coronal
    B. sagittal
    C. horizontal
    D. commuter
    (B, p. 89, factual)

12. In humans, the dorsal side of the spinal cord could also be described as what?

    A. ventral
    B. anterior
    C. sagittal
    D. posterior
    (D, p. 89, factual)

13.   A cross-section through the brain that shows structures as they
      would be seen from the front involves which plane?

      A. coronal
      B. sagittal
      C. horizontal
      D. transverse
      (A, p. 90, factual)

14.   Two structures on the same side of the body are said to be _____
      to each other.

      A. ventral
      B. medial
      C. contralateral
      D. ipsilateral
      (D, p. 90, factual)

15.   Which of the following means "toward the side, away from the
      midline"?

      A. lateral
      B. medial
      C. proximal
      D. ventral
      (A, p. 90, factual)

16.   If one structure is on the left side of the body and
      another is on the right, they are said to be _____ to each other.

      A. medial
      B. lateral
      C. ipsilateral
      D. contralateral
      (D, p. 90, factual)

17.   What is a bump or protuberance on the surface of the brain
      called?

      A. gyrus
      B. sulcus
      C. column
      D. lamina
      (A, p. 91, factual)

18.   Which two terms both refer to grooves found on the surface of the
      brain?

      A. sulcus and fissure
      B. gyrus and sulcus
      C. fissure and tract
      D. tract and lamina
      (A, p. 91, factual)

19.    What is a long, deep sulcus called?

       A. gyrus
       B. lamina
       C. fissure
       D. sulci
       (C, p. 91, factual)

**The Spinal Cord**

20.    The spinal cord communicates with:

       A. muscles below the level of the head.
       B. all sense organs and muscles in the human body.
       C. dorsal root ganglia only.
       D. ventral root ganglia only.
       (A, p. 89, factual)

21.    The dorsal roots of the spinal cord are sensory and the ventral
       roots are motor according to:

       A. Dale's law.
       B. Dale's principle.
       C. Sherrington.
       D. the Bell-Magendie law.
       (D, p. 90, factual)

22.    To what does the Bell-Magendie law refer?

       A. All branches of an axon release the same combination of
          transmitters.
       B. The dorsal roots of the spinal cord are sensory and the
          ventral roots are motor.
       C. The size of an action potential does not depend on the
          intensity of the initiating stimulus.
       D. Brain development proceeds from hindbrain to midbrain to
          forebrain.
       (B, p. 90, factual)

23.    What is the name given to a cluster of neurons outside the CNS?

       A. lamina
       B. column
       C. tract
       D. ganglion
       (D, p. 90, factual)

24.    Which of the following would be found outside the CNS?

       A. a tract
       B. a ganglion
       C. a sulcus
       D. a gyrus
       (B, p. 90, factual)

25.    The sensory nerves enter the spinal cord on which side?

       A. right
       B. left
       C. ventral
       D. dorsal
       (D, p. 90, conceptual)

26.    The motor nerves leave the spinal cord on which side?

       A. ventral
       B. dorsal
       C. right
       D. left
       (A, p. 90, conceptual)

27.    After damage to the dorsal roots of the spinal cord, an
       individual will suffer what kind of loss?

       A. sensation from the affected body area
       B. control of the peripheral muscles in the affected body area
       C. control of organs in the affected body area
       D. control of the muscles on the opposite side of the body
       (A, p. 91, conceptual)

28.    With respect to the spinal cord, where are the cell bodies for
       sensory neurons located?

       A. outside
       B. inside
       C. on the right
       D. on the left
       (A, p. 90, factual)

29.    With respect to the spinal cord, where are the cell bodies for
       motor neurons located?

       A. outside
       B. inside
       C. on the right
       D. on the left
       (B, p. 90, factual)

30.    Where would you find the dorsal root ganglia?

       A. at the base of the brain
       B. in the gray matter of the spinal cord
       C. in the white matter of the spinal cord
       D. outside, but near, the spinal cord
       (D, p. 90, conceptual)

31.    A cross section of the spinal cord indicates that gray matter is:

       A. densely packed with myelinated axons.
       B. composed mostly of unmyelinated axons.
       C. densely packed with cell bodies and dendrites.
       D. composed only of dendrites.
       (C, p. 90, factual)

32.    Gray matter in the brain and spinal cord is mainly composed of
       what structures?

       A. cell bodies and dendrites
       B. myelinated axons
       C. unmyelinated axons
       D. ganglia
       ("WWW" A, p. 90, factual)

33.    Where does most of the information traveling up and down the
       spinal cord (between the brain and body) travel?

       A. in the H-shaped gray matter
       B. in the H-shaped white matter
       C. in the gray matter on the outer portion of the spinal cord
       D. in the white matter on the outer portion of the spinal cord
       (D, p. 90, conceptual)

34.    Interneurons of the spinal cord:

       A. are almost all sensory neurons.
       B. are almost all motor neurons.
       C. are neither sensory nor motor neurons.
       D. are found only in the white matter of the spinal cord.
       (C, p. 90, factual)

35.    If the spinal cord is cut at a given segment, the brain loses
       sensation:

       A. at that segment only.
       B. at that segment and all segments above it.
       C. at that segment and all segments below it.
       D. at all other segments.
       (C, pp. 91, factual)

36.    If the spinal cord is cut at a given segment, the brain loses
       sensation:

       A. but not motor control over all parts of the body.
       B. and motor control over all parts of the body.
       C. but not motor control from that segment and all segments below
          it.
       D. and motor control from that segment and all segments below it.
       (D, pp. 91, factual)

**The Autonomic Nervous System**

37.    The sympathetic and parasympathetic combine to form which
       division of the nervous system?

       A. somatic
       B. autonomic
       C. central
       D. peripheral
       ("WWW" B, p. 91, factual)

38.    The autonomic nervous system:

       A. only receives information from the heart, intestines, and
          other organs.
       B. only sends information to the heart, intestines, and other
          organs.
       C. receives and sends information to the heart, intestines, and
          other organs.
       D. conveys messages from the sense organs to the central nervous
          system.
       (C, p. 91, factual)

39.    Which part of the nervous system prepares the body for "fight or
       flight" activities?

       A. sympathetic
       B. somatic
       C. parasympathetic
       D. peripheral
       (A, p. 91, factual)

40.    Which part of the nervous system consists of two paired chains of
       ganglia lying to the left and right of the spinal cord in its
       central regions?

       A. somatic nervous system
       B. sympathetic nervous system
       C. parasympathetic nervous system
       D. central nervous system
       (B, p. 91, factual)

41.    Which activity is increased by the sympathetic nervous system?

       A. salivation
       B. heart rate
       C. digestive activity
       D. activation of the immune system
       (B, p. 91, factual)

42.    Sympathetic ganglia:

       A. are not linked to one another.
       B. act somewhat more independently than do parasympathetic
          ganglia.
       C. are closely linked and often act as a single system.
       D. have short postganglionic fibers extending to internal organs.
       (C, p. 91, factual)

43.    In general, what is the relationship between the sympathetic and
       parasympathetic nervous systems?

       A. When one is active, the other is inactive.
       B. When one is active, the other is activated to the same degree.
       C. They are both constantly active, but to varying degrees.
       D. The activation of one is independent of the activation of the
          other.
       (C, p. 91, conceptual)

44.    In general, what is the relationship between the sympathetic and
       parasympathetic nervous systems?

       A. They work together to produce similar effects.
       B. They cannot be active at the same time.
       C. Their effects collectively summate.
       D. They produce opposite effects.
       (D, p. 91, factual)

45.    What, generally, is the relationship between the activity of the
       sympathetic and the parasympathetic nervous systems?

       A. The sympathetic controls internal organs while the
          parasympathetic controls peripheral organs.
       B. The sympathetic usually has specific, localized effects, while
          the parasympathetic has broad effects.
       C. They usually have opposite effects on the same organ.
       D. The sympathetic is involved in voluntary behavior, while the
          parasympathetic is involved in involuntary behavior.
       (C, p. 91, factual)

46.    Sympathetic is to _____ as parasympathetic is to _____.

       A. central nervous system; peripheral nervous system
       B. voluntary behavior; involuntary behavior
       C. arousal; relaxation
       D. neurotransmitters; hormones
       (C, p. 91, conceptual)

47.    Digestive activity is increased by the activation of which
       nervous system?

       A. the parasympathetic
       B. the sympathetic
       C. both the parasympathetic and sympathetic
       D. neither the parasympathetic nor the sympathetic
       (A, p. 91, factual)

48.    Erection of the hairs, known in humans as "goose bumps," is
       caused by activation of which nervous system?

       A. parasympathetic
       B. sympathetic
       C. central
       D. peripheral
       (B, p. 93, factual)

49.    You are walking after dark.  A sudden noise frightens you.  Your
       heart pounds, your pulse races, and your breathing rate
       increases.  These responses are due to your:

       A. parasympathetic nervous system.
       B. sympathetic nervous system.
       C. somatic nervous system.
       D. immune system.
       (B, pp. 91 , conceptual)

50.    Which of the following has input from both the sympathetic and
       parasympathetic nervous systems?

       A. sweat glands
       B. muscles that constrict blood vessels
       C. muscles that erect the hairs of the skin
       D. the heart
       (D, p. 91, conceptual)

51.    Which nervous system is also known as the craniosacral system?

       A. sympathetic
       B. parasympathetic
       C. central
       D. somatic
       (B, p. 92, factual)

52.    The craniosacral system is also known as the:

       A. peripheral nervous system.
       B. sympathetic nervous system.
       C. parasympathetic nervous system.
       D. somatic nervous system.
       (C, p. 92, factual)

53.  Which kinds of activities are produced from activation of the
     parasympathetic nervous system?

     A. fight-or-flight
     B. arousal of the body's organs
     C. a decrease in digestion
     D. calmness and relaxation
     (D, p. 91, conceptual)

54.  The parasympathetic nervous system has:

     A. long preganglionic and postganglionic axons.
     B. long preganglionic and short postganglionic axons.
     C. short preganglionic and short postganglionic axons.
     D. short preganglionic and long postganglionic axons.
     (B, p. 92, factual)

55.  Which neurotransmitter is most often used by the parasympathetic
     nervous system?

     A. dopamine
     B. serotonin
     C. acetylcholine
     D. norepinephrine
     (C, p. 92, factual)

56.  Acetylcholine is the only neurotransmitter released by:

     A. the sympathetic nervous system's postganglionic synapses.
     B. the parasympathetic nervous system's postganglionic axons.
     C. intrinsic neurons in the spinal cord.
     D. intrinsic neurons of the hippocampus.
     (B, p. 92, factual)

57.  Which neurotransmitter is most often used by the sympathetic
     nervous system?

     A. dopamine
     B. serotonin
     C. acetylcholine
     D. norepinephrine
     (D, p. 92, factual)

58.  Sympathetic is to _____ as parasympathetic is to _____.

     A. serotonin; dopamine
     B. dopamine; serotonin
     C. acetylcholine; norepinephrine
     D. norepinephrine; acetylcholine
     (D, p. 92, conceptual)

59.    What is a general effect of over-the-counter cold remedies?

A. They stimulate dopamine receptors.
B. They decrease activity of the autonomic nervous system.
C. They decrease activity of the parasympathetic nervous system.
D. They decrease activity of the sympathetic nervous system.
(C, p. 93, factual)

60.    Given their effects on the nervous system, what is one side
effect of over-the-counter cold remedies?

A. increased digestive activity
B. decreased salivation
C. decreased heart rate
D. increased sinus flow
(B, p. 93, conceptual)

61.    Given their effects on the nervous system, what is one side
effect of over-the-counter cold remedies?

A. increased digestive activity
B. increased salivation
C. increased heart rate
D. increased sinus flow
(C, p. 93, conceptual)

**The Hindbrain**

62.    The hindbrain is also known as the:

A. mesencephalon
B. prosencephalon
C. rhombencephalon
D. tegmentum
(C, p. 93, factual)

63.    Which of the following is NOT part of the hindbrain?

A. cerebellum
B. hippocampus
C. pons
D. medulla
(B, p. 93, factual)

64.    What consists of the medulla, the pons, and the cerebellum?

A. hindbrain
B. reticular formation
C. midbrain
D. forebrain
(A, p. 93, factual)

65.   What structure is composed of the medulla, pons, the midbrain,
      and certain central structures of the forebrain?

      A. limbic system
      B. thalamus
      C. brain stem
      D. cerebellum
      (C, p. 93, factual)

66.   The hindbrain consists of the:

      A. tectum, tegmentum, and reticular formation
      B. thalamus and hypothalamus
      C. spinal cord and cranial nerves
      D. medulla, pons, and cerebellum
      (D, p. 94, factual)

67.   Why is the medulla considered part of the brain rather than the
      spinal cord?

      A. because it developed later in evolution
      B. because it is contained in the skull
      C. because it develops from a separate group of neurons
      D. because it is composed only of interneurons
      (B, p. 94, conceptual)

68.   Breathing, heart rate, vomiting, salivation, coughing, and
      sneezing are all controlled by which structure?

      A. medulla
      B. thalamus
      C. cerebellum
      D. pons
      (A, p. 94, factual)

69.   As axons from the spinal cord enter the skull, which structure do
      they enter?

      A. midbrain
      B. forebrain
      C. medulla
      D. cerebellum
      (C, p. 94, conceptual)

70.   The medulla oblongata is located:

      A. just below the spinal cord.
      B. outside the dorsal root ganglia.
      C. within the skull.
      D. on the surface of each internal organ.
      (C, p. 94, factual)

71.    The medulla controls a number of reflexes through:

       A. the midbrain
       B. the forebrain
       C. cranial nerves
       D. skeletal nerves
       (C, p. 94, factual)

72.    How many pairs of cranial nerves do humans have?

       A. 8
       B. 10
       C. 12
       D. 16
       (C, p. 94, factual)

73.    Which major functions are controlled by the cranial nerves?

       A. activation of the peripheral nervous system
       B. eye movements, taste, and swallowing
       C. skeletal muscles of the trunk
       D. skeletal muscles of the extremities
       (B, p. 94, conceptual)

74.    Damage to which hindbrain structure would be most life-
       threatening?

       A. pons
       B. medulla
       C. cerebellum
       D. hypothalamus
       (B, p. 94, conceptual)

75.    Where are the nuclei located for most of the cranial nerves?

       A. in the cerebral cortex
       B. in the hypothalamus
       C. in the midbrain
       D. in the pons and medulla
       (D, p. 94-95, conceptual)

76.    Each cranial nerve originates in:

       A. the hypothalamus.
       B. a nucleus.
       C. the medulla
       D. the pons
       (B, p. 94, factual)

77.     Where are the nuclei located for cranial nerves I through IV?

        A. the midbrain and forebrain
        B. the hindbrain
        C. the pons and medulla
        D. the spinal cord
        (A, p. 94, factual)

78.     The pons acts as a bridge between:

        A. the hindbrain and the forebrain.
        B. the thalamus and the hypothalamus.
        C. one side of the nervous system and the other.
        D. the thalamus and the cerebral cortex.
        (C, p. 95, conceptual)

79.     The reticular formation is contained within the:

        A. brain stem.
        B. spinal cord.
        C. raphe system.
        D. cerebellum.
        (A, p. 95, factual)

80.     The descending portion of the reticular formation is one of
        several brain areas that control:

        A. the sensory areas of the brain.
        B. the sensory areas of the spinal cord.
        C. the motor areas of the brain.
        D. the motor areas of the spinal cord.
        (D, p. 95, factual)

81.     The ascending portion of the reticular formation sends outputs
        to:

        A. the raphe system.
        B. the cerebellum.
        C. much of the cerebral cortex.
        D. motor areas of the spinal cord.
        (C, p. 95, factual)

82.     The ascending portion of the reticular formation:

        A. controls the motor areas of the spinal cord.
        B. decreases attention while increasing arousal.
        C. controls the motor areas of the brain.
        D. increases arousal and attention.
        (D, p. 95, factual)

83.    The raphe system sends axons to the:

       A. forebrain.
       B. reticular formation.
       C. spinal cord.
       D. cerebellum.
       (A, p. 95, factual)

84.    The raphe system:

       A. increases the brain's readiness to respond to stimuli.
       B. is important for balance and coordination.
       C. controls the sensory areas of the spinal cord.
       D. regulates the rate of production of cerebrospinal fluid.
       (A, p. 95, factual)

85.    The cerebellum contributes to the control of what function?

       A. hunger
       B. temperature
       C. olfaction
       D. movement
       (D, p. 95, factual)

86.    Research indicates that the behavioral effects of the
       cerebellum may be due to its part in which activities?

       A. coordinating information from left and right hemispheres
       B. focusing and shifting attention and organizing sensory inputs
       C. interpreting visual stimuli
       D. coordinating the release of hormones
       (B, p. 95, conceptual)

87.    If an individual has difficulty typing, he may have suffered
       damage to the:

       A. cerebellum.
       B. midbrain.
       C. medulla.
       D. tectum.
       (A, p. 95, conceptual)

88.    If an individual has difficulty determining which rhythm is
       faster when presented with two or more, it is likely that she
       suffered damage to the:

       A. cerebellum.
       B. forebrain.
       C. tectum.
       D. medulla.
       (A, p. 95, conceptual)

### The Midbrain

89.    Which of the following is NOT part of the midbrain?

       A. tectum
       B. tegmentum
       C. pons
       D. superior colliculus
       (C, p. 95, factual)

90.    In which area of the brain would one find the tectum, tegmentum, superior and inferior colliculi, and substantia nigra?

       A. midbrain
       B. hindbrain
       C. reticular formation
       D. forebrain
       (A, p. 95, factual)

91.    As compared to humans, the midbrain in birds and reptiles is:

       A. smaller and less important.
       B. larger and more prominent.
       C. more asymmetric, with the right side much larger than the
          left.
       D. filled with more ventricles.
       (B, p. 95, factual)

92.    An important midbrain structure which deteriorates in Parkinson's disease is the:

       A. superior colliculus.
       B. inferior colliculus.
       C. tegmentum.
       D. substantia nigra.
       (D, p. 96, factual)

93.    What information can you provide someone about the neurotransmitter involved in Parkinson's disease?

       A. a dopamine pathway deteriorates
       B. a serotonin pathway deteriorates
       C. acetylcholine production increases
       D. both serotonin and acetylcholine pathways are affected
       (A, p. 96, conceptual)

### The Forebrain

94.    Which of the following is NOT part of the forebrain?

       A. cerebral cortex
       B. hippocampus
       C. thalamus
       D. medulla
       (D, p. 96, factual)

110

95.    The most prominent part of the mammalian brain is the:

       A. midbrain.
       B. hindbrain.
       C. forebrain.
       D. limbic system.
       ("WWW" C, p. 96, factual)

96.    The cerebral cortex is the:

       A. outer portion of the hindbrain.
       B. outer portion of the forebrain.
       C. inner portion of the forebrain.
       D. inner portion of the midbrain.
       (B, p. 96, factual)

97.    What does the term "cortex" mean, with respect to "cerebral cortex"?

       A. complexity
       B. expansion
       C. bark
       D. folded object
       (C, p. 96, factual)

98.    A group of forebrain structures is important for motivated and emotional behavior.  What is the name given to this group of structures?

       A. limbic system
       B. reticular formation
       C. tegmentum
       D. basal ganglia
       (A, p. 96, factual)

99.    The limbic system is important for:

       A. emotional behaviors.
       B. motor coordination.
       C. coordination between the eyes and ears.
       D. perceiving three-dimensional objects.
       (A, p. 96, factual)

100.   What does the term "limbic" mean with respect to limbic system?

       A. complexity
       B. expansion
       C. bark
       D. border
       (D, p. 96, factual)

101.  What is a function of the thalamus?

      A. sending sensory information to the cerebral cortex
      B. regulating sleep cycles
      C. directing the secretions of the hypothalamus
      D. moderating emotional outbursts
      (A, p. 96, factual)

102.  The diencephalon is composed of the:

      A. thalamus and basal ganglia.
      B. basal ganglia and hypothalamus.
      C. thalamus and hypothalamus.
      D. thalamus and hippocampus.
      (C, p. 96, factual)

103.  The term "thalamus" is derived from a Greek word meaning:

      A. avocado.
      B. bridal bed.
      C. side by side.
      D. relay.
      (B, p. 96, factual)

104.  Sensory information which is not processed by the thalamus
      includes:

      A. olfactory information.
      B. visual information.
      C. auditory information.
      D. somatosensory information.
      (A, p. 96, factual)

105.  Olfactory information is processed by the:

      A. thalamus via the olfactory bulbs.
      B. cortex via the olfactory bulbs.
      C. spinal cord.
      D. medulla.
      (B, p. 96, factual)

106.  An impairment of eating, drinking, temperature regulation, or
      sexual behavior suggests possible damage to which brain
      structure?

      A. midbrain
      B. hippocampus
      C. hypothalamus
      D. cerebellum
      ("WWW" C, p. 97, conceptual)

107.   The hypothalamus conveys messages to the:

       A. pituitary gland.
       B. skin regarding temperature regulation.
       C. retina.
       D. ventricles.
       (A, p. 97, factual)

108.   Secretions from which gland will also affect the secretion of
       hormones from the thyroid gland, adrenal gland, and ovaries or
       testes?

       A. thymus gland
       B. pineal gland
       C. pancreas
       D. pituitary gland
       (D, p. 97, factual)

109.   Which endocrine gland is physically connected to the
       hypothalamus?

       A. pituitary
       B. adrenal
       C. thymus
       D. pineal
       (A, p. 97, factual)

110.   The pituitary gland synthesizes and releases hormones:

       A. to the outside of the body.
       B. to the thalamus.
       C. into the bloodstream.
       D. to the hypothalamus.
       (C, p. 97, factual)

111.   A group of subcortical structures lying lateral to the thalamus
       is called the:

       A. superior colliculus.
       B. inferior colliculus.
       C. thalamic nuclei.
       D. basal ganglia.
       (D, pg. 97, factual)

112.   Which structure is not part of the basal ganglia?

       A. caudate nucleus
       B. hippocampus
       C. putamen
       D. globus pallidus
       (B, p. 97, factual)

113.   Which structure is likely to be damaged in Parkinson's disease,
       Huntington's disease, and other conditions that impair movement?

       A. thalamus
       B. basal ganglia
       C. limbic system
       D. reticular formation
       (B, p. 98, factual)

114.   Damage to the basal ganglia would most likely result in what kind
       of deficits?

       A. a movement disorder
       B. problems with visual perception
       C. problems with auditory perception
       D. a loss of pain sensation
       (A, p. 98, factual)

115.   Damage to the basal ganglia might result in:

       A. mania.
       B. depression.
       C. anorexia.
       D. hyperactivity.
       (B, p. 98, factual)

116.   The nucleus basalis sends information to the:

       A. hypothalamus.
       B. basal ganglia.
       C. cerebral cortex.
       D. hippocampus.
       (C, p. 99, factual)

117.   The nucleus basalis is a key part of the brain's system for:

       A. emotional response.
       B. attention.
       C. visual perception.
       D. auditory perception.
       (B, p. 99, factual)

118.   In which area of the brain is the hippocampus located?

       A. It is part of the hindbrain.
       B. It is part of the forebrain.
       C. It is part of the midbrain.
       D. It is part of the basal ganglia.
       (B, p. 99, factual)

119.   The hippocampus plays a major role in what function?

       A. innate sexual behavior
       B. temperature regulation
       C. memory
       D. secretion of hormones
       (C, p. 99, factual)

120.   An individual has difficulty remembering anything recent after
       brain damage, but all memories stored before the damage are
       intact.   The brain area damaged may be the:

       A. fornix
       B. hypothalamus
       C. hippocampus
       D. nucleus basalis
       (C, p. 99, conceptual)

121.   What brain structure links the hippocampus with the hypothalamus?

       A. thalamus
       B. nucleus basalis
       C. basal ganglia
       D. fornix
       (D, p. 99, factual)

122.   A fluid-filled channel in the center of the spinal cord is called
       the:

       A. ventricle.
       B. central canal.
       C. raphe system.
       D. meninge.
       (B, p. 99, factual)

123.   What is contained in the ventricles of the brain?

       A. glia
       B. cell bodies
       C. dendrites and axons
       D. cerebrospinal fluid
       (D, p. 99, factual)

124.   How many ventricles exist in the adult human brain?

       A. they exist only in children's brains
       B. 2
       C. 4
       D. there are too many to count accurately
       (C, p. 99, factual)

125.   What do the ventricles, central canal, and subarachnoid space
       have in common?

       A. All are part of the forebrain.
       B. All are filled with cerebrospinal fluid.
       C. All are involved in cognitive functioning.
       D. All are filled with blood.
       (B, p. 99, factual)

126.   The choroid plexus:

       A. cushions the brain.
       B. protects the brain from infection.
       C. is another name for the ventricles.
       D. forms the cerebrospinal fluid.
       (D, p. 99, factual)

127.   What is a function of the cerebrospinal fluid?

       A. to cushion the brain
       B. to hold blood in reserve for emergencies
       C. to maintain the blood-brain barrier
       D. to allow the head to float in water
       (A, p. 99, factual)

128.   Meningitis:

       A. are the membranes surrounding the brain.
       B. forms the cerebrospinal fluid.
       C. is an inflammation of the membranes surrounding the brain.
       D. is the process of cerebrospinal fluid gradually being
          reabsorbed into the blood vessels of the brain.
       (C, p. 99, factual)

129.   What causes meningitis?

       A. a genetic deficiency of dopamine receptors
       B. an excess of cerebrospinal fluid
       C. the presence of blood in the cerebrospinal fluid
       D. inflammation of membranes around the brain and spinal cord
       (D, p. 99, factual)

130.   Membranes that surround the brain and spinal cord are called:

       A. CSF
       B. ventricles
       C. meninges
       D. hydrocephali
       (C, p. 99, factual)

131.   What causes hydrocephalus?

       A. poorly developed skull bones in an infant
       B. interruption of blood flow to the brain around the time of
          birth
       C. obstruction in the flow of cerebrospinal fluid
       D. damage to one of the cranial nerves
       (C, p. 100, factual)

132.   Hydrocephalus is usually associated with:

       A. a lack of nutrition.
       B. an obstruction of the flow of CSF.
       C. an excess of hormones.
       D. a constriction of the skull bones.
       (B, p. 100, factual)

**Module 4.2: The Cerebral Cortex**

133.   Each hemisphere of the cerebral cortex receives most of its input
       from the _____ side of the body and controls the muscles on the
       _____ side.

       A. contralateral; ipsilateral
       B. ipsilateral; contralateral
       C. ipsilateral; ipsilateral
       D. contralateral; contralateral
       (D, p. 102, factual)

134.   Contralateral is to _____ as ipsilateral is to _____.

       A. same side; opposite side
       B. opposite side; same side
       C. front side; back side
       D. back side; front side
       (B, p. 102, factual)

135.   Which of the following is gray matter?

       A. the outer surfaces of the cerebral cortex
       B. the inner surface of the cerebral cortex
       C. the cerebral ventricles
       D. the axons of the brainstem and spinal cord
       (A, p. 102, factual)

136.   What composes the outer surface of the cerebral hemispheres?

       A. gray matter
       B. white matter
       C. glial cells
       D. myelinated axons
       (A, p. 102, factual)

137. What is the large bundle of axons connecting the two hemispheres of the brain?

    A. the corpus callosum
    B. the limbic system
    C. the midbrain
    D. the thalamus
    (A, p. 102, factual)

138. Each half of the hemisphere communicates with the other half through a bundle of axons called the:

    A. anterior commissure.
    B. hypothalamus.
    C. ventricles.
    D. meninges.
    ("WWW" A, p. 102, factual)

139. Which of the following is true about laminae in the cerebral cortex?

    A. All cortical areas contain 6 layers.
    B. Odd numbered laminae contain only neurons; even numbered laminae contain only glia.
    C. The laminae vary in thickness in different areas.
    D. Each layer corresponds to a different sensory modality.
    (C, p. 102, factual)

140. The mammalian cortex contains up to _____ laminae.

    A. 2
    B. 6
    C. 12
    D. 24
    (B, p. 102, factual)

141. Lamina V is thickest in the:

    A. primary sensory area.
    B. secondary sensory areas.
    C. primary motor areas.
    D. spinal cord.
    (C, p. 102, factual)

142. Lamina IV is prominent in:

    A. all the primary sensory areas.
    B. the secondary sensory areas.
    C. primary motor areas.
    D. spinal cord.
    (A, p. 102, factual)

143.    Lamina IV is absent from the:

        A. primary visual areas.
        B. primary auditory areas.
        C. somatosensory areas.
        D. motor cortex.
        (D, p. 102, factual)

144.    What is true about all of the cells in a given column in the
        cerebral cortex?

        A. They have the same shape.
        B. They are the same size.
        C. They are involved in the same function.
        D. They are connected to one another by a single horizontal cell.
        (C, p. 102, factual)

**The Occipital Lobe**

145.    Which lobe of the cerebral cortex is most important for visual
        information?

        A. occipital
        B. parietal
        C. temporal
        D. frontal
        ("WWW" A, p. 103, factual)

146.    What deficits does a person suffer after damage to the striate
        cortex in the occipital lobe?

        A. deafness
        B. blindness
        C. loss of touch and other body sensations
        D. loss of fine motor control
        (B, p. 103, factual)

147.    Another name for the primary visual cortex is the:

        A. striate cortex.
        B. parietal lobe.
        C. central sulcus.
        D. postcentral gyrus.
        (A, p. 103, factual)

148.    Cortical blindness is a result of destruction of:

        A. any part of the cortex.
        B. the striate cortex.
        C. the parietal cortex.
        D. the central sulcus.
        (B, p. 103, factual)

149.  An individual has normal eyes and normal pupillary reflexes but
      no pattern perception or visual imagery.  This person suffers
      from:

      A.  imagery deficit syndrome.
      B.  cortical blindness.
      C.  parietal lobe degeneration.
      D.  retinal degeneration.
      (B, p. 103, factual)

150.  Which part of the cerebral cortex is most important for the sense
      of touch?

      A.  occipital lobe
      B.  parietal lobe
      C.  temporal lobe
      D.  frontal lobe
      ("WWW" B, p. 103, factual)

151.  The postcentral gyrus in the parietal lobe is the primary area
      for which type of sensation?

      A.  touch
      B.  vision
      C.  hearing
      D.  smell
      (A, p. 103, factual)

152.  One of the deepest grooves in the surface of the cortex is the:

      A.  central sulcus.
      B.  postcentral gyrus.
      C.  precentral gyrus.
      D.  postcentral sulcus.
      (A, p. 103, factual)

153.  What is the primary target area on the cerebral cortex for touch
      and other skin sensations?

      A.  olfactory bulbs
      B.  striate cortex
      C.  precentral gyrus
      D.  postcentral gyrus
      (D, p. 103, factual)

154.  What is the primary target area in the cortex for information
      regarding muscle-stretch and joint receptors?

      A.  primary somatosensory cortex.
      B.  occipital lobe.
      C.  central sulcus.
      D.  precentral gyrus.
      (A, p. 103, factual)

155. Of the four bands of cells that make up the postcentral gyrus:

    A. all four receive deep pressure information.
    B. all four receive light touch information.
    C. two receive deep pressure information.
    D. two receive light touch information.
    (D, p. 103, factual)

156. Someone who suddenly loses the ability to identify objects by feeling them has probably suffered damage to what area of the cerebral cortex?

    A. parietal lobe
    B. temporal lobe
    C. frontal lobe
    D. corpus callosum
    (A, p. 103, conceptual)

157. A blind person who suddenly loses the ability to read Braille has probably suffered damage to what area of the cerebral cortex?

    A. temporal lobe
    B. frontal lobe
    C. occipital lobe
    D. parietal lobe
    (D, p. 103, conceptual)

158. What is one of the common symptoms of damage to the parietal lobe?

    A. inability to describe what something will look like from another angle
    B. loss of social inhibitions
    C. outbursts of unprovoked anxiety or aggressive behavior
    D. trouble recognizing faces and other highly complex visual stimuli
    (A, p. 104, factual)

159. You have just become a neurologist. Your first patient consistently neglects the left side of his body. You should suspect that he has suffered damage to what area of the cerebral cortex?

    A. the left temporal lobe
    B. the right temporal lobe
    C. the left parietal lobe
    D. the right parietal lobe
    (D, p. 104, factual)

160.    A symptom of right-hemisphere parietal lobe damage is the
        tendency to ignore the:

        A. ipsilateral side of the body and world.
        B. dorsal areas of the body.
        C. contralateral side of the body and world.
        D. Ventral areas of the body.
        (C, p. 104, factual)

161.    "Neglect" occurs after damage to the:

        A. left parietal lobe only.
        B. right parietal lobe, one part of the right frontal lobe, or
           the connection between these two areas.
        C. left parietal lobe, one part of the left frontal lobe, or the
           connection between these two areas.
        D. left occipital lobe, one part of the right temporal lobe, or
           the connections between these two areas.
        (B, p. 104, factual)

162.    "Neglect" has been shown to be a problem with:

        A. vision.
        B. touch.
        C. attention.
        D. memory.
        (C, p. 104, factual)

**The Temporal Lobe**

163.    What is the primary area of the cerebral cortex for auditory
        sensations?

        A. occipital
        B. parietal
        C. temporal
        D. frontal
        (C, p. 105, factual)

164.    The temporal lobe of the cerebral cortex is the primary target
        for which kind of sensory information?

        A. somatosensory, including touch
        B. the simplest aspects of vision
        C. gustatory
        D. auditory
        (D, p. 105, factual)

165. Which lobe seems to be especially involved in the comprehension of spoken language in humans?

    A. occipital
    B. parietal
    C. frontal
    D. temporal
    (D, p. 105, factual)

166. Which lobe contributes to perception of movement and recognition of faces?

    A. occipital lobe.
    B. parietal lobe.
    C. temporal lobe.
    D. frontal lobe.
    (C, p. 105, factual)

167. A tumor in the temporal lobe gives rise to:

    A. flashes of light.
    B. visual hallucinations.
    C. olfactory hallucinations.
    D. prolonged yawning.
    (B, p. 105, factual)

168. Visual hallucinations are often associated with tumors in which brain area?

    A. temporal lobe
    B. corpus callosum
    C. parietal lobe
    D. frontal lobe
    ("WWW" A, p. 105, factual)

169. Monkeys with Kluver-Bucy syndrome fail to show normal fears to stimuli such as snakes and fire.  This disorder is a result of damage to which lobe?

    A. occipital
    B. parietal
    C. temporal
    D. frontal
    (C, p. 105, factual)

170. Monkeys with Kluver-Bucy syndrome fail to show normal fears and anxieties after:

    A. temporal lobe damage.
    B. parietal lobe damage.
    C. occipital lobe damage.
    D. frontal lobe damage.
    (A, p. 105, factual)

171.  Which lobe contains the primary motor cortex and the prefrontal
      cortex?

      A. occipital
      B. parietal
      C. temporal
      D. frontal
      (D, p. 106, factual)

172.  Which lobe contains the precentral gyrus?

      A. occipital
      B. parietal
      C. temporal
      D. frontal
      (D, p. 106, factual)

173.  Where is the precentral gyrus located?

      A. in the posterior portion of the frontal lobe
      B. in the anterior portion of the frontal lobe
      C. in the anterior portion of the parietal lobe
      D. in the posterior portion of the temporal lobe
      (A, p. 106, factual)

174.  The precentral gyrus is essential for what type of control?

      A. fine movements
      B. coordination between vision and hearing
      C. emotions
      D. hunger and thirst
      (A, p. 106, factual)

175.  Which is the only area of the cerebral cortex known to receive
      input from ALL sensory modalities?

      A. the thalamus
      B. the prefrontal cortex
      C. the striate cortex
      D. the parietal lobe
      (B, p. 106, factual)

176.  Prefrontal lobotomies were conducted in the United States in an
      attempt to:

      A. restore memory.
      B. repair brain damage.
      C. control psychological damage.
      D. control socially unacceptable impulses.
      ("WWW" C, p. 107, factual)

177.    What is a common effect of prefrontal cortex damage?

        A. difficulty recognizing faces and other complex visual stimuli
        B. outbursts of unprovoked anxiety and aggressive behavior
        C. apathy, distractibility, and loss of facial expressions
        D. neglect of the opposite side of the body
        (C, p. 107, factual)

178.    People with lobotomies generally:

        A. failed to inhibit socially unacceptable impulses.
        B. demonstrated superior memory.
        C. were highly sensitive to somatosensory information.
        D. developed severe anxieties.
        (A, p. 107, factual)

179.    The prefrontal cortex is important for:

        A. the processing of visual information.
        B. working memory.
        C. language acquisition.
        D. recognizing faces.
        (B, p. 107, factual)

180.    Which kind of brain damage often causes people to lose their
        social inhibitions and to ignore the rules of polite conduct?

        A. damage to the corpus callosum
        B. damage to the cerebellum
        C. damage to the prefrontal cortex
        D. damage to the striate cortex
        (C, p. 107, factual)

181.    What part of the cortex is especially important for the delayed
        response task?

        A. prefrontal cortex
        B. primary visual cortex
        C. precentral gyrus
        D. parietal lobe
        (A, p. 107, factual)

182.    If the prefrontal cortex is damaged, an individual may:

        A. engage in incomplete or badly planned actions.
        B. sleep 18-22 hours per day.
        C. show deficits in all types of memory.
        D. lose memory for faces.
        ("WWW" A, p. 107, factual)

183.  A person showers with his clothes on and pours water on the tube
      of toothpaste instead of on the toothbrush.  He probably suffers
      from damage to the:

      A. occipital lobe.
      B. striate cortex.
      C. prefrontal cortex.
      D. parietal cortex.
      (C, p. 107, factual)

**How do the Pieces Work Together?**

184.  Karl Lashley supported the idea that:

      A. the brain works as a whole and all parts contribute equally.
      B. all parts of the brain feed their information into a central
         processor in the left prefrontal cortex.
      C. maze running is controlled by the posterior cerebellum.
      D. maze running depends only on perception of body location.
      (A, p. 108, factual)

185.  The "binding problem" is the issue of how we:

      A. convert sensory information into a pattern that produces
         movement.
      B. perceive visual, auditory and other aspects of a stimulus as a
         single object.
      C. transfer information between the left and right hemispheres.
      D. communicate between the word comprehension and word production
         areas of the brain.
      (B, p. 108, factual)

186.  Which of the following is true about the cortical areas that are
      sometimes known as "association areas"?

      A. They do have the main control of thinking and reasoning.
      B. They would be better described as additional sensory areas.
      C. They get most of their input from other areas of the cerebral
         cortex.
      D. They integrate information from more than one sensory system.
      (B, pp. 108-109, conceptual)

187.  A frequency known as gamma waves produces action potentials at
      the rate of:

      A. 10-20 per second.
      B. 20-30 per second.
      C. 20-50 per second.
      D. 30-80 per second.
      (D, p. 109, factual)

188.  When people failed to recognize a drawn face presented to them
      during an experimental procedure, it was found that gamma waves:

      A. increased in frequency.
      B. did not emerge.
      C. emerged in nonvisual areas of the brain.
      D. appeared only when the face was presented upside down.
      (B, p. 109, factual)

189.  When a cat responds to a sudden stimulus, the brain's activity
      patterns in many areas:

      A. desynchronizes.
      B. slows down to about half its usual level.
      C. synchronizes.
      D. stops.
      (C, p. 109, factual)

190.  The area of the brain known to be important for "binding" is the:

      A. lateral geniculate nucleus of the thalamus.
      B. central sulcus.
      C. inferior (lower) parietal cortex.
      D. corpus callosum.
      (C, p. 110, factual)

191.  Individuals with bilateral parietal lobe damage:

      A. have difficulty binding the different aspects of perception.
      B. bind different aspects of vision only.
      C. become hyperactive.
      D. show an increase in synchrony of brain activity.
      (A, p. 110, factual)

192.  Establishing a link between synchrony of various brain areas and
      binding:

      A. is virtually impossible.
      B. will answer all questions researchers have regarding
         perception.
      C. will not necessarily answer *why* synchrony produces binding.
      D. will resolve the centuries old mind-brain question.
      (C, p. 110, factual)

**Chapter 5**                          **The Development and Plasticity of the Brain**

**Module 5.1: Development of the Brain**

1.     Developing the ability to solve the object permanence task
       requires:

       A. the development of the temporal lobe.
       B. the development of the prefrontal cortex.
       C. that a child be at least two years of age.
       D. the development of neurons and synapses in the brain stem
          between the ages 7½ and 12 months.
       (B, p. 116, factual)

2.     What is a physiological explanation for why children under the
       age of 9 months fail to show object permanence?

       A. the relatively slow development of the prefrontal cortex
       B. the early lack of communication between the two hemispheres
       C. the lack of a fully developed visual cortex
       D. the relatively slow development of the thalamus
       (A, p. 116, conceptual)

3.     The human central nervous system:

       A.   begins to form during the fetal stage.
       B.   is unlike all other vertebrate central nervous systems in its
            developmental process.
       C.   begins to form when the embryo is about two weeks old.
       D.   begins to form when the embryo is about two months old.
       (C, p. 116, factual)

4.     Early in development, how does the nervous system begin?

       A. as a tube surrounding a fluid-filled cavity
       B. as a spherical structure in the center of the embryo
       C. as a diffuse system of cells scattered throughout the body
       D. as a single layer of cells covering the heart and other
          internal organs
       (A, p. 116, factual)

5.     When do the ventricles and the central canal of the spinal cord
       form?

       A. shortly after birth in humans
       B. just as the forebrain starts its rapid phase of growth
       C. early in embryonic development
       D. during the third trimester
       (C, p. 116, conceptual)

6.      What developmental pattern characterizes the cerebral cortex?

        A. inside out
        B. outside to the inside
        C. bottom to top
        D. top to bottom
        (A, p. 116, conceptual)

7.      What main variation exists between vertebrates in the embryonic
        development and growth of the nervous system?

        A. the sequence of the development of various structures
        B. the speed of development
        C. the number of cavities within the neural tube
        D. whether the anterior or posterior end differentiates into the
           forebrain
        (B, p. 116, factual)

8.      The brain's developmental process among vertebrates:

        A. is the same with virtually no variation.
        B. varies mainly in speed and duration.
        C. varies in the number of ventricles which eventually develop.
        D. varies in structural sequence.
        (B, p. 116, factual)

9.      At what point does the brain weigh 1,000 g, which is almost as
        much as the average adult brain.

        A. by the sixth month after conception
        B. by birth
        C. by 1 year old
        D. by early adolescence
        (C, p. 117, factual)

10.     The average adult brain weights approximately:

        A. 650 g.
        B. 1,300 g.
        C. 2,600 g.
        D. 5,200 g.
        (B, p. 117, factual)

11.     What is the production of new neurons called?

        A. differentiation
        B. migration
        C. myelination
        D. proliferation
        (D, p. 117, factual)

12.    What is proliferation?

    A. the production of new cells
    B. the movement of primitive neurons and glia
    C. the formation of dendrites and an axon
    D. the insulation process that occurs on some axons
    (A, p. 117, factual)

13.    Proliferation occurs:

    A. at the top of the spinal column.
    B. around the vesicles.
    C. around the ventricles.
    D. at the expanding edge of the brain.
    (C, p. 117, factual)

14.    What term describes the movement of primitive neurons and glia
       within the developing nervous system?

    A. differentiation
    B. migration
    C. myelination
    D. proliferation
    (B, p. 117, factual)

15.    What is migration?

    A. the production of new cells
    B. the movement of primitive neurons and glia
    C. the gradual formation of dendrites and an axon
    D. the insulation process that occurs on some axons
    (B, p. 117, factual)

16.    Migration requires:

    A. a precise chemical environment.
    B. cells which are myelinated.
    C. mature neurons.
    D. neurons with fully developed dendrites.
    (A, p. 117, factual)

17.    What is the process called when a primitive neuron begins to
       develop dendrites and an axon?

    A. differentiation
    B. migration
    C. myelination
    D. proliferation
    (A, p. 117, factual)

18.    What is differentiation?

       A. the production of new cells
       B. the movement of primitive neurons and glia
       C. the formation of dendrites and an axon
       D. the insulation process that occurs on some axons
       (C, p. 117, factual)

19.    What is the general relationship of dendritic growth relative to
       axon growth?

       A. Axons grow before dendrites.
       B. Axons and dendrites grow at the same time.
       C. Dendrites grow before axons.
       D. It depends on the type of neuron.
       (A, p. 117, factual)

20.    During development, the axon grows:

       A. after differentiation is complete.
       B. during migration.
       C. after the dendrites have completed their growth.
       D. at the same time as the dendrites.
       (B, p. 117, factual)

21.    When does most dendritic growth in a newly forming neuron occur?

       A. prior to migration
       B. during migration
       C. prior to the growth of the axon
       D. at the time when incoming axons are due to arrive
       (D, p. 117, factual)

22.    The shape of neurons:

       A. is the same throughout the brain.
       B. is something that develops after birth.
       C. depends mainly on the thickness of the myelin.
       D. is different throughout the brain.
       ("WWW" D, p. 117, factual)

23.    What happens if an immature neuron is transplanted to another
       area of the brain early in its development?

       A. It makes its way back to its original location.
       B. It takes on all the characteristics of neighboring neurons.
       C. It develops as other cells in the area from which it was
          taken.
       D. It dies.
       (B, p. 117, factual)

24.   If you transplant later stage immature neurons to another area of
      the brain:

      A. they migrate back to their original location.
      B. they will take on all of the properties of their new location.
      C. they will retain some of the properties of their old location.
      D. they will retain all of the properties of their old location.
      (C, p.117, factual)

25.   Myelination is a process:

      A. common to all vertebrate axons.
      B. common to all vertebrate dendrites.
      C. common to some vertebrate axons.
      D. which occurs in response to injury.
      (C, p. 117, factual)

26.   Myelination occurs in:

      A. all animals.
      B. all vertebrates, but only vertebrates.
      C. all mammals, but only mammals.
      D. only humans.
      (B, p. 117, factual)

27.   For some axons, glial cells produce an insulating sheath that
      makes rapid transmission possible.  What is this process called?

      A. differentiation
      B. migration
      C. myelination
      D. proliferation
      (C, p. 117, factual)

28.   In humans, where does myelination first occur?

      A. in the spinal cord
      B. in the hindbrain
      C. in the midbrain
      D. in the forebrain
      (A, p. 117, factual)

29.   Myelination in the human brain:

      A. is complete upon birth.
      B. is complete around the second birthday.
      C. is complete sometime shortly after adolescence.
      D. continues well into the adult years.
      (D, p. 117, factual)

30.    Glomeruli of the mouse olfactory bulb:

    A. are not present until three weeks of age.
    B. are not present until adulthood.
    C. expand and grow during early development.
    D. are responsible for cell migration.
    (C, p. 117, factual)

31.    Why is it that all neurons in a healthy adult brain have made appropriate connections?

    A. Chemical messages from our muscles tell our brain how many neurons to form, and that number perfectly matches the connections required.
    B. If an axon does not make the appropriate connections by a certain age, it dies.
    C. We are born with all connections formed.
    D. Connections form rapidly, but we learn to use whatever connections have formed.
    (B, p. 118, factual)

32.    Why is it that every axon in an adult mammal has a target cell (muscle cell or other neuron) with which it makes synaptic contact?

    A. Each target cell causes the growth of a neuron and its axon.
    B. After formation, axons release a chemical that causes a target cell to form.
    C. Axons that fail to find a target cell die.
    D. An axon will make contact with any kind of cell and adjust its function as necessary.
    (C, p. 118, factual)

33.    Which cells receive nerve growth factor (NGF)?

    A. neurons in the central nervous system as they differentiate
    B. migrating neurons in the parasympathetic nervous system
    C. neurons in the sympathetic nervous system that successfully form lasting synapses
    D. peripheral neurons that innervate parts of the body that increase in size as the body grows
    (C, p. 118, conceptual)

34.    What is signaled by nerve growth factor (NGF)?

    A. that a target cell has "accepted" an axon
    B. which target cell a growing axon should connect with
    C. that axons should elongate as the body grows bigger
    D. the need for new neurons to form in brain areas that are lacking in neurons
    (A, p. 118, conceptual)

35.      Nerve Growth Factor (NGF):

         A. promotes the survival and growth of the axon.
         B. is a fuel metabolized by neurons.
         C. promotes programmed cell death.
         D. is a hormone first released at puberty.
         (A, p. 118, factual)

36.      Programmed mechanism of cell death is called:

         A. NGF
         B. apoptosis
         C. neurotophin
         D. BDNF
         (B, p. 118, factual)

37.      Apoptosis:

         A. is a programmed mechanism of cell death.
         B. promotes the survival and growth of the axon.
         C. promotes the survival and growth of dendrites.
         D. promotes the activity of neurons.
         (A, p. 118-119, factual)

38.      What is apoptosis?

         A. the growth of an axon in response to NGF
         B. the leakage of transmitters from vesicles
         C. a program of "suicide" by a neuron
         D. dendritic branching in the sympathetic nervous system
         (C, p. 118-119, factual)

39.      When does apoptosis occur?

         A. when an axon is exposed to NGF
         B. when dendrites are exposed to NGF
         C. when an axon receives too little NGF
         D. when dendrites receive too little NGF
         (C, p. 118-119, conceptual)

40.      If a sympathetic nervous system axon does not receive enough
         nerve growth factor, the neuron will:

         A. kill itself.
         B. grow a shorter axon.
         C. compensate by growing more dendrites.
         D. decrease its velocity of action potentials.
         (A, p. 118, factual)

41.    Some neurons die during development because:

       A. they are surrounded by glia.
       B. they do not receive enough GABA.
       C. they receive too much NGF.
       D. they fail to receive enough NGF.
       (D, p. 118, conceptual)

42.    Nerve growth factor attracts:

       A. all growing dendrites.
       B. all growing axons.
       C. the growing axons of the sympathetic nervous system.
       D. the growing dendrites of all cranial nerves.
       (C, p. 118, conceptual)

43.    Apoptosis is to necrosis as:

       A. murder is to suicide.
       B. active is to passive.
       C. regeneration is to degeneration.
       D. birth is to death.
       (B, pp. 118-119, conceptual)

44.    Necrosis is:

       A. cell suicide.
       B. the death of neurons as a result of injury.
       C. the destruction of neurons by neighboring neurons.
       D. a secretion of a chemical in response to injury.
       (B, p. 119, factual)

45.    What is the function of neurotrophins?

       A. They inhibit proliferation.
       B. They promote survival of axons.
       C. The neuron uses them as fuel.
       D. They signal that an axon has been "rejected."
       (B, p. 119, factual)

46.    What happens to an axon that does not receive enough
       neurotrophins from a target cell?

       A. It will branch out and form other synapses on other cells.
       B. It will manufacture its own neurotrophins.
       C. It degenerates and dies.
       D. It will fail to reabsorb transmitters that have already been
          released.
       (C, p. 119, factual)

47. At later stages of the neuron's development, neurotrophins:

    A. increase the branching of axons.
    B. cause the neuron's death.
    C. become converted into myelin.
    D. connect the axon to axons of adjoining cells.
    (A, p. 119, factual)

48. In response to nervous system injury, neurotrophins:

    A. cause the neuron's death.
    B. reduce inflammation due to this injury.
    C. increase regrowth of damaged axons.
    D. promote apoptosis.
    (C, p. 119, factual)

49. Which statement most accurately describes embryonic development of the nervous system in humans?

    A. The majority of cells remain as primitive neurons until birth.
    B. All synapses that are formed are permanent.
    C. Neurons form before birth; synapses form after birth.
    D. Far more neurons are produced than will ultimately survive.
    (D, p. 119, conceptual)

50. What is true about massive cell death in the brain during prenatal development?

    A. It usually indicates a genetic abnormality.
    B. It is an indication of restricted blood flow to the fetus.
    C. It is usually due to an autoimmune disorder.
    D. It is normal.
    (D, p. 119, conceptual)

51. Which of the following is a likely explanation for the excess proliferation of neurons in early development?

    A. to compensate for connection errors
    B. to use up excess stored fuel
    C. to increase learning capacity when it is most needed
    D. to prevent apoptosis
    (A, p. 119, factual)

52. Which of the following is the mostly likely explanation for the excess proliferation of neurons?

    A. to allow the nervous system to match incoming axons to receiving cells.
    B. to allow for cell death in the event of injury.
    C. to allow for genetic error.
    D. to allow for the proliferation of dendrites.
    (A, p. 119, factual)

53.   Compared to an adult, a fetus has:

A. more neurons.
B. approximately the same number of neurons.
C. about half the number of neurons.
D. about one-tenth the number of neurons.
(A, p. 119, factual)

**Pathfinding by Axons**

54.   Weiss believed that when he grafted an extra leg onto a
      salamander adjacent to one of the hindlegs:

A. each axon developed a branch that found its way to the correct
   muscle in the extra limb.
B. the muscles in the extra limb sent out special messages to
   attract the axons.
C. neurons which had not yet made connections developed them with
   the extra limb.
D. each muscle received many signals and responded only to the
   ones it was "tuned" to.
(D, p. 120, factual)

55.   What happened when Weiss grafted an extra leg onto a salamander
      adjacent to one of the hindlegs?

A. The new leg gradually took over for the old.
B. The new leg withered and died.
C. Nerves from the old leg attached to the new in a random
   fashion.
D. Branches of axons from the old leg attached to corresponding
   muscles in the new.
(D, p. 120, conceptual)

56.   What process occurs when axons attempt to form connections to a
      grafted limb in a salamander?

A. Axons send messages similar to radio signals to which specific
   muscles respond.
B. Axons connect randomly and muscles learn to coordinate through
   experience.
C. Axons find their way to corresponding muscles in the new leg.
D. A lack of nerve growth fiber leads to the degeneration of the
   new leg.
(C, p. 120, conceptual)

57.   If you cut the optic nerve of a newt, what happens?

      A. The fibers grow back and attach to random targets, so they see
         a scrambled picture.
      B. The fibers grow back and attach to their original targets,
         resulting in normal vision.
      C. The newt remains blind, since neurons do not regenerate.
      D. The fibers attach to multiple targets, resulting in blurry
         vision.
      (B, p. 121, factual)

58.   What happened after Roger Sperry cut a newt's optic nerve and
      rotated the eye?  Axons from what used to be the dorsal part of
      the retina (now located on the ventral side) grew back to the
      target areas:

      A. that ordinarily get input from the dorsal retina.
      B. that ordinarily get input from the ventral retina.
      C. that ordinarily get input from the center of the retina.
      D. equally and diffusely.
      (A, p. 121, conceptual)

59.   What visual capabilities did Sperry's newt have after Sperry cut
      the optic nerve and rotated the eye?

      A. It regained normal vision.
      B. It saw the world upside down and backwards.
      C. It required experience to relearn how to see.
      D. It remained blind.
      (B, p. 121, factual)

60.   What happens when an axon is damaged in a goldfish or amphibian's
      optic nerve?

      A. The organism is permanently blind in one part of the visual
         field.
      B. The axon will regrow and randomly connect with any open target
         cell.
      C. The axon will regrow but fail to make a connection.
      D. The axon will regrow to the general area where it originally
         went.
      (D, p. 121, conceptual)

61.   When Sperry cut a newt's optic nerve and rotated the eye by 180
      degrees, each axon:

      A. degenerated.
      B. regenerated to a random location.
      C. regenerated to the area where it had originally been.
      D. regenerated, but to the opposite part of the original target
         area.
      (C, p. 121, conceptual)

62.    Which of the following best describes the process by which
       developing axons find their general target areas?

       A. completely random growth
       B. shape attraction
       C. electrical attraction
       D. chemical attraction
       ("WWW" D, p. 121, factual)

63.    How widely each axon spreads its branches, once it has reached
       its target, is determined by:

       A. how large the neuron is.
       B. neurotrophins.
       C. glucose.
       D. the distance between that neuron and the thalamus.
       (B, p. 121, factual)

64.    Axons sort themselves over the surface of the target area:

       A. by following a gradient of chemicals.
       B. through apoptosis.
       C. through necrosis.
       D. based on their size.
       (A, p. 121, factual)

65.    Which of the following are selective as axons form synapses with
       target cells?

       A. axons, but not target cells
       B. target cells, but not axons
       C. both axons and target cells
       D. neither axons nor target cells
       (C, p. 121, conceptual)

66.    What is meant by neural Darwinism?

       A. The brains of higher primates are the ones that are most
          similar to those of humans.
       B. Most individual differences in the brain are due to genetic
          mutations.
       C. Successful neurons develop while less successful neurons
          weaken or die.
       D. Successful neurons reproduce while less successful neurons do
          not.
       (C, p. 122, conceptual)

### Fine-Tuning by Experience

67.   Keeping animals in a varied environment with stimulation leads to
      which change in neuronal structure?

      A. increased branching of dendrites
      B. increased speed of action potentials
      C. increased density of Nodes of Ranvier along the axon
      D. division of mature neurons to form additional neurons
      ("WWW" A, p. 122-123, factual)

68.   What is different about rats raised in an enriched
      environment in comparison to rats raised in an impoverished
      environment?

      A. a more pleasant personality
      B. improved learning performance
      C. better parenting skills
      D. nothing
      (B, p. 123, factual)

69.   Enriched environments:

      A. enhance the sprouting of dendrites, but not axons.
      B. enhance the sprouting of axons, but not dendrites.
      C. enhance the sprouting of axons and dendrites.
      D. increase the length of the axon.
      (C, p. 123, factual)

70.   One portion of the brain in mynah birds is known to be essential
      to the birds' ability to sing.  How does this area appear at one
      year compared to when the bird was born?

      A. It has fewer, but larger, dendritic spines.
      B. It has fewer and smaller dendritic spines.
      C. It has more dendritic spines.
      D. It has more, and larger, axons.
      (A, p. 123, factual)

71.   A magnetoencephalograph (MEG) measures:

      A. the powerful magnetic fields generated by your skin.
      B. the powerful magnetic fields generated by your brain.
      C. the faint magnetic fields generated by your skin.
      D. the faint magnetic fields generated by your brain.
      (D, pp. 124, factual)

72.   Brain cells that are neither neurons nor glia, but which are
      capable of dividing and then differentiating into neurons or glia
      are called:

      A. parallel fibers.
      B. intrinsic cells.
      C. stem cells.
      D. glomeruli.
      (C, p. 125, factual)

73.   Stem cells:

      A. line the interior of the ventricles of the brain.
      B. originate in the olfactory bulbs of the brain.
      C. destroy glial cells.
      D. are found in the brain stem.
      (A, p. 125, factual)

74.   What has been found in adults who demonstrate perfect pitch?

      A. an area of greater development in the left temporal lobe
      B. an area of greater development in the left frontal lobe
      C. a longer basilar membrane and greater number of hair cells in
         each ear
      D. impaired visual acuity
      (A, p. 125, factual)

75.   Which of the following aspects of brain and neural functioning
      can be most clearly altered by experience?

      A. velocity of action potentials
      B. structure of dendrites and axons
      C. chemical constituents of the ventricles
      D. number of laminae in the cerebral cortex
      (B, p. 125, factual)

76.   Musicians who use the left hand to finger the violin strings have
      some alterations in one brain area, detectable by
      magnetoencephalography.   That brain area is the:

      A. left hemisphere prefrontal cortex.
      B. right hemisphere prefrontal cortex.
      C. left hemisphere postcentral gyrus.
      D. right hemisphere postcentral gyrus.
      (D, p. 125, factual)

77.    What information is used by postsynaptic cells of the lateral
       geniculate (in the thalamus) in a developing fetal brain to
       determine that incoming axons all come from spots near one
       another in the retina?

       A. similarity of neurotransmitters
       B. similarity of size
       C. simultaneous activity
       D. presence or absence of myelin
       (C, p. 126, factual)

78.    Which of the following would be more damaging to an adult brain
       than to the brain of an infant or fetus?

       A. exposure to alcohol
       B. infections like German measles
       C. iodine deficiency in the diet
       D. All of these are more damaging to an infant brain.
       (D, p.126, factual)

**Proportional Growth of Brain Areas**

79.    The development of each brain area depends on:

       A. the rate but not the duration of the process.
       B. the duration but not the rate of the process.
       C. both the rate and duration of the process.
       D. how many genes are allocated for each area.
       (C, p. 126, factual)

80.    In relation to the overall brain size, the olfactory bulbs in
       humans, compared to many other mammals:

       A. are very large.
       B. are much smaller.
       C. are essentially the same size.
       D. have greater asymmetry between the left and the right
          hemispheres.
       (B, p. 126, conceptual)

81.    If you know the total brain size of a mammal:

       A. you could accurately predict the corresponding sizes of
          different brain areas, with no exceptions.
       B. it would not give you any clue as to the sizes of different
          brain areas.
       C. you could accurately predict the sizes of nearly all large
          brain areas except the olfactory bulbs.
       D. you could accurately predict the corresponding sizes of brain
          areas in all mammals, except for humans.
       (C, p. 127, conceptual)

82.    From the total brain mass of a mammal, we can most accurately
       predict:

       A. the total body mass of the animal.
       B. the mass of almost any major structure within the brain.
       C. performance on a standardized test of animal intelligence.
       D. amount of genetic similarity between that animal and humans.
       (B, p. 127-128, factual)

83.    If Himalayan anteaters have a larger cerebral cortex than
       Mongolian anteaters, then probably:

       A. Himalayan anteaters also have larger subcortical areas.
       B. Mongolian anteaters have larger subcortical areas.
       C. Mongolian anteaters have a larger corpus callosum.
       D. Himalayan anteaters have a lower metabolic rate.
       (A, p. 127-128, factual)

84.    A number of studies have attempted to correlate brain size with
       IQ scores in humans.  Which of the following trends seems to
       occur in the data?

       A. Studies using more accurate measurements of brain size have
          found higher correlations.
       B. Positive correlations emerge only in older studies using less
          accurate measures of brain size.
       C. Positive correlations emerge only if the same researcher
          measures the brain size and administers the IQ tests.
       D. Regardless of how brain size and IQ are measured, the
          correlations are very close to zero.
       (A, pp. 127-128, conceptual)

85.    How is it that smaller female brains perform as well as larger
       male brains?

       A. IQ tests are biased in favor of females.
       B. Females are more organized than males, and so are their
          brains.
       C. Testosterone interferes with frontal cortex activity.
       D. There is no definitive answer.
       (D, p. 128, conceptual)

86.    Which procedure would an investigator use to measure which brain
       areas are most active at a given moment in a living human?

       A. a PET scan
       B. a CAT scan
       C. an MRI
       D. autoradiography
       (C, p. 128, factual)

**The Vulnerable Developing Brain**

87.　An iodine deficiency in the diet can lead to an inadequate production of thyroid hormones.　What is the result if this occurs in an infant or developing fetus?

　　A. Down's syndrome
　　B. mental retardation
　　C. Tourette's syndrome
　　D. accelerated body growth
　　(B, p. 129, factual)

88.　What modern day practice helps prevent an inadequate production of thyroid hormones?

　　A. fluoride in drinking water
　　B. processed sugar
　　C. iodized salt
　　D. artificial sweeteners
　　(C, p. 129, factual)

89.　The most common treatment for ADD and ADHD is:

　　A. a stimulant drug.
　　B. an antidepressant.
　　C. a tranquilizer drug.
　　D. an antipsychotic drug.
　　(A, p. 129, factual)

90.　In infants, anesthetic drugs:

　　A. suppress synaptic activity of neurons.
　　B. work as they do with adults.
　　C. are ineffective.
　　D. act as neurotophins.
　　(A, p. 129, factual)

91.　What condition would be suspected if a young child shows decreased alertness, hyperactivity, mental retardation, motor problems, a heart defect, and abnormal facial features?

　　A. fetal alcohol syndrome
　　B. Turner's syndrome
　　C. Klinefelter's syndrome
　　D. PKU
　　(A, p. 129, factual)

92.　What brain abnormalities are found in children with fetal alcohol syndrome?

　　A. short axons with few branches
　　B. short dendrites with few branches
　　C. lack of dopamine receptors
　　D. enlarged ventricles
　　("WWW" B, p. 129, factual)

93.    How much alcohol, if any, can a pregnant woman drink without
       worrying about the negative effects on her child?

       A. the equivalent of two cocktails a day
       B. the equivalent of one beer a day
       C. anything less than what causes her to act drunk
       D. It is best to abstain completely.
       (D, p. 129, factual)

94.    In general, the more the mother drinks during pregnancy:

       A. the more impulsive the child.
       B. the more likely her child is to be diagnosed as clinically
          depressed.
       C. the smaller the cerebral ventricles of her child.
       D. the thicker the myelin sheaths of her child's axons.
       (A, p. 129, factual)

95.    Children of mothers who use cocaine during pregnancy:

       A. have a slightly higher birth weight.
       B. are likely to develop Turner's syndrome.
       C. have a slightly lower IQ score.
       D. are born with severe abnormalities resembling cerebral palsy.
       (C, p. 130, factual)

96.    Children of mothers who smoke cigarettes during pregnancy are at
       an increased risk of:

       A. intellectual deficits.
       B. Korsakoff's syndrome.
       C. Rett syndrome.
       D. Parkinson's disease.
       ("WWW" A, p. 130, factual)

**Module 5.2:  Recovery of Function After Brain Damage**

**Causes of Human Brain Damage**

97.    Closed head injury is:

       A. the most common cause of brain damage in young adults.
       B. usually fatal.
       C. the most common cause of Korsakoff's syndrome.
       D. related to Alzheimer's disease.
       (A, p. 132, factual)

98.    A sharp blow to the head resulting from an assault or trauma that
       does not actually puncture the brain is called a:

       A. stroke.
       B. cerebrovascular accident.
       C. hemorrhage.
       D. closed head injury.
       (D, p. 132, factual)

99.   Closed head injury results in damage because of:

      A. blood clots that interrupt normal blood flow to the brain.
      B. excessive deficit of neurotrophins.
      C. a temporary deficit of neurotrophins.
      D. hemorrhage.
      (A, p. 132, factual)

100.  The most common type of stroke is:

      A. caused when an artery ruptures.
      B. apoptosis.
      C. a penumbra.
      D. caused when a blood clot closes an artery.
      (D, p. 132, factual)

101.  A stroke which is caused when an artery ruptures is also known
      as:

      A. ischemia.
      B. hemorrhage.
      C. closed head injury.
      D. penumbra.
      (B, p. 132, factual)

102.  Which of the following should NOT be recommended for stroke
      victims?

      A. tissue plasminogen activator
      B. tranquilizers
      C. food restriction
      D. cooling the brain
      (B, pp. 132-133, factual)

103.  Woodpeckers do not get concussions because:

      A. they have more cerebrospinal fluid that any other bird or
         mammal.
      B. they strike a hard surface in an almost perfect arc.
      C. they avoid rotating their heads during impact.
      D. their skulls are not as hard as those of other birds or
         mammals.
      (C, p. 133, factual)

104.  Stroke kills neurons:

      A. only in the immediate vicinity of the stroke.
      B. only in the penumbra.
      C. in two waves.
      D. unless tranquilizers are prescribed almost immediately.
      (C, p. 133, factual)

105.   After a stroke, cells in the penumbra:

    A. are the first to die.
    B. help to remove dead or dying cells in the area of damage.
    C. quickly become more active, compensating for the area of damage.
    D. may die days or weeks after a stroke.
    (D, p. 133, factual)

106.   After a stroke, cells in the penumbra:

    A. die quickly.
    B. may die a year after the stroke.
    C. may die days or weeks afterwards.
    D. are protected by the blood-brain barrier.
    (C, p. 133, factual)

107.   Penumbra, as related to stroke, refers to the:

    A. type of stroke that has been suffered.
    B. brain region unaffected by the stroke.
    C. brain cells that are immediately destroyed by the stroke.
    D. brain region that surrounds the immediate damage.
    (D, p. 133, factual)

108.   In hemorrhage, cells in the penumbra:

    A. lose much of their oxygen.
    B. lose much of their glucose.
    C. are flooded with excess oxygen.
    D. act quickly to strengthen the blood-brain barrier.
    (C, p. 133, factual)

109.   After ischemia, penumbra cells:

    A. transform from neurons into glia.
    B. are invaded by waste products.
    C. break down the blood-brain barrier.
    D. increase the velocity of their action potentials.
    (B, p. 133, factual)

110.   In ischemia, cells in the penumbra:

    A. lose much of their oxygen and glucose supplies.
    B. are flooded with excess oxygen and other blood products.
    C. accumulate excessive amounts of neurotophins.
    D. develop a thicker than usual myelin sheath.
    (A, p. 133, factual)

111.   Ischemia is to _____ as hemorrhage is to _____:

A. older individuals; younger individuals
B. proximal; distal
C. obstruction; rupture
D. barely noticeable; lethal
(C, p. 132, factual)

112.   What kind of cells proliferate after a stroke?

A. penumbra cells
B. glial cells
C. ischemia cells
D. cancer cells
("WWW" B, p. 134, factual)

113.   After either ischemia or hemorrhage, edema forms because:

A. the pH of brain fluids has changed.
B. the molarity of brain fluids has changed.
C. the blood-brain barrier has broken down.
D. mitochondria interfere with neural activity.
(C, p. 134, factual)

114.   Ischemia and hemorrhage kill neurons by:

A. understimulating them.
B. overstimulating them.
C. overactivating the sodium-potassium pump.
D. depleting the glutamate supply available to neurons.
(B, p. 134, factual)

115.   Damage due to stoke can be minimized by administering a drug which:

A. breaks up blood clots.
B. overstimulates neurons in and around the damaged area.
C. increases the release of glutamate.
D. slows down the sodium-potassium pump.
(A, p. 134, factual)

116.   Tissue Plasminogen activator (tPA):

A. is recommended for hemorrhage.
B. overstimulates glutamate receptors.
C. should be administered a few days after stroke.
D. is helpful in cases of ischemia.
(D, p. 134, factual)

117.   Tissue Plasminogen activator (tPA):

   A. is not recommended for hemorrhage.
   B. overstimulates glutamate receptors.
   C. should be administered a few days after stroke.
   D. is not recommended for ischemia.
   (A, p. 134, factual)

118.   In research aimed at minimizing damage due to stroke,
       attempts to prevent overstimulation of cells have produced:

   A. very promising results.
   B. disappointing results.
   C. a complex interaction between age of patient and season of the
      year.
   D. positive results in humans, but not so for animals.
   (B, p. 134, factual)

119.   Some researchers believe that ischemia kills cells by apoptosis.
       This occurs because the:

   A. cells are so disturbed that their self-destruct programs are
      activated.
   B. cell has so little oxygen.
   C. cell has so little glutamate available for release.
   D. cells accumulate excessive neurotrophins.
   (A, p. 134, conceptual)

120.   Researchers have tried using drugs that block apoptosis.  Results
       have been:

   A. favorable in animals and human trials.
   B. favorable in animal trials but too costly to try with humans.
   C. favorable in animal trials but difficult or impractical to
      apply to humans.
   D. unfavorable in all research trials.
   (C, p. 134, factual)

121.   To date, the most effective laboratory method minimizing the
       damage resulting from stroke in nonhuman animals has been to:

   A. use drugs which trap free radicals.
   B. use drugs which effect cannabinoids.
   C. use neurotrophins which block apoptosis.
   D. cool the brain.
   ("WWW" D, p. 135, factual)

**Adjustments and Potential Recovery After Brain Damage**

122.  A deafferented limb:

    A. has lost its sensory input.
    B. has lost its motor control.
    C. is an amputated limb.
    D. is one which an organism uses spontaneously.
    (A, p. 135, factual)

123.  A monkey with a deafferented limb:

    A. cannot control the muscles of that limb.
    B. moves that limb whenever it uses its contralateral limb.
    C. uses it spontaneously, even though the animal has lost
       sensation to that body part.
    D. does not use it, even though it can still control the muscles.
    (D, p. 135, factual)

124.  What is a lesion?

    A. an area of brain next to a blood vessel
    B. a cell that lines the surface of a ventricle
    C. a fluid-filled space in the brain
    D. an area that has been damaged
    (D, p. 136, factual)

125.  A lesion is to _____ as an ablation is to _____.

    A. temporary; permanent
    B. destruction; removal
    C. surgery; stroke
    D. neurons; behavior
    (B, p. 136, conceptual)

126.  A researcher interested in making a small lesion deep within the
      brain would be most likely to use which of the following
      techniques?

    A. cut the tissue with a knife
    B. remove tissue with vacuum suction
    C. insert an electrode with a stereotaxic device and apply
       current
    D. block the flow of blood in arteries that supply that area of
       the brain
    (C, p. 136, factual)

127.  What procedure do experimenters use to produce a "sham lesion"?

A. Produce a lesion on one side of the brain and not the other.
B. Make a lesion in an area of the brain that was believed to be damaged already.
C. Introduce an electrode and then remove it without passing any current.
D. Pass a current through an electrode touching only the skull.
(C, p. 136, factual)

128.  What is the purpose of creating a sham lesion?

A. to destroy a brain area believed to be interfering with normal behavior
B. to assess the effects of introducing an electrode
C. to test the stereotaxic map
D. to create a path for injecting chemicals
(B, p. 136, conceptual)

129.  Diaschisis refers to the:

A. increase in activity of neurons surrounding a damaged area.
B. decreased activity of surviving neurons after other neurons are damaged.
C. increased activity in the cerebral cortex after damage to any part of the brain.
D. increased activity in the hypothalamus after damage to any part of the brain.
(B, p. 137, factual)

130.  What does the research on diaschisis imply about drugs that block norepinephrine, such as those used to control blood pressure?

A. They should be given quickly and in large doses following a stroke.
B. They should be avoided as much as possible if used to treat recent stroke victims.
C. They more than double the chances of a stroke.
D. They facilitate replacement of destroyed neurons in the central nervous system.
(B, p. 137, factual)

131.  To promote recovery, stroke victims should be given:

A. stimulant drugs immediately after the stroke.
B. any drug which decreases dopamine.
C. stimulant drugs a few days after the stroke.
D. tranquilizers a few days after the stroke.
(C, p. 137, factual)

132. Recovery from stroke is:

    A. impaired by tranquilizers.
    B. enhanced by tranquilizers.
    C. impaired by stimulant drugs if administered days after the
       stroke.
    D. enhanced by stimulant drugs if administered immediately after
       the stroke.
    (A, p. 137, factual)

133. A damaged axon:

    A. will never grow back.
    B. can grow back under certain circumstances.
    C. will grow back if its dendrites do also.
    D. will only grow back if it is myelinated.
    (B, p. 137, factual)

134. Which axons will regenerate to a significant degree if cut or
    crushed?

    A. those in invertebrates but not in vertebrates
    B. only those which are unmyelinated
    C. those in the central nervous system but not in the peripheral
       nervous system
    D. those in the peripheral nervous system but not in the central
       nervous system
    ("WWW" D, p. 137, factual)

135. After a cut through the spinal cord, axons grow back enough to
    restore functioning in certain _____ but not in _____.

    A. adults; infants
    B. infants; adults
    C. fish; mammals
    D. mammals; primates
    (C, p. 137, factual)

136. What is one impediment to regeneration of axons in the mammalian
    central nervous system?

    A. inhibitory chemicals secreted by the damaged portion of the
       axon
    B. bacterial infections caused by the decaying tissue
    C. large amounts of scar tissue
    D. inhibitory messages sent from the cell nucleus when an axon is
       damaged
    (C, p. 137, factual)

137.  What is one reason why axons regenerate better in the peripheral
      nervous system of mammals?  The peripheral nervous system:

      A. has fewer myelinated axons.
      B. has glial cells that destroy scar tissue.
      C. maintains a temperature closer to that at which embryonic
         cells form.
      D. produces a chemical that promotes axon growth.
      (D, p. 137, factual)

138.  Central nervous system axons regenerate much better in fish than
      in mammals because:

      A. fish nerves do not have to travel so far to reach their
         target.
      B. fewer fish nerves are covered with myelin.
      C. fish produce chemicals which promote regeneration.
      D. fish generally have a lower body temperature.
      (C, p. 137, factual)

139.  Central nervous system axons regenerate much better in fish than
      in mammals because fish:

      A. nerves do not have to travel so far to reach their target.
      B. myelin does not secrete proteins that inhibit axon growth, as
         does myelin in mammals.
      C. nerves have so much more myelin than do mammal nerves.
      D. myelin secretes a protein that accelerates regeneration.
      (B, p. 137, factual)

140.  Damaged axons regrow better in the young because:

      A. less myelin has formed.
      B. less astrocytes have formed.
      C. more myelin has formed.
      D. they have more growth-inhibiting proteins.
      (A, p. 137, factual)

141.  After central nervous damage, astrocytes:

      A. degenerate and die.
      B. secrete proteins that inhibit axon regrowth.
      C. secrete proteins that enhance some regrowth of axons.
      D. help develop thicker myelin sheaths around surviving axons.
      (B, p. 137, factual)

142.  Hemiplegia is caused by a:

      A. cut all the way through the spinal cord.
      B. cut part way through the spinal cord.
      C. Lesion on one side of the brain.
      D. stroke centered in the medulla.
      (B, p. 137, factual)

143.  If some of the axons innervating a given cell are destroyed or if
      they become inactive, what compensatory process takes place in
      the remaining presynaptic cells?

      A. activation of previously silent synapses
      B. removal of toxins
      C. denervation supersensitivity
      D. collateral sprouting
      (D, p. 138, conceptual)

144.  What is the term for the new branches that may form in uninjured
      axons after damage to surrounding axons?

      A. collateral sprouts
      B. bifurcations
      C. denervation supersensitivity
      D. diaschisis
      (A, p. 138, factual)

145.  After damage to a set of axons, neurotrophins induce nearby:

      A. injured axons to form new branches.
      B. injured dendrites to form new branches.
      C. uninjured axons to form new branches.
      D. uninjured dendrites to form new branches.
      (C, p. 138, factual)

146.  After loss of about half of the cells in a rat's locus coeruleus:

      A. the rat dies.
      B. the rat becomes comatose.
      C. collateral sprouts fill in most of the vacated synapses in the
         cerebral cortex.
      D. glia cells in the locus coeruleus transform into neurons.
      (C, p. 138, factual)

147.  After damage to the connections to the left hippocampus from the
      left entorhinal cortex, sprouts develop from the:

      A. left entorhinal cortex.
      B. right entorhinal cortex.
      C. left hippocampus.
      D. right hippocampus.
      (B, p. 138, factual)

148.  Damage to some of the axons that innervate a given structure may
      give rise to:

      A. collateral sprouting, but not denervation supersensitivity.
      B. denervation supersensitivity, but not collateral sprouting.
      C. both collateral sprouting and denervation supersensitivity.
      D. neither collateral sprouting nor denervation supersensitivity.
      (C, p. 138, factual)

149.    Where does denervation supersensitivity take place?

        A. In the presynaptic membrane.
        B. In both the presynaptic membrane and the postsynaptic
           membrane.
        C. In the postsynaptic membrane.
        D. In glial cells.
        (C, pp. 139, factual)

150.    What can be determined through autoradiography?

        A. how neurons communicate with each other
        B. where certain chemicals are located in the brain
        C. brain anatomy in a living person
        D. any effects on the brain of prolonged exposure to fumes in a
           car
        (B, p. 139, factual)

151.    Certain axons innervating a given neuron are damaged.  What
        compensatory change is likely to take place in that postsynaptic
        cell?

        A. collateral sprouting
        B. removal of toxins
        C. denervation supersensitivity
        D. decrease in glucose utilization
        (C, p. 139, factual)

152.    Denervation supersensitivity refers to an increase in what?

        A. production and release of neurotransmitters
        B. growth of axon branches
        C. responses to neurotransmitters
        D. polarization of the membrane at rest
        (C, p. 139, factual)

153.    Denervation supersensitivity is to _____ as disuse
        supersensitivity is to _____:

        A. destruction of incoming axons; inactivity of incoming axons
        B. inactivity of incoming axons; destruction of incoming axons
        C. postsynaptic neurons; presynaptic neurons
        D. presynaptic neurons; postsynaptic neurons
        (A, p. 139, factual)

154.    If supersensitivity takes place, what can one expect to find
        regarding the number of receptors?

        A. an increased number in the presynaptic cell
        B. a decreased number in the presynaptic cell
        C. an increased number in the postsynaptic cell
        D. a decreased number in the postsynaptic cell
        (C, p. 139, factual)

155. What is one reason for gradual behavioral recovery from brain damage?

    A. Uninjured areas of the brain develop new functions to take over the ones that were lost.
    B. Glia cells are transformed into neurons.
    C. Additional myelin forms on the axons that were not destroyed.
    D. Postsynaptic cells deprived of input become supersensitive.
    ("WWW" D, p. 139, factual)

156. One way to demonstrate denervation supersensitivity is to:

    A. damage axons that release dopamine.
    B. damage dendrites that receive dopamine.
    C. inject large amounts of dopamine or dopamine precursors.
    D. inject apomorphine in order to damage neurons.
    (A, p. 139, factual)

157. Studies with rats demonstrate that after damage to axons that release dopamine, the denervated side of the brain is:

    A. dopamine depleted.
    B. minimally sensitive to dopamine.
    C. supersensitive to dopamine.
    D. more sensitive than usual to all other neurotransmitters.
    (C, p. 139, factual)

158. People who lose most of the axons in some dopamine pathways still maintain nearly normal behavior.  This is because after some of the axons are lost the:

    A. presynaptic membrane develops denervation supersensitivity.
    B. postsynaptic membrane develops denervation supersensitivity.
    C. remaining axons decrease their release of transmitter.
    D. denervated side of the brain becomes less sensitive to dopamine.
    (B, pp. 139, factual)

159. Suppose a finger is amputated.  What will happen to the part of the cerebral cortex that used to respond to that finger?

    A. It will degenerate and die.
    B. It will remain alive but forever inactive.
    C. It will be active at times when the individual would have used that finger.
    D. It will become responsive to other fingers or part of the palm.
    (D, p. 141, factual)

160.  A section of the somatosensory cortex ordinarily responds to the
      third finger of the left hand.  If that finger is amputated, to
      what will the cells in this part of the cortex respond?

      A. nothing
      B. the second and fourth fingers and part of the palm
      C. the third finger of the right hand
      D. the entire left hand and the entire right hand
      (B, p. 141, factual)

161.  A cortical cell originally responded to stimulation of the middle
      finger.  After amputation of that finger it begins responding to
      the second and fourth fingers.  What most likely accounts for
      this?

      A. synaptic reorganization
      B. growth of completely new axons
      C. altered pattern of blood vessels in the brain
      D. a psychotic reaction
      (A, p. 141, factual)

162.  Investigators recorded activity from the cerebral cortex of
      monkeys that had an entire limb deafferented twelve years
      earlier.  Much to their surprise, what did they find?

      A. The organization of this area of the cortex had not been
         changed at all by the operation.
      B. This whole cortical area had become responsive to the face.
      C. This whole cortical area had become response to the opposite
         limb.
      D. This whole cortical area had developed motor instead of
         sensory functions.
      (B, p. 141, factual)

163.  What evidence have researchers found to explain how a whole
      cortical area associated with a deafferented or amputated limb
      becomes reinnervated?

      A. Associated axons in the spinal cord and brainstem also form
         sprouts.
      B. Cortical axons can sprout for distances up to 10 mm.
      C. The cortical area actually degenerates and other areas expand.
      D. Some sensory neurons from the limb remain active.
      (A, p. 141, factual)

164.  Sensations from phantom limbs:

      A. come from the stump of the amputated limb.
      B. are a result of brain reorganization.
      C. do not have a neural basis.
      D. can be diminished if more of the limb in removed surgically.
      (B, p. 141, factual)

165.    The part of the cortex responsive to the feet is immediately next
        to the part responsive to the:

        A. leg.
        B. arm.
        C. genitals.
        D. head.
        (C, pp. 141-142, factual)

166.    Histology involves the study of the:

        A. detailed structure of tissue.
        B. genetic contributions of parents and grandparents.
        C. history of neuroscience.
        D. changes in a single neuron over time.
        (A, p. 142, factual)

167.    Histochemistry deals with the:

        A. genetic contributions of an organism's predecessors.
        B. chemical components of tissues.
        C. changes in a single neuron over time.
        D. chemical changes in a person's body due to drug use.
        (B, p. 142, factual)

168.    One way to relieve the pain associated with a phantom limb is to:

        A. remove more of the amputated limb.
        B. have the amputee learn to use an artificial limb.
        C. stimulate that part of the cortex.
        D. help them understand that there is no neural basis for these
           sensations.
        (B, p. 142, factual)

169.    Recovery from brain damage is possible:

        A. across all ages, and researchers do not find any age
           differences.
        B. but younger populations have greater difficulty adjusting.
        C. but as we grow older, the brain becomes less capable of
           recovery.
        D. generally only among individuals under 60 years of age.
        (C, p. 143, factual)

170.    Recovery from brain damage:

        A. becomes more difficult in old age.
        B. is unlikely to last more than a few years.
        C. is more extensive in young adults than for either children or
           older adults.
        D. begins to develop about two months after the damage occurred.
        (A, p. 143, factual)

171. The Kennard principle suggests that the degree of recovery from brain damage will be more complete in:

    A. adults than in children.
    B. children than in adults.
    C. humans than in nonhumans.
    D. nonhumans than in humans.
    (B, pp. 143-144, factual)

172. Which of the following findings CONTRADICTS the Kennard principle?

    A. People seem to recover from brain damage, but can deteriorate again in old age.
    B. Fish recover from spinal cord damage better than mammals.
    C. Brain damage in infancy sometimes produces greater deficits than damage in adulthood.
    D. Organisms recover better from a series of small lesions than from a single, large lesion.
    (C, p. 144, factual)

173. How do the effects of brain damage early in life compare to damage in adulthood?

    A. They produce equal effects.
    B. Early damage produces greater effects.
    C. Early damage produces less of an effect.
    D. It depends on a number of other factors.
    (D, p. 144, factual)

174. Under what circumstances do children generally recover better than adults from brain damage?

    A. when it is caused by an infection
    B. when it is caused by inadequate oxygen
    C. when it is caused by exposure to alcohol
    D. when it is confined to one hemisphere of the brain
    (D, p. 144, conceptual)

175. Which of the following is likely after extensive brain damage in an infant rat?

    A. After damage to one hemisphere, the other hemisphere grows larger than usual.
    B. After damage to one hemisphere, the other hemisphere grows small than usual.
    C. After damage to the anterior portions of the brain, the posterior portions grow larger than usual.
    D. After damage to the posterior portions of the brain, the anterior portions grow larger than usual.
    (A, p. 144, factual)

176.  Removal of a young rat's _____ leads to _____ in the posterior
      portion of the cortex.

      A. anterior cortex; reduced development
      B. left hemisphere; reduced development
      C. right hemisphere; increased thickness
      D. anterior cortex; increased thickness
      (A, p. 144, factual)

177.  Damage to an infant monkey's orbital frontal cortex produced:

      A. no behavioral changes.
      B. deficits on the delayed alternation task.
      C. improved performance on the delayed alternation task.
      D. death.
      (B, p. 144, factual)

178.  Because the dorsolateral prefrontal cortex does not mature in
      monkeys until age two years, damage to that structure in infancy
      produces what kind of effect?

      A. Deficits from which the animal can recover at age two years.
      B. Severe deficits from which the animal can never recover.
      C. Mild deficits at first which grow more severe at age two
         years.
      D. No deficit, either immediately or later.
      (C, p. 144, factual)

179.  Damage to the dorsal lateral prefrontal cortex is to _____ as the
      orbital frontal cortex is to _____.

      A. increasing deficits; decreasing deficits
      B. decreasing deficits; increasing deficits
      C. cognitive deficits; emotional deficits
      D. emotional deficits; cognitive deficits
      (A, p. 144, conceptual)

180.  Damage to the dorsal lateral prefrontal cortex of an infant
      monkey:

      A. initially produces only a moderate deficit on the delayed
         alternation task.
      B. initially produces a powerful deficit on the delayed
         alternation task.
      C. does not change the monkey's behavior.
      D. produces deficits that repeatedly increase and decrease,
         increase and decrease again, as the monkey grows older.
      (A, p. 144, factual)

181.   Some people with frontal lobe damage behave in socially
       inappropriate ways.  What is generally true about these people?

       A. They are no longer capable of acceptable behavior.
       B. They are totally unaware of what they are doing.
       C. They can gradually recover their social skills through
          therapy.
       D. They usually spontaneously recover most of their social skills
          with or without therapy.
       (C, p. 145, factual)

182.   After damage to the visual cortex, a rat no longer approaches the
       white card it has been trained to approach.  What is the evidence
       that the rat has not completely forgotten the task?

       A. It can relearn the task faster than it can learn to approach a
          black card.
       B. After a delay, it spontaneously regains the memory and
          approaches a white card.
       C. After several unreinforced sessions, it begins responding
          correctly.
       D. Its heart rate increases when looking at a white card but not
          when looking at a black card.
       (A, p. 145, factual)

183.   In dealing with brain-damaged patients, the usual goal is to:

       A. get the patients to rely on other people for the skills that
          they have lost.
       B. get the patients to make as much use as possible of the
          impaired systems
       C. promote physical changes in the brain, such as collateral
          sprouting.
       D. encourage complete inactivity to enable the brain to engage in
          restorative processes.
       (B, p. 145, factual)

184.   After damage to the visual cortex, rats are most likely to pay
       attention to and learn the meaning of visual stimuli when:

       A. no other stimuli are present.
       B. tactile stimuli are present but irrelevant.
       C. tactile stimuli are present but redundant.
       D. a tactile stimulus signals reward and a visual stimulus does
          not.
       (A, p. 145, factual)

185.  A human has suffered brain damage that impairs vision.  Based on research, what would be good advice for the therapists working with this patient?

   A. Give up on vision and concentrate on the use of the patient's other senses.
   B. Pair each visual stimulus with a tactile stimulus that means the same thing.
   C. Be sure that in addition to visual stimuli, tactile stimuli are present, but irrelevant.
   D. Minimize the presence of other stimuli when the patient is supposed to attend to vision.
   (D, p. 145, conceptual)

186.  Recovery of behavior after several kinds of brain damage in animals has been shown to be facilitated by daily injections of which substance?

   A. calcium blockers
   B. sodium
   C. 6-OHDA
   D. potassium
   (A, p. 146, factual)

187.  Gangliosides:

   A. are calcium blockers.
   B. reduce regeneration of dendrites.
   C. increase scar tissue in damaged brains.
   D. promote the restoration of damaged brains.
   (D, p. 146, factual)

188.  Gangliosides probably:

   A. guide axons to the correct locations to form synapses.
   B. increase scar tissue in damaged brains.
   C. destroy synapses.
   D. increase dendritic branching.
   (A, p. 146, factual)

189.  Which hormone has been shown to decrease the effects of brain damage or to improve recovery from that damage?

   A. vasopressin
   B. renin
   C. progesterone
   D. parathyroid hormone
   (C, p. 146, factual)

190.    What is the current status of transplanting fetal cells as a
        therapy for damaged brains?

        A. It is the predominant therapy for Parkinson's disease.
        B. Results have been disappointing, but research continues.
        C. It is highly successful when used, but seldom used.
        D. The idea has been abandoned.
        (B, p. 146, factual)

191.    In general, what can we say about recovery for brain-damaged
        patients in the future?

        A. There is very little hope of recovery.
        B. Researchers are optimistic, but they need to evaluate many
           possible therapies.
        C. Drug therapies have clear advantages over all other
           approaches.
        D. Brain grafts are the only real answer.
        ("WWW" B, p. 146, factual)

**Module 6.1: Visual Coding and the Retinal Receptors**

**Reception, Transduction, and Coding**

1.    With reference to the sensory system, "reception" is:

    A. the absorption of physical energy.
    B. the conversion of physical energy into an electrochemical
       pattern in the neurons.
    C. the rate of activity within a given neuron.
    D. a one-to-one correspondence between the physical stimulus and
       the neural response.
    (A, p. 152, factual)

2.    What process involves the conversion of physical energy from some
      external stimulus into an electrochemical pattern in the neurons?

    A. coding
    B. reception
    C. transduction
    D. reconstitution
    (C, p. 152, factual)

3.    With reference to the sensory systems, what does "transduction"
      mean?

    A. the absorption of physical energy
    B. the changing of one sensory modality to another (e.g.
       converting written words into sounds)
    C. a one-to-one correspondence between the physical stimulus and
       the neural response
    D. the conversion of physical energy into an electrochemical
       pattern in the neurons
    (D, p. 152, factual)

4.    When speaking of sensory systems, "coding" refers to:

    A. the absorption of physical energy.
    B. the rate of activity within a given neuron.
    C. the conversion of physical energy into an electrochemical
       pattern in the neurons.
    D. a one-to-one correspondence between the physical stimulus and
       the neural response.
    (D, p. 152, factual)

5.    The three processes of sensory perception, in order of
      occurrence, are:

    A. coding, transduction, reception.
    B. reception, coding, transduction.
    C. transduction, reception, coding.
    D. reception, transduction, coding.
    ("WWW" D, p. 152, factual)

6.   The depolarization of a visual receptor is part of which perceptual process?

     A. coding
     B. transduction
     C. reception
     D. induction
     (B, p. 152, conceptual)

7.   What is a receptor potential?

     A. a local depolarization or hyperpolarization of a receptor membrane
     B. the potential that a receptor has to develop into a mature cell
     C. the potential that a receptor has to absorb energy
     D. conscious awareness of sensation
     (A, p. 152, factual)

8.   Where would you find a receptor potential?

     A. in the membrane of a receptor neuron
     B. in the synaptic cleft between a receptor neuron and an interneuron
     C. in a motor neuron
     D. in the nucleus of a receptor cell
     (A, p. 152, conceptual)

9.   Who believed that the brain's representation of a physical stimulus had to resemble the stimulus itself?

     A. Albert Einstein
     B. Rene Descartes
     C. Johannes Muller
     D. Hermann von Helmholtz
     (B, pp. 152, factual)

10.  When touch is absorbed by a sensory receptor, the energy is transduced into a local depolarization or hyperpolarization. What is this called?

     A. an action potential
     B. a receptor potential
     C. an opponent process
     D. conscious awareness of sensation
     (B, pp. 152, factual)

11.   The "law of specific nerve energies" states that:

      A. perception of a repeated stimulus fades.
      B. every stimulation of the optic nerve is perceived as light.
      C. the speed of action potentials varies depending on the
         strength of the stimulus.
      D. any stimulation above the threshold produces an action
         potential.
      (B, p. 153, conceptual)

12.   Which of the following is true according to the law of specific
      nerve energies?

      A. Any stimulation of the auditory nerve is perceived as sound.
      B. A single nerve can convey either auditory or visual
         information.
      C. Each sensory system has a unique electrical charge.
      D. If one sensory system becomes inactive, others will
         compensate.
      (A, p. 153, conceptual)

13.   Which of the following (if true) would MOST violate the law of
      specific nerve energies?

      A. A single neuron conveys visual information at one time and
         auditory information at another.
      B. A single neuron is excited by light of one wavelength, but
         inhibited by another.
      C. The activity of a single neuron contributes to the perception
         of both sweet and salty tastes.
      D. Two auditory neurons produce action potentials in the presence
         of the same sound.
      (A, p. 153, conceptual)

14.   Who originally proposed the law of specific nerve energies?

      A. Albert Einstein
      B. Rene Descartes
      C. Johannes Muller
      D. Hermann von Helmholtz
      (C, p. 153, factual)

15.   According to the law of specific nerve energies, how does the
      brain tell the difference between one sensory modality and
      another?

      A. by which neurotransmitter is released
      B. by which neurons are active
      C. by the velocity of the action potentials
      D. by the amplitude of the action potentials
      (B, p. 153, factual)

16.    According to the law of specific nerve energies, a given nerve
       has the option of sending:

       A. many different kinds of messages in response to light.
       B. many different kinds of messages in response to sound.
       C. one kind of response to light and a different kind of response
          to sound.
       D. only action potentials.
       (D, p. 153, factual)

17.    In light of what we know today, we must modify the law of
       specific nerve energies to include which possibility?

       A. A receptor can signal light by one response and sound by a
          different response.
       B. Any artificial stimulation of a receptor is perceived as pain.
       C. A change in the intensity of a stimulus may be indicated by a
          neurotransmitter change.
       D. An increase in firing may indicate one color and a decrease
          may indicate another color.
       (D, p. 153, factual)

18.    Which of the following is NOT used by the nervous system to
       convey information about a stimulus?

       A. the temporal rhythm of action potentials
       B. the frequency of action potentials
       C. which particular neurons are active
       D. the size of action potentials
       (D, p. 153, conceptual)

**The Eye and its Connections to the Brain**

19.    Light enters the eye through an opening in the center of the iris
       called the:

       A. retina.
       B. cornea.
       C. pupil.
       D. macula.
       (C, p. 153, factual)

20.    Visual receptors line the:

       A. retina.
       B. cornea.
       C. pupil.
       D. iris.
       ("WWW" A, p. 153, factual)

21.  Light from the left half of the world strikes what part of the
     retina?

     A. the left half
     B. the right half
     C. the whole retina equally
     D. it depends of the wavelength
     (B, p. 153, factual)

22.  Light from above our head strikes the:

     A. left side of the retina.
     B. right side of the retina.
     C. top half of the retina.
     D. bottom half of the retina.
     (D, p. 153, factual)

23.  Which of the following characterizes the fovea?

     A. It has the greatest perception of detail.
     B. It surrounds the point of exit of the optic nerve.
     C. It falls in the shadow cast by the pupil.
     D. It has more rods than cones.
     (A, pp. 153-154, factual)

24.  The central portion of the macula:

     A. is where the optic nerve exits the back of the eyeball.
     B. is specialized for acute, detailed vision.
     C. contains mostly rods.
     D. contains many blood vessels and ganglion cell axons.
     (B, p. 154, factual)

25.  If you want to see something in fine detail, you should focus the
     light on which part of your retina?

     A. the optic nerve
     B. the fovea
     C. an area containing mostly rods
     D. the cornea
     (B, p. 154, conceptual)

26.  Why does the fovea provide the clearest, most detailed visual
     information?

     A. There are so few blood vessels and ganglion cells there.
     B. It is closest to the pupil.
     C. It surrounds the optic nerve.
     D. It is at the top of the retina where there are many rods.
     (A, p. 154, factual)

27.   Why does the fovea provide the clearest, most detailed visual information?

      A. It is closest to the pupil.
      B. It surrounds the optic nerve.
      C. Receptors are tightly packed there.
      D. There are many blood vessels for supplying energy.
      (C, p. 154, factual)

28.   What is true about the retinas of predatory birds such as hawks?

      A. They have no discernible fovea.
      B. They have a greater density of receptors than do humans on the top half of the retina.
      C. They have a greater density of receptors than do humans on the bottom half of the retina.
      D. They are virtually indistinguishable from the retinas of humans.
      (B, p. 154, factual)

29.   What is a physiological basis for the expression "eyes like a hawk"?

      A. Hawks have no blind spot.
      B. Hawks have a "visual streak".
      C. Hawks have eyes occupying over half their head.
      D. Hawks have rods in the fovea and cones in the periphery.
      (C, p. 154, conceptual)

30.   How do the retinas of many bird species differ from the retinas of humans?

      A. Many species of birds have two foveas per eye while humans have only one fovea per eye.
      B. Many species of birds have smaller foveas than do humans.
      C. Many species of birds have less density of visual receptors on the top half of their retinas than do humans.
      D. Many species of birds have foveas composed mainly of bipolar cells while humans have retinas composed mainly of cones.
      (A, p. 154, factual)

31.   How do the retinas of predatory birds such as hawks differ from the retinas of humans?

      A. Hawks have one fovea; humans have two.
      B. Hawks have mostly cones; humans have mostly bipolar cells.
      C. Hawks see better above them than below them; humans see better below them than above them.
      D. Hawks have more receptors on the top half of their retinas than do humans.
      (D, p. 154, factual)

32.    How do the retinas of predatory birds, such as hawks, differ from
       the retinas of prey species, such as rats?

       A. Hawks have one fovea; rats have two.
       B. Hawks have greater density of receptors on the top half of
          their retinas than do rats.
       C. Hawks do not have bipolar cells in the retina; rats have an
          abundance of bipolar cells in the retina.
       D. Hawks have mostly rods, whereas rats have mostly cones.
       (B, p. 154, factual)

33.    In vertebrate retinas, receptors send their messages:

       A. straight to the brain.
       B. immediately to ganglion cells within the retina.
       C. to bipolar cells within the retina.
       D. to the periphery of the retina first, ganglion cells next, and
          bipolar cells last.
       (C, p. 154, factual)

34.    What is the correct sequence through which visual information
       passes?

       A. receptor cells, then ganglion cells, then bipolar cells
       B. ganglion cells, then receptor cells, then bipolar cells
       C. bipolar cells, then receptor cells, then ganglion cells
       D. receptor cells, then bipolar cells, then ganglion cells
       (D, p. 155, factual)

35.    In what order does light pass through the retina?

       A. receptor cells, ganglion cells, bipolar cells
       B. ganglion cells, bipolar cells, receptor cells
       C. receptor cells, bipolar cells, ganglion cells
       D. bipolar cells, receptor cells, ganglion cells
       (C, p. 155, factual)

36.    The optic nerve is composed of axons from which kind of cell?

       A. rods and cones
       B. bipolar cells
       C. horizontal cells
       D. ganglion cells
       (D, p. 155, factual)

37.    Why is the blind spot blind?

       A. It contains too many amacrine cells.
       B. It contains no rods or cones.
       C. It is in the shadow of the pupil.
       D. Excessive lateral inhibition interferes with reception at this
          spot on the retina.
       (B, p. 155-156, factual)

38.    What is the name of the point at which the optic nerve leaves the
       retina?

       A. the blind spot
       B. the fovea
       C. the optic chiasm
       D. the ganglion
       (A, p. 156, factual)

39.    Which condition might increase the size of a person's blind spot?

       A. attention deficit disorder
       B. cataracts
       C. masturbation
       D. glaucoma
       (D, p. 156, factual)

**Visual Receptors:   Rods and Cones**

40.    Where are the rods and cones of the eye located?

       A. in the optic nerve
       B. in the cornea
       C. in the pupil
       D. in the retina
       (D, p. 156, factual)

41.    What are the two kinds of receptors in the retina?

       A. bipolar and ganglion cells
       B. ganglion and rods
       C. rods and cones
       D. amacrine and horizontal
       (C, p. 156, factual)

42.    In comparison to the rods, what is true about the cones?

       A. They are more common toward the periphery of the retina.
       B. They are more sensitive to detail.
       C. They are more sensitive to dim light.
       D. They are more common in rodents and other nocturnal animals.
       (B, p. 156, factual)

43.    In comparison to cones, what is true about rods?

       A. They are more common toward the center of the retina.
       B. They are more sensitive to detail.
       C. They are more sensitive to dim light.
       D. They reach their peak firing levels slowly.
       (C, p. 156, factual)

44.    Rods are to _____ as cones are to _____.

       A. the periphery; the fovea
       B. red; blue
       C. vertebrates; invertebrates
       D. reading text; reading road signs
       (A, pp. 156, conceptual)

45.    Most retinal cones are concentrated in the:

       A. periphery.
       B. fovea.
       C. right half of each retina.
       D. top part of each retina.
       (B, pp. 156, factual)

46.    Peripheral vision mainly depends upon:

       A. the fovea.
       B. Cones.
       C. rods.
       D. just a few receptors.
       (C, p. 157, factual)

47.    Walking down a dark street at night, Joe is startled by the
       movement of a cat that he sees out of the "corner of his eye."
       Why is he is unable to see the cat when he looks directly at it?

       A. The fovea is mostly rods.
       B. Cones are less sensitive to dim light.
       C. Dark adaptation occurs more quickly in the center than it does
          peripherally.
       D. There is a higher ratio of receptors to ganglion cells in the
          fovea.
       (B, p. 157, application)

48.    Why do humans perceive faint light better in the periphery of the
       eye?

       A. Receptors in the periphery are closer to the pupil.
       B. The fovea is closer to the retina's blind spot than peripheral
          receptors are.
       C. More receptors in the periphery than in the fovea funnel input
          to each ganglion cell.
       D. Ganglion cells in the periphery transmit their information to
          a larger brain area.
       (C, p. 157, conceptual)

49.    Which receptors are responsible for the perception of color?

       A. cones
       B. rods
       C. both rods and cones
       D. horizontal and amacrine cells
       (A, p. 157, factual)

50.     What is one reason why you can see faint light better in the
        periphery than you can near the fovea?

        A. Each receptor cell in the periphery transmits its information
           to many different postsynaptic cells.
        B. The periphery is closer to the point where the optic nerve
           exits the eyeball.
        C. The opsin found in cones is more sensitive to light than the
           opsin found in rods.
        D. Ganglion cells in the periphery pool information from a larger
           number of receptors.
        (D, p. 157, conceptual)

51.     What percentage of adults with normal vision are color blind in
        the extreme periphery of the visual field?

        A. 0%
        B. 25%
        C. 50%
        D. 100%
        (D, p. 157, conceptual)

52.     Why are humans unable to distinguish colors in their extreme
        peripheral vision?

        A. As light is bent through the pupil, different wave lengths are
           distorted to different degrees.
        B. The periphery of the retina responds only to bright lights.
        C. The periphery of the retina contains only rods.
        D. The cornea and lens focus all colored lights onto the fovea.
        ("WWW" C, p. 157, conceptual)

53.     How does light excite a rod or cone?

        A. It heats up the fluid in the receptor.
        B. It converts 11-cis-retinal into all-trans-retinal.
        C. It converts leu-enkephalin into met-enkephalin.
        D. It ionizes neutral sodium into a positively charged ion.
        (B, p. 157, factual)

54.     What retinal cells contain photopigments?

        A. amacrine cells
        B. horizontal cells
        C. cones only
        D. rods and cones
        (D, p. 157, factual)

55.     Light energy converts 11-cis-retinal to:

        A. opsins.
        B. unstable proteins.
        C. all-trans-retinal.
        D. sodium.
        (C, p. 157, factual)

56.   How does the chemical 11-cis-retinal contribute to vision?

      A. It changes the focus of the lens.
      B. It changes light energy into a hyperpolarization of a
         receptor.
      C. It travels between one receptor and another to spread
         excitation.
      D. It deflects light from the retina to prevent overstimulation.
      (B, p. 157, conceptual)

57.   Chemicals that release energy when struck by light are called:

      A. photooptics.
      B. photopigments.
      C. opsins.
      D. kestrels.
      (B, p. 157, factual)

58.   Photopigments in rods and cones are derived from what source?

      A. vitamin A
      B. thiamine
      C. phenylalanine
      D. vitamin K
      (A, p. 157, factual)

59.   When second-messenger molecules in the retina close sodium
      channels in the cell membrane, the receptor cells:

      A. depolarize.
      B. hyperpolarize.
      C. increase the inhibition of the bipolar cells.
      D. inhibit ganglion cells.
      (B, p. 157, factual)

60.   The approximate range of wavelengths detectable by the human eye
      is:

      A. 40-70 nm
      B. 400-700 nm
      C. 700-7,000 nm
      D. 20-20,000 nm
      (B, p. 157, factual)

61.   Rats have one kind of cone. This translates into:

      A. the inability to discriminate among colors.
      B. the ability to see as many colors as do humans, but only one
         color at any given time.
      C. a cone which is universal for detecting all colors.
      D. the ability to see only green.
      (A, p. 157-158, conceptual)

62.   It is believed that rats have only one kind of cone.  According
      to the Young-Helmholtz theory, what should be true of their color
      vision?

      A. They cannot distinguish one color from another.
      B. They can distinguish between only red and green.
      C. They can distinguish between only yellow and blue.
      D. They can see only one color at a time.
      (A, pp. 158, conceptual)

63.   Who developed the trichromatic theory?

      A. Hering
      B. Muller
      C. Weiss and Sperry
      D. Young and Helmholtz
      (D, p. 158, factual)

64.   According to the Young-Helmholtz theory, what is the basis for
      color vision?

      A. a different receptor for each color
      B. three kinds of cones
      C. a single receptor that produces different responses for each
         color
      D. the combined influences of rods and cones
      (B, p. 158, factual)

65.   According to the Trichromatic Theory we perceive color by:

      A. the ratio of activity among three types of rods.
      B. pairs of opposites: red-green, yellow-blue, and white-black.
      C. the ratio of activity among three types of cones.
      D. the ratio of cone activity to rod activity.
      (C, p. 158, factual)

66.   The trichromatic theory, developed in the 1800's, proposed the
      existence of three types of cones.  Modern physiological
      techniques have established the existence of how many types of
      cones?

      A. only one
      B. three
      C. at least a dozen
      D. over fifty
      (B, p. 158, factual)

67.   Initially, researchers determined how many types of receptors we
      have for determining color:

      A. through psychophysical observations.
      B. through the use of biochemical methods.
      C. through genetic markers.
      D. by developing a trichromatic spectrometer.
      (A, p. 158, factual)

68.  More than a century ago, researchers had evidence that the human
     retina contained three kinds of color-sensitive receptors.  What
     was the basis of their evidence?

     A. observations of negative after-images
     B. studies of how people adapt to various degrees of light or
        darkness
     C. chemical measurements on the receptors themselves
     D. experiments on mixing colors together
     (D, p. 158, conceptual)

69.  Which theory emphasizes the idea that color vision depends on the
     relative responses of three kinds of cone?

     A. Young-Helmholtz theory
     B. opponent-process theory
     C. retinal theory
     D. volley theory
     (A, p. 158, factual)

70.  What is perceived when all types of cones are simultaneously and
     equally active?

     A. a bright light
     B. black
     C. white
     D. random flashes
     (C, p. 158, factual)

71.  What is the distribution of cones over the central portion of the
     retina?

     A. The short, medium, and long-wavelength cones are equally
        abundant.
     B. Long- and medium-wavelength cones are the most abundant.
     C. Short-wavelength cones are most abundant.
     D. Cones for detecting the color blue are the most abundant.
     (B, p. 158, factual)

72.  At the level of rods and cones the _____ theory seems to fit
     best, while at the level of the bipolar cells the _____ theory
     seems to fit best.

     A. opponent process; volley
     B. volley; trichromatic
     C. opponent process; trichromatic
     D. trichromatic; opponent process
     (D, pp. 158-159, conceptual)

73.    Who developed the opponent process theory?

       A. Young and Helmholtz
       B. Hering
       C. Muller
       D. Weiss and Sperry
       (B, p. 159, factual)

74.    After you stare at a bright green object for a minute and look
       away, you see red.  Which theory attempts to explain this
       finding?

       A. Young-Helmholtz theory
       B. trichromatic theory
       C. opponent-process theory
       D. color-constancy theory
       (C, p. 159, factual)

75.    According to the opponent-process theory of color vision, how do
       we perceive color?

       A. in terms of red vs. green and yellow vs. blue
       B. by the ratio of firing by three types of cone
       C. by the ratio of firing of rods to cones
       D. by the ratio of activity between the left eye and the right
          eye
       (A, p. 159, factual)

76.    If bipolar cell A in the visual system increases its rate of
       firing when responding to the color red, it will decrease its
       rate of firing when stimulated by what color?

       A. blue
       B. green
       C. white
       D. yellow
       (B, p. 159, factual)

77.    For humans, why is there no such thing as the color reddish
       green?

       A. There are not enough bipolar cells with inputs from red and
          green cones.
       B. Some neurons enable red light to excite them while green light
          simultaneously inhibits them.
       C. Bipolar cells do not respond simultaneously to inputs from red
          and green cones.
       D. Red and green cones occupy places on the retina that are so
          distant from each other that the information cannot converge
          at the optic nerve simultaneously.
       (B, p. 159, factual)

78.    Which theory accounts for color constancy?

       A. the trichromatic theory
       B. the opponent-process theory
       C. the retinex theory
       D. the Young-Helmholtz theory
       (C, p. 160, factual)

79.    Color constancy is the ability to:

       A. constantly see color no matter what the environmental
          conditions may be.
       B. see color, even in very faint light.
       C. differentiate among many colors and hues.
       D. recognize the color of an object despite changes in lighting.
       (D, p. 160, factual)

80.    According to the retinex theory, if you were to put on glasses
       which produced a reddish tint:

       A. you would be unable to identify the true color of objects.
       B. the cortex would subtract some red from each object to
          determine the true color.
       C. bipolar cells would inhibit information coming from red cones
          so you could accurately determine the color of objects.
       D. you could still identify the true color of objects because the
          red cones would tire quickly and cease firing.
       (B, p. 160, factual)

81.    In the most common form of color blindness people have difficulty
       distinguishing:

       A. between blue and yellow.
       B. between green and blue.
       C. between red and green.
       D. among all colors.
       ("WWW" C, p. 161, factual)

82.    What is the relationship of color blindness between males and
       females?

       A. Males are more likely to be color blind.
       B. Females are more likely to be color blind.
       C. Males and females show roughly equal susceptibility to color
          blindness.
       D. Males are more likely to report problems with color vision,
          but females are more likely to actually be color blind.
       (A, p. 161, factual)

**Module 6.2:  The Neural Basis of Visual Perception**

83.    Which of the following is true about the human visual system?

    A. Some people with otherwise normal vision are unable to detect motion.
    B. Females are more likely than males to be color blind.
    C. Only one kind of cone is necessary to discriminate colors.
    D. Cones are more sensitive than rods to dim light.
    (A, p. 163, factual)

**An Overview of the Mammalian Visual System**

84.    Which cells make inhibitory contact with bipolar cells?

    A. amacrine
    B. horizontal
    C. rods
    D. cones
    (B, p. 163, factual)

85.    The optic nerves from the right and left eye initially meet at the:

    A. optic chiasm.
    B. lateral geniculate nucleus.
    C. hypothalamus.
    D. cerebral cortex.
    ("WWW" A, p. 163, factual)

86.    In humans the optic nerves from the two eyes follow what pathway?

    A. They go directly to the ipsilateral hemisphere, without contacting each other.
    B. They go directly to the contralateral hemisphere, without contacting each other.
    C. Half of the axons from each eye cross to the other side at the optic chiasm.
    D. They combine to send identical information to each hemisphere.
    (C, p. 163, factual)

87.    Where does the optic nerve send most of its information?

    A. directly to the cerebral cortex
    B. to the lateral geniculate
    C. to the superior colliculus
    D. directly to the occipital lobe
    (B, p. 163, factual)

88.  The occipital lobe receives visual information directly from what
     source?

     A. the optic nerves
     B. the optic chiasm
     C. the superior colliculus
     D. the lateral geniculate of the thalamus
     (D, p. 163, conceptual)

89.  Branches of the optic nerve go directly to what areas of the
     brain?

     A. lateral geniculate and cerebral cortex
     B. superior colliculus and cerebral cortex
     C. lateral geniculate and superior colliculus
     D. prefrontal cortex and occipital lobe
     (C, p. 163, conceptual)

**Mechanisms of Processing in the Visual System**

90.  What is the relationship between the number of rods and the
     number of cones in the human retina?

     A. There are more rods than cones.
     B. There are more cones than rods.
     C. There are approximately equal numbers of rods and cones.
     D. Infants and children have more cones, but adults have more
        rods.
     (A, p. 163, factual)

91.  The receptive field of a receptor is the:

     A. point at which the optic nerve exits the retina.
     B. axon hillock.
     C. point in space from which light strikes the receptor.
     D. point where light shines on, and excites, the visual cortex.
     (C, p. 165, factual)

92.  Stimulating a receptor leads to either excitation or inhibition
     of a particular neuron; the receptor is part of that neuron's:

     A. stimulus field.
     B. convergence field.
     C. receptive field.
     D. bipolar area.
     (C, p. 165, conceptual)

93.  If light shines in the receptive field of a bipolar cell of the visual system, what effect will it have on the activity of that cell?

     A. It will have no effect.
     B. It will excite the cell.
     C. It will inhibit the cell.
     D. It may excite or inhibit the cell.
     (D, p. 165, conceptual)

94.  How do researchers find the receptive field of a cell in the visual system?

     A. Determine which structure sends axons to the cell.
     B. Determine where the cell sends its own axon.
     C. Measure the extent of the cell's dendrites.
     D. Shine light on various parts of the retina and determine the cell's responses.
     (D, p. 165, factual)

95.  While light is striking a visual receptor, light begins also to strike the receptor next to it.  What effect will this additional light have on the response of the first cell?

     A. excitation
     B. inhibition
     C. no effect
     D. first inhibition, then excitation
     (B, p. 165, conceptual)

96.  In the vertebrate retina, which cells are responsible for lateral inhibition?

     A. horizontal cells
     B. ganglion cells
     C. bipolar cells
     D. glial cells
     (A, p. 166, conceptual)

97.  What is responsible for sharpening contrast at visual borders?

     A. receptive fields
     B. lateral inhibition
     C. retinal disparity
     D. the direction in which the light shines
     (B, p. 166, factual)

98.   Suppose someone has a genetic defect that prevents the formation
      of horizontal cells in the retina.  Which visual phenomenon is
      most likely to be impaired?

      A. lateral inhibition
      B. movement perception
      C. dark adaptation
      D. size constancy
      (A, p. 166, conceptual)

99.   Horizontal cells receive their input from _____; they send output
      to _____.

      A. rods and cones; ganglion cells
      B. rods and cones; bipolar cells
      C. bipolar cells; ganglion cells
      D. cones; rods
      (B, p. 166, factual)

100.  Suppose someone has a genetic defect that prevents the formation
      of horizontal cells in the retina.  Which visual phenomenon is
      most likely to be impaired?

      A. color perception
      B. movement perception
      C. dark adaptation
      D. perception of sharp edges
      (D, p. 166, conceptual)

101.  Suppose light strikes a row of visual receptors, cells 1-20. Of
      the bipolar cells connected to those 20 cells, which ones will
      experience the LEAST lateral inhibition?

      A. those connected to all the even-numbered cells
      B. those connected to all the odd-numbered cells
      C. those connected to the cells in the middle (8-12)
      D. those connected to the cells on the edges (1 and 20)
      (D, pp. 166, conceptual)

102.  Suppose light strikes equally all the receptors in one circular
      patch on the retina.  Considering lateral inhibition, which cells
      will respond most vigorously?

      A. those connected to cells in the center of the circle
      B. those connected to cells on the border of the circle
      C. those connected to all cells in the circle, to the same extent
      D. those connected to cells outside the circle
      (B, pp. 166, conceptual)

103.  Suppose light strikes all the cells in one circular patch on the retina equally.  Why might some of the cells respond more vigorously?

     A. The lens diffracts more energetic light onto the border of the circle.
     B. Cells in the center adapt at once to the unchanging light.
     C. Cells on the border receive lateral inhibition from one side and not the other.
     D. Cells closer to the pupil receive more excitation.
     (C, pp. 166, conceptual)

104.  With regard to lateral inhibition, when light falls on a surface, the receptors just inside the border are _____, and those just outside the border are ____.

     A. most responsive; least responsive
     B. least responsive; most responsive
     C. mildly responsive; mildly responsive
     D. inhibited; excited
     (A, pp. 166, factual)

**Concurrent Pathways in the Visual System**

105.  Which ganglion cells, if any, are located mostly in or near the fovea?

     A. parvocellular
     B. magnocellular
     C. koniocellular
     D. They are all distributed equally.
     (A, p. 168, factual)

106.  Small receptive fields are to _____ as large receptive fields are to _____.

     A. parvocellular cells; magnocellular cells
     B. magnocellular cells; parvocellular cells
     C. magnocellular cells; koniocellular
     D. koniocellular cells; parvocellular cells
     (A, p. 168, conceptual)

107.  Small cell bodies are to _____ as large cell bodies are to _____:

     A. parvocellular cells; magnocellular cells
     B. magnocellular cells; parvocellular cells
     C. magnocellular cells; koniocellular
     D. koniocellular cells; parvocellular cells
     (A, p. 168, conceptual)

108.  Magnocellular cells are to _____ as parvocellular cells are to
      _____.

      A. wake-sleep cycles; movement
      B. movement; color
      C. detail; color
      D. color; wake-sleep cycles
      (B, p. 168, conceptual)

109.  Which cells send their axons to the lateral geniculate nucleus of
      the thalamus?

      A. all koniocellular cells
      B. all magnocellular cells
      C. all magnocellular cells and most koniocellular cells
      D. most magnocellular cells and all parvocellular cells
      (D, p. 168, factual)

110.  Which ganglion cells, if any, are most sensitive to depth and
      brightness?

      A. parvocellular
      B. magnocellular
      C. koniocellular
      D. There are no differences among the three.
      (B, p. 168, factual)

111.  Within the cerebral cortex, the pathway in the visual system
      responsible for color information also seems to be responsible
      for what other information?

      A. movement
      B. brightness
      C. distance
      D. dark adaptation
      (B, p. 169, conceptual)

112.  The parvocellular and magnocellular pathways:

      A. completely commingle from the retina to the lateral geniculate
         nucleus.
      B. remain fairly distinct from the retina to the lateral
         geniculate nucleus.
      C. both carry all the important information primates need about
         brightness.
      D. leave the retina and synapse in the visual cortex.
      (B, p. 169, factual)

113.  Axons from the lateral geniculate extend directly to which part
      of the cortex?

      A. primary visual cortex
      B. precentral gyrus
      C. postcentral gyrus
      D. prefrontal cortex
      ("WWW" A, p. 168, factual)

114.  Axons from the lateral geniculate extend to which area of the
      cerebral cortex?

      A. precentral gyrus
      B. postcentral gyrus
      C. prefrontal cortex
      D. occipital lobe
      (D, p. 168, factual)

115.  Where does the visual information from the lateral geniculate
      area go?

      A. to the retina
      B. to the primary visual cortex
      C. to the thalamus
      D. to the hypothalamus
      (A, p. 168, factual)

116.  The primary visual cortex is also known as the:

      A. lateral geniculate nucleus.
      B. striate cortex.
      C. area V2.
      D. parvocellular area.
      (B, p. 168, factual)

117.  What is another designation for the striate cortex?

      A. V1
      B. V2
      C. V3
      D. V4
      (A, p. 168, factual)

118.  The primary visual cortex sends its information:

      A. to the lateral geniculate nucleus.
      B. to area V1.
      C. to area V2.
      D. back to the retina.
      (C, p. 168, factual)

119.  Once information is sent to the secondary visual cortex it:

      A. has reached its final processing destination.
      B. may return to the primary visual cortex.
      C. goes mostly to the primary motor cortex.
      D. is sent back to the lateral geniculate nucleus.
      (B, p. 168, factual)

120.  The parvocellular and magnocellular pathways:

      A. split into three pathways at the optic chiasm.
      B. split into three pathways within the cerebral cortex.
      C. join together at the optic chiasm.
      D. join together once within the cerebral cortex.
      (B, p. 169, factual)

121.  Once within the cerebral cortex, the parvocellular pathway
      continues as a pathway sensitive to:

      A. details of shape.
      B. color.
      C. brightness.
      D. movement.
      (A, p. 169, factual)

122.  Once within the cerebral cortex, the magnocellular pathway
      continues, with a ventral branch sensitive to:

      A. details of shape.
      B. facial features.
      C. movement.
      D. brightness.
      (C, p. 169, Factual)

123.  Once within the cerebral cortex, the magnocellular pathway
      continues, with a dorsal branch important for:

      A. details of shape.
      B. color and brightness.
      C. movement.
      D. integrating vision with action.
      (D, p. 169, factual)

124.  Once within the cerebral cortex, a mixed pathway of magnocellular
      and parvocellular cells is important for:

      A. brightness and color.
      B. integrating vision with action.
      C. details of shape.
      D. distinguishing facial features.
      (A, p. 169, factual)

125.  Within the visual cortex, three major pathways are responsible
      for these aspects of vision:

      A. people, animals, objects.
      B. large objects, small objects, backgrounds.
      C. shape, movement, color.
      D. current perception, memory, imagination.
      (C, p. 169, factual)

126.  Within the cerebral cortex, where, if anywhere, do the shape,
      movement, and color/brightness pathways converge to share
      information?

      A. interblobs of area V1
      B. thick stripes of areas V2
      C. temporal cortex
      D. apparently nowhere
      (C, p. 169, factual)

127.  Once within the cerebral cortex, the pathway associated with
      integrating vision with movement next leads to the:

      A. temporal cortex.
      B. parietal cortex.
      C. visual cortex.
      D. frontal lobe.
      (B, p. 169, factual)

128.  Ventral stream:

      A. refers to the pathway specialized for detecting movement.
      B. refers to the pathway specialized for identifying objects.
      C. is another name for the temporal cortex.
      D. is another name for the parietal cortex.
      (B, p. 169, factual)

129.  The visual paths in the temporal cortex collectively are referred
      to as the:

      A. ventral stream.
      B. dorsal stream.
      C. parvomagnocellular pathway.
      D. magnoparvocellular pathway.
      (A, p. 169, factual)

130.  The visual path in the parietal cortex is referred to as the:

      A. ventral stream.
      B. dorsal stream.
      C. parvocellular pathway.
      D. magnocellular pathway.
      (B, p. 169, factual)

131.  The dorsal stream is important for:

      A. identifying size of objects.
      B. finding objects and grasping them.
      C. determining color and brightness.
      D. identifying the shape of objects.
      (B, p. 169, factual)

132.  Damage to the ventral stream may interfere with:

      A. describing the location of objects which can be seen.
      B. stepping over objects in the way.
      C. walking toward something seen.
      D. reaching out to grasp an object.
      (A, p. 169, factual)

133.  Damage to the dorsal stream may interfere with:

      A. describing what is seen.
      B. perceiving the movement of an object.
      C. remembering something seen at a previous time.
      D. reaching out to grasp an object.
      (D, p. 169, factual)

134.  An individual suffers damage to the temporal cortex, but
      maintains an intact parietal cortex.  This may result in an
      inability to:

      A. step over or go around objects in their way.
      B. remember objects seen previously.
      C. reach out and grasp an object.
      D. describe the size or shape of objects they see.
      (D, p. 169, factual)

135.  An individual suffers damage to the parietal cortex, but
      maintains an intact temporal cortex.  This may result in an
      inability to:

      A. describe the size of objects they see.
      B. describe the shape of objects they see.
      C. walk toward something they hear.
      D. reach out and grasp an object.
      (D, p. 169, factual)

**The Cerebral Cortex:  The Shape Pathway**

136.  Hubel and Wiesel won a Nobel Prize for their work describing the
      function of cells in what area?

      A. the retina
      B. the lateral geniculate area of the thalamus
      C. the temporal lobe
      D. the primary visual cortex
      ("WWW" D, pp. 170, factual)

137.  Who drew the first distinction among different types of cells of
      the primary visual cortex?

      A. Roger Sperry
      B. Rita Levi-Montalcini
      C. Santiago Ramon y Cajal
      D. David Hubel and Torsten Wiesel
      (D, p. 170, factual)

138.  What is the shape of the receptive field to which a simple cell
      in the primary visual cortex responds?

      A. circle of a particular radius
      B. circle with a hole in the middle
      C. bar in a particular orientation
      D. bar of a particular length
      (C, p. 170, conceptual)

139.  What shape are the receptive fields of most cells in the primary
      visual cortex?

      A. bars or edges
      B. circles
      C. squares
      D. points
      (A, p. 170, factual)

140.  What type of cell responds to a pattern of light in a particular
      orientation anywhere within its large receptive field, regardless
      of the exact location of the stimulus?

      A. simple
      B. complex
      C. hypercomplex
      D. end-stopped
      (B, p. 170, factual)

141.  Which cell responds most strongly to a stimulus moving
      perpendicular to its axis?

      A. simple
      B. complex
      C. hypercomplex
      D. end-stopped
      (B, p. 170, factual)

142.    If we compare the receptive fields of two simple cells in the
        primary visual cortex, chosen at random, in what way are they
        most likely to differ?

        A. orientation (angle)
        B. shape
        C. whether they respond to colored light as well as white light
        D. whether they respond to a single point of light
        (A, p. 170, conceptual)

143.    What is one way to determine whether a given cell in the primary
        visual cortex is "simple" or "complex"?

        A. the shape of its receptive field
        B. whether its receptive field is monocular or binocular
        C. whether it can respond equally to lines in more than one
           location
        D. whether it is sensitive to the orientation of the stimulus
        (C, p. 170-171, factual)

144.    Suppose a given cell in the primary visual cortex has a receptive
        field shaped like a bar, with no strong inhibitory field at
        either end of the bar.  It can respond to a bar-shaped pattern of
        light of the correct orientation at any location in its receptive
        field. What kind of cell is this?

        A. simple
        B. complex
        C. hypercomplex
        D. polycomplex
        (B, p. 170-171, conceptual)

145.    What is the shape of the receptive field to which a simple cell
        in the primary visual cortex responds?

        A. circle of a particular radius
        B. circle with a hole in the middle
        C. bar in a particular orientation
        D. bar of a particular length
        (C, p. 170-171, conceptual)

146.    Which kind of cell in the primary visual cortex, if any, has the
        smallest receptive field?

        A. simple
        B. complex
        C. hypercomplex
        D. There are no differences among the three.
        (A, p. 170-171, conceptual)

147.  What would an investigator find concerning the properties of
      cells in a single column of the visual cortex?

      A. They have receptive fields in the same location in the visual
         field.
      B. They have receptive fields of the same angle of orientation.
      C. Moving from dorsal to ventral through the column, each
         receptive field is slightly larger than the previous one.
      D. Their receptive fields vary randomly.
      (B, p. 171, conceptual)

148.  Where are cells of the visual cortex that have receptive fields
      of the same orientation generally located?

      A. in a single column of the cortex
      B. distributed throughout the cortex
      C. in a straight line along the surface of the cortex
      D. in a curved line along the surface of the cortex
      (A, p. 171, factual)

149.  Cells within a given column respond best to:

      A. lines of many different orientations.
      B. lines of a single orientation.
      C. stationary circles of light.
      D. circles of light which move from left to right.
      (B, p. 171, factual)

150.  It has been suggested that neurons in areas V1 and V2 might be:

      A. feature detectors.
      B. most responsive to stationary circles of light.
      C. most responsive to shape constancy.
      D. most responsive to stationary wide bars of light.
      (A, p. 172, factual)

151.  If you stare at a waterfall long enough to fatigue feature-
      detector neurons responsive to downward motion, then look at the
      rocks and trees next to the waterfall, how will the rocks and
      trees appear?

      A. stationary, but the colors will fade
      B. stationary, but you will temporarily lose vision for detail
      C. to move upward
      D. to move downward
      (C, p. 172 factual)

152.  Most visual researchers suggest that area V1 neurons respond most
      strongly to:

      A. spatial frequencies.
      B. round shapes.
      C. faces.
      D. edges.
      (A, p. 173, factual)

153.  Which of the following has the largest receptive fields and the
      greatest preferential sensitivity to highly complex visual
      patterns, such as faces?

      A. inferior temporal cortex
      B. superior colliculus
      C. lateral geniculate
      D. striate cortex
      (A, p. 173-174, conceptual)

154.  Cells in the inferior temporal cortex respond vigorously to their
      preferred shape:

      A. but only if the stimulus is also the preferred color.
      B. as long as it is also a particular size.
      C. as long as it is stationary.
      D. regardless of its exact size or position on the retina.
      (D, p. 173-174, conceptual)

155.  How do the receptive fields of the inferior temporal cortex
      compare to the those of the striate cortex?

      A. They are located lower in the retina.
      B. They are sensitive to larger, more complicated patterns.
      C. They are smaller and more symmetrical.
      D. They are more sensitive to identifying exact locations.
      (B, p. 173-174, conceptual)

156.  To what does "shape constancy" refer?

      A. All neurons within a single column have the same shape of
         dendritic tree.
      B. We can recognize objects even at different orientations.
      C. Objects described from memory are described as more
         symmetrical than they actually were when we saw them.
      D. No matter how big we get, our mothers still see us as
         children.
      (B, p. 174, conceptual)

157.  What is the inability to recognize visual objects called?

      A. visual apraxia
      B. visual adipsia
      C. visual agnosia
      D. visual aphasia
      (C, p. 174, factual)

158.  What characterizes someone with visual agnosia?

      A. cannot perceive colors
      B. can point to objects reported as unseen
      C. cannot recognize visual objects
      D. cannot see
      (C, p. 174, factual)

159.    What difficulty does someone with prosopagnosia have?

    A. focusing on colored objects
    B. seeing items located in the left visual field
    C. recognizing faces
    D. processing information from more than one sensory modality at
       a time
    (C, p. 174, factual)

160.    Joe has suffered brain damage that has left him unable to
    recognize the faces of his wife and children, although he can
    identify them by their voices.  What is Joe's condition?

    A. aphasia
    B. motion blindness
    C. lateral inhibition
    D. prosopagnosia
    (D, pp. 174, conceptual)

161.    What would someone who suffers from prosopagnosia be UNABLE to
    describe?

    A. relatives and friends by the sounds of their voices
    B. whether a face is familiar or unfamiliar
    C. whether a face is that of a male or female
    D. whether a face is that of an old or a young person
    (B, pp. 174, factual)

162.    What can people who suffer from prosopagnosia recognize?

    A. relatives and friends by the sound of their voices
    B. faces of people they knew before the damage
    C. faces of people they have met after the damage
    D. faces of famous people
    (A, pp. 174, factual)

163.    Of the four choices below, which would someone with prosopagnosia
    be most likely to recognize?

    A. faces of their family members
    B. faces of famous personalities
    C. their pets
    D. The Declaration of Independence
    (D, p. 174-175, conceptual)

164.    In addition to having difficulty recognizing faces, people with
    prosopagnosia may have difficulty:

    A. reading.
    B. with all types of memory.
    C. with their vision.
    D. recognizing different kinds of plants and animals.
    (D, pp. 174-175, factual)

165.  Neurons responding specifically to faces have been found in the:

      A. inferior temporal cortex.
      B. inferior parietal cortex.
      C. lateral geniculate nucleus.
      D. striate cortex.
      (A, p. 175, factual)

166.  No known type of brain damage causes a person to lose the ability
      to recognize one person without impairing the ability to
      recognize others.  What inference can we draw from this fact?

      A. Visual recognition depends on simple cells, not complex cells.
      B. Visual recognition depends on complex cells, not simple cells.
      C. Visual recognition depends on cells in the lateral geniculate.
      D. No one cell is solely responsible for recognizing any one
         facial pattern.
      (D, p. 175, conceptual)

167.  When individuals with intact brains recognize faces, activity:

      A. increases in the fusiform gyrus.
      B. decreases in the fusiform gyrus.
      C. increases in the fovea.
      D. decreases in the prefrontal cortex.
      (A, p. 175, factual)

**The Cerebral Cortex:   The Color Pathway**

168.  Color perception depends MOSTLY on the:

      A. magnocellular pathway.
      B. parvocellular pathway.
      C. superior colliculus.
      D. lateral geniculate.
      (B, p. 176, factual)

169.  A path of cells highly sensitive to color emerges in parts of:

      A. area V1.
      B. area V2.
      C. area V4.
      D. koniocellular pathway.
      (A, p. 176, factual)

170.  Color constancy refers to:

      A. continuing to recognize the color of an object despite changes
         in lighting.
      B. the color of an object which is inherent in the object itself.
      C. skin tones not permanently affected by exposure.
      D. the process of mixing light to create colors.
      ("WWW" A, p. 176, factual)

171. Color constancy depends on which part of the nervous system?

    A. rods
    B. the postcentral gyrus
    C. area V4 of the occipital lobe
    D. area V1 of the temporal lobe
    (C, p. 176, factual)

172. Monkeys with damage to area V4 lose:

    A. vision.
    B. color vision.
    C. color constancy.
    D. shape constancy.
    (C, p. 176, factual)

173. Animals with damage to area V4 cells have difficulty:

    A. paying attention to large, bright stimuli.
    B. paying attention to colorful stimuli.
    C. shifting their attention from bright stimuli to less bright
       stimuli.
    D. shifting their attention from one face to another.
    (C, p. 176, factual)

**The Cerebral Cortex:  The Motion and Depth Pathways**

174. Of the following, which is most specialized for stereoscopic
    depth perception?

    A. magnocellular pathway
    B. parvocellular pathway
    C. superior colliculus
    D. lateral geniculate
    (A, p. 176, factual)

175. What is stereoscopic depth perception?

    A. differentiating the distance of a sound by the input of each
       ear
    B. the sound-tracking system used by bats
    C. using differences in what each eye sees to assess distance
    D. assuming that an object that overlaps another is closer
    (C, p. 176, conceptual)

176. When cells in the middle temporal cortex respond to visual
    stimuli, their response depends mostly on what characteristic(s)?

    A. the speed and direction of movement
    B. the exact shape of the object
    C. the color and brightness of the object
    D. the exact location of the object in visual space
    (A, p. 176, factual)

177.  What area contains specialized cells for the detection of motion?

      A. V2
      B. V3
      C. V4
      D. V5
      (D, p. 176, factual)

178.  Cells in V5 and the medial superior temporal cortex selectively
      respond to which characteristic of visual stimuli?

      A. color
      B. movement
      C. particular shapes
      D. brightness
      (B, p. 176, factual)

179.  Where might one find cells that respond to the movement of an
      object in a specific direction and at a specific speed?

      A. in the medial superior temporal cortex
      B. in the striate cortex
      C. in the retina
      D. in the lateral geniculate
      (A, p. 176, factual)

180.  Where might one find cells that respond best to moving borders
      within specific receptive fields?

      A. in the striate cortex
      B. in the middle temporal cortex
      C. in the retina
      D. in the lateral geniculate
      (B, p. 176-177, factual)

181.  Where might one find cells that respond best to the movement of
      an object relative to its background?

      A. in the medial superior temporal cortex
      B. in the striate cortex
      C. in the retina
      D. in the lateral geniculate
      (A, p. 176-177, factual)

182.  What will a person fail to recognize after damage to cortical
      tissue in and around area V5?

      A. color
      B. faces
      C. motion
      D. objects in the upper half of the visual field
      (C, p. 176, conceptual)

183.  Cells in the _____ prevent us from confusing eye movements with
      object movements.

      A. ventral part of area MST
      B. dorsal part of area MST
      C. motor cortex
      D. occipital lobe
      (A, p. 177, factual)

184.  Which of the following would be easiest for someone who is motion
      blind?

      A. dressing themselves
      B. driving a car
      C. taking the dog for a walk
      D. filling a pitcher with water
      (A, p. 177, conceptual)

185.  People with motion blindness probably have suffered damage to:

      A. striate cortex.
      B. middle-temporal cortex.
      C. corpus callosum.
      D. retina.
      (B, p. 177, factual)

**Visual Attention**

186.  Shifting of attention is associated with increased activity in
      part of the:

      A. occipital lobe.
      B. temporal lobe.
      C. parietal lobe.
      D. frontal lobe.
      (C, p. 177, factual)

187.  What is meant by "suppressed vision during eye movements"?

      A. The visual cortex actually "shuts down" while the eyes are
         moving.
      B. If eye movement is too small or too fast, you will not see the
         movement.
      C. The activity of the eye muscles interferes with vision.
      D. The eyes can remain focused even as the head is moving.
      (A, p. 177, factual)

### The Binding Problem Revisited:  Visual Consciousness

188. The argument that the lateral geniculate is not conscious of
     visual information is based on the observation that:

     A. people who are asked to attend to the position of an object
        decrease their attention to its color.
     B. the parvocellular and magnocellular paths converge on the same
        cells in the pineal gland.
     C. most people are not conscious of whether a stimulus struck the
        left or right eye.
     D. a hypnotic suggestion to "become blind" suppresses activity in
        the lateral geniculate.
     (C, p. 178, factual)

189. Blindsight refers to:

     A. the ability to localize visual objects within an apparently
        blind visual field.
     B. the ability to merge together information from your two eyes
        even though they do not see the exact same picture.
     C. a brain with no conscious vision.
     D. the inability to see flashing light.
     (A, p. 178, factual)

## Module 6.3: Development of the Visual System

### Infant Vision

190. Which of the following characterizes the vision of infants?

     A. Infants see better in the periphery than in the center of
        vision.
     B. Infants have tunnel vision.
     C. Infants cannot distinguish colors.
     D. Infants cannot detect complex patterns until at least six
        months old.
     (A, p. 181, factual)

191. In what way does infant vision differ from adult vision?

     A. Infants do not have peripheral vision.
     B. Infants have trouble focusing their attention on visual
        stimuli.
     C. Infants have trouble shifting their attention away from visual
        stimuli.
     D. Infants have rods, but no cones.
     (C, p. 181, factual)

192.    In what way does infant vision differ from adult vision?

        A. Infants have trouble focusing their attention on visual
           stimuli.
        B. Infants have rods but no cones.
        C. Infants do not have well-developed vision near the fovea.
        D. Infants do not have peripheral vision.
        (C, p. 181, factual)

193.    How do cartoonists frequently indicate that a character
        (regardless of species) is an infant?

        A. They draw pupils that are tiny with respect to the rest of the
           eye.
        B. They draw the character with a bald head.
        C. They put diapers on the character.
        D. They draw eyes large with respect to the head.
        (D, p. 181, factual)

194.    At what age can infants focus on faces and other patterns?

        A. from very shortly after birth
        B. not until approximately two months of age
        C. at approximately six months
        D. at birth, but the image must hit the fovea
        (A, p. 181, factual)

**Effects of Experience on Visual Development**

195.    What are the properties of neurons in the visual cortex of a very
        young kitten at the moment when it first opens its eyes?

        A. They respond almost indiscriminately to all visual stimuli.
        B. They have receptive fields similar to those of normal adult
           cats.
        C. They have only circular, as opposed to edge or bar shaped,
           receptive fields.
        D. They have a wide variety of receptive fields, including some
           of odd shapes not found in adult cats.
        (B, p. 181-182, conceptual)

196.    If a kitten is reared with one eye shut, what happens to the
        cells in its visual cortex?  They become sensitive to:

        A. both eyes equally, the same as a kitten reared normally.
        B. both eyes, but more so to the eye that has been inactive.
        C. only the eye that has been inactive.
        D. only the eye that has been active.
        ("WWW" D, p. 181-182, conceptual)

197. Cortical neurons in the visual cortex of a kitten or a cat will
     lose the ability to respond to stimuli in one eye if the eye is
     sutured shut for:

     A. the first 8 days after birth.
     B. the first 2 months of life.
     C. any two month period in adult life.
     D. any one month period.
     (B, p. 182, factual)

198. Most of the neurons in the visual cortex of very young kittens
     respond to:

     A. one eye, but later develop binocular control.
     B. one eye, and continue that way.
     C. both eyes, but later fine tune to only one.
     D. both eyes, and continue that way.
     (D, p. 182, conceptual)

199. If both eyes of a very young kitten are sutured shut for the
     first few weeks:

     A. the kitten will be blind once the sutures are removed.
     B. one eye will develop sight, but the other will not.
     C. the cortex remains responsive to both eyes.
     D. there is degeneration of cortical neurons.
     (C, p. 182, factual)

200. What would be the likely outcome of a person who was blind at
     birth, and had vision restored later in life by the removal of
     cataracts (clouded lenses)?

     A. quick development of normal vision
     B. trouble describing the shapes of objects
     C. trouble identifying the location of light
     D. inability to use touch and sound cues to maneuver around in
        a building
     (B, p. 182, factual)

201. Under what conditions, if any, will a cell in the visual cortex
     of a cat respond to light in an eye that has been closed for the
     first few months of life?

     A. under all conditions
     B. under no conditions
     C. if has the opportunity to coordinate with the "active" eye
     D. if the "active" eye is closed for a while
     (D, p. 182-183, conceptual)

202.  What is true about cortical neurons that have become insensitive
      to an eye that was sutured shut during the critical period?

      A. Nothing can restore sensitivity to stimuli in that eye.
      B. That eye will gradually recover after years of exposure to
         normal visual stimuli.
      C. Some sensitivity can be recovered if the other eye is sutured
         shut for a few months.
      D. Some sensitivity can be recovered if both eyes are sutured
         shut for a few months.
      (C, p. 182, conceptual)

203.  According to research on visual development in animals, what is
      probably the best way to treat amblyopia ex anopsia?

      A. Cover both eyes for a few months early in life.
      B. Cover the strong eye for a period of time early in life.
      C. Cover the lazy eye for a period of time early in life.
      D. Cover the strong eye for a period of time during adulthood.
      (B, p. 183, conceptual)

204.  By comparing the slightly different inputs from the two eyes, you
      achieve:

      A. amblyopia ex anopsia.
      B. amblyopia differential.
      C. stereoscopic depth perception.
      D. contrasting imagery.
      (C, p. 184, factual)

205.  In depth perception, different views are received by each eye,
      depending on the distance of the object being viewed.  What is
      this called?

      A. retinal disparity
      B. amblyopic differential
      C. astigmatic contrast
      D. contrasting imagery
      (A, p. 184, conceptual)

206.  The fine tuning of binocular vision depends on:

      A. genetic instructions.
      B. experience.
      C. the development of eye muscles in later childhood years.
      D. amblyopic ex anopsia.
      ("WWW" B, p. 184, factual)

207.  What would the effect be if an experimenter covered the eye of a
      kitten in an alternating pattern (left eye one day; right the
      next)?

      A. The cat would eventually lose all vision.
      E. The kitten would eventually develop the ability to pay
         attention to two stimuli at the same time.
      C. The kitten would never learn to focus its eyes on stimuli.
      D. Most cortical neurons would respond to stimuli in one eye or
         the other, but not both.
      (D, p. 184, factual)

208.  If a kitten sees alternately with only one eye one day and the
      other eye the next day during its critical period for visual
      development, what happens to its visual cortex?

      A. Its cells become virtually unresponsive to all visual stimuli.
      B. One eye will become dominant and the other lazy.
      C. Each cortical cell will become responsive to just one eye.
      D. Cells will respond to either eye, but the responses will be
         sluggish.
      (C, p. 184, conceptual)

209.  What is strabismus?

      A. a failure of the two eyes to focus on the same thing at the
         same time
      B. a blurring of vision caused by asymmetrical curvature of the
         eye
      C. stereoscopic depth perception
      D. the ability to perceive a flashing light as if it were a
         moving object
      (A, p. 184, factual)

210.  Children with strabismus fail to develop:

      A. perception of movement.
      B. the ability to recognize faces.
      C. stereoscopic depth perception.
      D. any kind of depth perception.
      (C, p. 184, factual)

211.  What is one reason why some children fail to develop normal depth
      perception?

      A. Their optic nerves are too far away from their foveas.
      B. Their occipital lobe matured before their lateral geniculate.
      C. They suffered strabismus early in life.
      D. They lacked experiences in hand-eye coordination early in
         life.
      (C, p. 184, factual)

212.   Correction of strabismus in adulthood:

       A. is not possible.
       B. will improve depth perception.
       C. will not affect depth perception.
       D. leads to better depth perception.
       (C, p. 184, factual)

213.   What is an important characteristic that determines that two
       axons, coming from corresponding locations in each eye, will
       establish strong connections with a single cortical cell?

       A. They release the same neurotransmitter.
       B. They are active in a synchronous manner.
       C. They form synapses on the same dendritic branch of the
          cortical cell.
       D. They are either both excitatory or both inhibitory.
       (B, p. 184, factual)

214.   Astigmatism refers to the:

       A. sensitive period for development of vision.
       B. ability to see horizontal and vertical lines.
       C. asymmetric curvature of eyes.
       D. inability to detect motion.
       (C, p. 184, factual)

215.   What happens to the visual cortex of a kitten that is reared in
       an environment consisting entirely of horizontal lines?

       A. It develops the same properties as a kitten reared in a normal
          environment.
       B. It becomes insensitive to horizontal lines.
       C. It becomes sensitive to almost nothing but horizontal lines.
       D. It becomes inactive, failing to respond to any visual stimuli
          at all.
       (C, p. 184, factual)

216.   A strong astigmatism during the first year or so of life can
       produce effects in the human brain similar to those found in what
       kinds of experiments on cats?

       A. covering one eye during the sensitive period
       B. covering both eyes during the sensitive period
       C. destroying individual cells by implanting electrodes
       D. restricting visual stimulation to one particular orientation
       (D, p. 184, conceptual)

217.  What is the condition involving blurred vision for either
      horizontal or vertical lines?

      A. strabismus
      B. prosopagnosia
      C. blindsight
      D. astigmatism
      (D, p. 184, factual)

218.  What can cause a permanent blurring of vision for either
      horizontal or vertical lines?

      A. pressure on the optic chiasm
      B. weak muscles controlling the lens of the eyes
      C. asymmetric curvature of the eyes
      D. damage to the corpus callosum
      (C, p. 184, factual)

219.  Researchers produced a kitten that could see stationary objects,
      but was blind to moving stimuli, by:

      A. covering one eye during the critical period.
      B. covering both eyes during the critical period.
      C. allowing the kitten to freely move in an environment made up
         entirely of stationary objects.
      D. raising the kitten in an environment illuminated only by a
         strobe light.
      (D, p. 185, factual)

220.  The effects of blindness on the human cortex include:

      A. deterioration of most of the visual cortex.
      B. certain parts of the visual cortex becoming responsive to
         auditory and touch information.
      C. the temporal lobe taking over visual cortex functions.
      D. the parietal lobe taking over the visual cortex functions.
      (B, p. 185, factual)

1.    What is the basis for differences in sensory abilities across
      species?

      A. The larger the organism, the more intense the stimulus must be
         to be detected.
      B. All organisms detect all stimuli, but only focus on those
         involved in survival.
      C. Organisms detect a range of stimuli that is biologically
         relevant for that species.
      D. The larger the organism, the larger the range of stimuli
         detected.
      (C, p. 191, conceptual)

2.    Which of the following, if any, would be able to see ultraviolet
      light?

      A. a bee
      B. a human
      C. a chimpanzee
      D. No living thing has been found to detect ultraviolet light.
      (A, p. 191, factual)

3.    Which of the following is true about the stimuli detectable by
      the auditory and visual systems of humans?

      A. Humans can detect all sights and sounds, as long as they are
         above a minimal intensity.
      B. Humans respond to a narrower range of stimuli than most other
         species.
      C. Humans are sensitive to all the stimuli lower organisms can
         detect, as well as some they cannot.
      D. Humans are sensitive to only a limited range of stimuli.
      (D, p. 191, factual)

## Module 7.1: Audition

### Sound

4.    What is the intensity of a sound wave called?

      A. frequency
      B. loudness
      C. amplitude
      D. tone
      (C, p. 192, factual)

5.    What is the perception of the intensity of a sound wave called?

      A. pitch
      B. frequency
      C. amplitude
      D. loudness
      (D, p. 192, factual)

6.    A very intense compression of air produces:

      A. sound waves of great amplitude.
      B. sound waves of low amplitude.
      C. a very soft sound.
      D. a very low sound.
      (A, p. 192, factual)

7.    Pitch is a perception related to which aspect of sound?

      A. amplitude
      B. frequency
      C. intensity
      D. across-fiber pattern coding
      (B, p. 192, factual)

8.    What occurs to a tone as the number of cycles per second
      increases?

      A. Pitch gets higher.
      B. Pitch gets lower.
      C. Loudness increases.
      D. Loudness decreases.
      (A, p. 192, conceptual)

9.    Loudness is to _____ as pitch is to _____.

      A. frequency; intensity
      B. amplitude; frequency
      C. pitch; tone
      D. amplitude; intensity
      (B, p. 192, conceptual)

10.   Amplitude is to _____ as frequency is to _____.

      A. loudness; pitch
      B. pitch; loudness
      C. pitch; tone
      D. loudness; intensity
      (A, p. 192, factual)

11.   Who would be most likely to hear a 20,000 Hz tone?

      A. a 5-year-old girl
      B. an elderly man
      C. an elderly woman
      D. a 40-year-old trained musician
      ("WWW" A, p. 192, conceptual)

12.    An average healthy adult can hear pitches in what frequency
       range?

       A. 1 - 5,000 Hz
       B. 15 - 20,000 Hz
       C. 100 - 100,000 Hz
       D. 1000 - 20,000 Hz
       (B, p. 192, factual)

13.    Suppose the highest pitch you can hear is about 20,000 Hz.   Under
       what circumstances will that limit change?

       A. It drops naturally as you grow older.
       B. It drops if you go several months without listening to any
          high pitches.
       C. It drops only as a result of injury or disease.
       D. It increases with musical training.
       (A, p. 192, factual)

14.    What is the function of the pinna?

       A. It vibrates in synchrony with high-frequency tones.
       B. It protects the eardrum from overstimulation.
       C. It filters out distracting sounds.
       D. It helps us locate the source of sounds.
       (D, p. 193, factual)

15.    The eardrum is also known as the:

       A. pinna.
       B. ossicle.
       C. tympanic membrane.
       D. cochlea.
       (C, p. 193, factual)

16.    What is another name for the tympanic membrane?

       A. eardrum
       B. pinna
       C. auditory nerve
       D. cochlea
       (A, p. 193, factual)

17.    The eardrum vibrates at:

       A. a much higher frequency than the sound waves that hit it.
       B. half the frequency of the sound waves that hit it.
       C. the same frequency as the sound waves that hit it.
       D. a constant frequency regardless of the frequency of the sound.
       (C. p. 193, factual)

18.   Three small bones connect the tympanic membrane to the oval
      window.  What is the function of these bones?

      A. They hold the tympanic membrane in place.
      B. They convert airwaves into waves of greater pressure.
      C. They spread out the air waves over an area of larger diameter.
      D. They change the frequency of air waves into lower frequencies
         that can be heard.
      (B, p. 193, factual)

19.   Which of the following is NOT one of the small bones of the
      middle ear?

      A. malleus
      B. stapes
      C. incus
      D. calamus
      (D, p. 193, factual)

20.   The tympanic membrane is to the _____ as the oval window is to
      the _____.

      A. anvil; hammer
      B. stirrup; anvil
      C. inner ear; middle ear
      D. middle ear; inner ear
      (D, p. 193, factual)

21.   Why is it important for sound vibrations to be amplified as they
      pass through the ear?

      A. The inner membrane gets less sensitive with age.
      B. More force is needed to create waves in fluid.
      C. Much of the vibration is lost in the eardrum.
      D. Too much is lost through friction.
      (B, pp. 193-194, factual)

22.   To what does the stapes (stirrup) connect?

      A. tympanic membrane
      B. scala media
      C. oval window
      D. basilar membrane
      (C, p. 193, factual)

23.   The malleus, incus, and stapes are small bones:

      A. in the inner ear.
      B. in the outer ear.
      C. which transmit information from the outer ear to the middle
         ear.
      D. which transmit information from the tympanic membrane to the
         oval window.
      (D, p. 193, factual)

24.    The cochlea is part of the:

    A. middle ear.
    B. inner ear.
    C. tympanic membrane.
    D. oval window.
    (B, p. 194, factual)

25.    The scala tympani makes up part of the:

    A. tympanic membrane.
    B. middle ear.
    C. cochlea.
    D. ossicles.
    (C, p. 194, factual)

26.    A cross-section of the cochlea shows:

    A. three long fluid-filled tunnels.
    B. one long fluid-filled tunnel.
    C. three small bones collectively known as ossicles.
    D. hair cells attached to the tympanic membrane.
    (A, p. 194, factual)

27.    What is the name of the receptor cells of the auditory system?

    A. rods and cones
    B. sound bulbs
    C. hair cells
    D. basilar membranes
    (C, p. 194, factual)

28.    Where are the auditory receptor cells located?

    A. in the semicircular canal
    B. on the tympanic membrane
    C. on the basilar membrane
    D. in the malleus
    (C, p. 194, factual)

29.    The cochlea vibrates with a shearing action because the:

    A. tectorial membrane is more rigid than the basilar membrane.
    B. basilar membrane is more rigid than the tectorial membrane.
    C. tectorial and basilar membranes are equally rigid.
    D. tectorial and basilar membranes are equally flexible.
    (A, p. 194, factual)

**Pitch Perception**

30.  According to the frequency theory, the:

     A. tectorial membrane vibrates in synchrony with the auditory
        nerve.
     B. auditory nerve is responsible for perception of sound but not
        loudness.
     C. basilar membrane vibrates in synchrony with a sound.
     D. basilar membrane is tuned to a specific frequency and vibrates
        whenever that frequency is present.
     (C, p. 194, factual)

31.  What is the major problem for the frequency theory of sound
     perception?

     A. It cannot account for perception of low pitch sounds.
     B. It cannot account for perception of low amplitude sounds.
     C. It requires the cochlea to vibrate, and it does not.
     D. Neurons cannot respond as quickly as the theory requires.
     (D, p. 194, conceptual)

32.  "Every sound causes one location along the basilar membrane to
     resonate, and thereby excites neurons in that area."  This is one
     way to state which theory about pitch perception?

     A. volley principle
     B. frequency theory
     C. place theory
     D. opponent-process theory
     (C, p. 194, conceptual)

33.  Which of the following assumptions is necessary for the place
     theory of pitch perception, but NOT for the frequency theory?

     A. Various auditory neurons respond best to different
        wavelengths.
     B. The response of an auditory neuron declines if a sound is
        repeated many times.
     C. The louder a sound, the more auditory neurons respond to it.
     D. Most times we hear a combination of many wavelengths, not a
        pure tone.
     (A, p. 194, conceptual)

34.  The fact that the refractory period limits the firing rate of a
     neuron is problematic for which theory(ies)?

     A. frequency theory
     B. place theory
     C. volley theory
     D. both the frequency theory and the place theory
     (A, p. 194, conceptual)

35.  The fact that the various parts of the basilar membrane are
     tightly bound together is problematic for which theory(ies)?

     A. the frequency theory
     B. the place theory
     C. the volley theory
     D. both the frequency theory and the place theory
     (B, p. 194, conceptual)

36.  The current view of how we perceive sounds less than 100 Hz is
     based on:

     A. the frequency of action potentials.
     B. the area along the basilar membrane that responds most
        strongly.
     C. volleys of responses.
     D. the asymmetrical positioning of an individual's ears.
     (A, p. 194, conceptual)

37.  No auditory neuron can fire in synchrony with a sound:

     A. below 50 Hz.
     B. between 50 and 100 Hz.
     C. between 100 and 1000 Hz.
     D. above 1000 Hz.
     (D, p. 194, factual)

38.  The current view of how we perceive high frequencies, such as
     8000 Hz, is based on:

     A. the frequency of responses by each auditory neuron.
     B. volleys of responses by many auditory neurons.
     C. where along the basilar membrane neurons fire most rapidly.
     D. the ratio of firing among three types of receptor.
     (C, p. 195, conceptual)

39.  What is the current view of how we perceive frequencies greater
     than 1,000 but less than 5,000 Hz?

     A. It is based on the frequency of responses by each auditory
        neuron.
     B. It is based on volleys of responses by many auditory neurons.
     C. It is based on the area along the basilar membrane where
        neurons fire most rapidly.
     D. It is based on the ratio of firing among three types of
        receptor.
     (B, p. 195, conceptual)

40.    Currently, the most prevalent theory of pitch perception is:

       A. the frequency theory.
       B. the place theory.
       C. the volley principle.
       D. a combination of frequency, place, and volley principles,
          depending on the frequency of the tone.
       (D, p. 194-195, conceptual)

41.    Perception of a low tone is to _____ as perception of a high tone
       is to _____.

       A. volley principle; frequency theory
       B. frequency theory; place theory
       C. place theory; volley principle
       D. gate theory; frequency theory
       (B, p. 194, conceptual)

42.    The basilar membrane is narrowest:

       A. where the cochlea is narrowest.
       B. where the cochlea is widest.
       C. at the apex.
       D. halfway between the base and apex.
       (B, p. 195, factual)

43.    The basilar membrane is stiffest:

       A. where the cochlea is narrowest.
       B. halfway between the base and apex.
       C. at the apex.
       D. at its base.
       (D, p. 195, factual)

44.    What differences have been found along the length of the basilar
       membrane?

       A. electrical charge and salinity
       B. viscosity and polarity
       C. width and stiffness
       D. density of hair cells
       (C, p. 195, factual)

45.    Where is the basal membrane most sensitive to the vibrations of
       very high-frequency sound waves?

       A. closest to the cochlea
       B. at the apex, farthest from the cochlea
       C. about halfway between the cochlea and the apex
       D. It is equally sensitive across the entire membrane.
       (A, p. 196, factual)

46.    Where do high frequency tones produce maximum displacement?

       A. at the base of the basilar membrane
       B. at the apex of the basilar membrane
       C. at the narrow end of the cochlea
       D. in the eighth cranial nerve
       (A, p. 196, factual)

47.    Where is the basal membrane most sensitive to the vibrations of
       low-frequency sound waves?

       A. closest to the cochlea
       B. at the apex, farthest from the cochlea
       C. about half-way between the cochlea and the apex
       D. It is equally sensitive across the entire membrane.
       (B, p. 196, factual)

48.    In the brain, an important crossover occurs which enables each
       hemisphere to get its major auditory input from the:

       A. same ear.
       B. opposite ear.
       C. superior colliculus.
       D. inferior olive.
       (B, p. 196, factual)

49.    Most auditory information is sent to which hemisphere of the
       brain?

       A. the ipsilateral side
       B. the contralateral side
       C. the left hemisphere
       D. It depends on whether the individual is dominant for audition
          in the right or the left hemisphere.
       (B, p. 196, conceptual)

50.    To what lobe of the cerebral cortex is auditory information sent?

       A. occipital
       B. temporal
       C. parietal
       D. frontal
       ("WWW" B, p. 196, factual)

51.    Within the primary auditory cortex, most cells respond
       selectively to a particular:

       A. loudness.
       B. rhythm.
       C. frequency.
       D. word.
       (C, p. 196, factual)

52.   A tonotopic map refers to:

   A. an auditory cortex map of sounds.
   B. a diagram of which kinds of sounds are most common in
      different parts of the world.
   C. a diagram comparing the different tones to which different
      species are sensitive.
   D. a map showing connections between the auditory cortex and the
      visual cortex.
   (A, p. 196, factual)

53.   People with massive damage to the primary auditory cortex:

   A. are rendered completely deaf.
   B. are rendered deaf to only high-frequency sounds.
   C. cannot recognize combinations or sequences of sounds.
   D. can no longer hear and recognize simple sounds.
   (C, p. 196, factual)

54.   To what kinds of tones do cells in the primary auditory cortex
      respond best?

   A. low-pitch tones
   B. high-pitch tones
   C. single tones
   D. complex combinations of tones
   (C, p. 196, factual)

55.   What is the result of damage to the primary auditory cortex?

   A. tone deafness
   B. complete deafness
   C. difficulty in responding to sequences of sounds
   D. inability to hear sounds other than one's own voice
   (C, p. 196, factual)

56.   In which situation would deficits from damage to the primary
      auditory cortex be most noticeable to an observer?

   A. driving a car
   B. responding to a ringing telephone
   C. tuning a guitar
   D. carrying on a conversation
   (D, p. 196, conceptual)

57.   The auditory cortex has a ventral pathway in the:

   A. prefrontal cortex.
   B. cochlear nucleus.
   C. temporal lobe.
   D. parietal lobe.
   (A, p. 196, factual)

58.  There is a dorsal pathway of the auditory cortex:

     A. providing information about where a sound originates.
     B. providing information about what a sound represents.
     C. specifically for high-frequency sounds.
     D. specifically for low-frequency sounds.
     (A, p. 196, factual)

59.  There is a ventral pathway of the auditory cortex:

     A. providing information about where a sound originates.
     B. providing information about what a sound represents.
     C. specifically for high-frequency sounds.
     D. specifically for low-frequency sounds.
     (B, p. 196, factual)

**Hearing Loss**

60.  What kind of deafness is the result of damage to the cochlea or
     the hair cells?

     A. conductive
     B. nerve
     C. temporary
     D. hysterical
     (B, p. 197, factual)

61.  What can most people with nerve deafness hear?

     A. some frequencies of sound better than others
     B. external sounds, but not their own voices
     C. soft sounds better than loud sounds
     D. nothing at all
     (A, p. 197, factual)

62.  Conductive deafness is also known as:

     A. nerve deafness.
     B. middle ear deafness.
     C. inner ear deafness.
     D. outer ear deafness.
     (B, p. 197, factual)

63.  People with conductive deafness:

     A. often have an abnormal cochlea.
     B. often have an abnormal auditory nerve.
     C. often suffer damage to the hair cells.
     D. can benefit from surgery or hearing aids.
     (D, p. 197, factual)

64.    What can people with conductive deafness hear?

       A. high-pitched sounds but not low-pitched sounds
       B. their own voice better than external sounds
       C. sounds, but not pitch; everything is monotone
       D. nothing at all
       (B, p. 197, factual)

65.    Nerve deafness is to _____ as conductive deafness is to _____.

       A. the inner ear; the middle ear
       B. the middle ear; the inner ear
       C. disease; exposure to loud noises
       D. age; disease
       (A, p. 197, conceptual)

66.    Which of the following is true for both nerve deafness and
       conductive deafness?

       A. Both can be temporary.
       B. Both can usually be corrected by surgery.
       C. Both can be caused by certain diseases.
       D. Both can involve a normal cochlea and a normal auditory nerve.
       (C, p. 197, factual)

67.    Which of the following is true for nerve deafness?

       A. It is usually temporary.
       B. It often can be corrected by surgery.
       C. It will involve a normal cochlea and auditory nerve.
       D. It can result from damage to the cochlea.
       (D, p. 197, factual)

68.    Which of the following statements about nerve deafness is FALSE?

       A. It can be caused by inadequate oxygen to the brain at birth.
       B. Hearing aids can compensate for some of the hearing loss.
       C. Prolonged exposure to loud noise is one of the most common
          causes.
       D. With surgical treatment it is possible to regain normal
          hearing.
       (D, p. 197, factual)

69.    Nerve deafness is also referred to as:

       A. inner ear deafness.
       B. middle ear deafness.
       C. conductive deafness.
       D. outer ear deafness.
       (A, p. 197, factual)

70.  If the cochlea suffers damage but it is confined to one part of
     the cochlea, that individual will:

     A. lose all hearing.
     B. lose hearing of certain frequencies of sound.
     C. lose hearing but it will be confined to that part of the
        cochlea as well as those areas immediately adjacent to it.
     D. lose hearing of certain loudnesses of sound.
     ("WWW" B, p. 197, factual)

71.  Tinnitus is often:

     A. suffered by those with conductive deafness.
     B. seen in the very young.
     C. due to a phenomenon like the phantom limb.
     D. due to differential loudness.
     (C, p. 197, factual)

72.  Which statement about tinnitus is FALSE?

     A. Many people with nerve deafness experience tinnitus.
     B. Many people with conductive deafness experience tinnitus.
     C. Tinnitus is common among the elderly.
     D. Tinnitus is a frequent or constant ringing in the ears.
     (B, p. 197, factual)

73.  Which of the following apparently depends on a process similar to
     phantom limbs?

     A. tinnitus
     B. dyslexia
     C. stuttering
     D. echolocation
     (A, p. 197, factual)

**Localization of Sounds**

74.  Comparisons between which two responses are helpful in locating
     the source of a sound?

     A. between the base and the apex of the basilar membrane
     B. between the middle ear and the inner ear
     C. between the left ear and the right ear
     D. between the start of the sound and the end of the sound
     (C, p. 198, conceptual)

75.  A sound shadow refers to:

     A. out of phase sound waves.
     B. in phase sound waves.
     C. the time it takes sound waves to reach the ears.
     D. how much louder a high-frequency sound is for the ear closest
        to the sound.
     (D, p. 198, factual)

76.  Which two factors determine whether or not there will be a "sound shadow"?

     A. loudness and ear size
     B. head size and frequency
     C. frequency and cochlea size
     D. suddenness of onset and loudness
     (B, p. 198, conceptual)

77.  What sound characteristics can be compared between the two ears to locate the source of the sound?

     A. sound shadows and frequency
     B. frequency and amplitude
     C. loudness and timing
     D. timbre and rhythm
     (C, p. 198, conceptual)

78.  For what kind of sounds can differences in loudness be used most accurately for localization?

     A. loud
     B. soft
     C. low-pitched
     D. high-pitched
     (D, p. 199, factual)

79.  Timing differences can be used most accurately for localizing:

     A. low-pitched sounds.
     B. high-pitched sounds.
     C. loud sounds.
     D. bird alarm calls.
     (A, p. 199, factual)

80.  For localizing sounds, loudness is a good cue for _____; timing is a good cue for _____.

     A. rapid onset; gradual onset
     B. gradual onset; rapid onset
     C. high-frequency; low-frequency
     D. low-frequency; high-frequency
     (C, pp. 199, conceptual)

81.  Head size affects which method(s) of sound localization?

     A. loudness
     B. phase differences
     C. both loudness and phase differences
     D. neither loudness nor phase differences
     (C, p. 199, factual)

82.    What is true about localization abilities of animals with small
       heads, such as mice?

       A. They can localize tones better than humans.
       B. They can use phase differences, but not loudness differences.
       C. They can use loudness differences but only for high frequency
          tones.
       D. They can use phase differences but only for low frequency
          tones.
       (C, p. 199, factual)

83.    Elephants and other animals with large heads:

       A. can hear high-pitched sounds better than most other species.
       B. cannot hear low-pitched sounds as well as smaller animals.
       C. cannot hear high-pitched sounds as well as smaller animals.
       D. cast good sound shadows.
       (C, p. 199, factual)

84.    Small animals with their ears close together hear by:

       A. detecting phase differences.
       B. detecting loudness differences in low-frequency sounds.
       C. casting a sound shadow, for high-frequency sounds.
       D. casting a sound shadow, for low-frequency sounds.
       (C, p. 199, factual)

85.    Which of the following would be LEAST able to use phase
       differences as a means of sound localization?

       A. chimpanzees
       B. humans
       C. elephants
       D. ground squirrels
       (D, p. 199, conceptual)

## Module 7.2: The Mechanical Senses

### Vestibular Sensation

86.    What does the vestibular system detect?

       A. the degree of stretch of muscles
       B. vibrations on the skin
       C. the location of sounds
       D. movement of the head
       (D, p. 201, factual)

87.     After damage to the vestibular system, what would someone have
        trouble doing?

        A. localizing sounds
        B. detecting odors
        C. discriminating temperature of the skin
        D. maintaining balance
        (D, p. 201, conceptual)

88.     Which two structures provide information about vestibular
        sensation?

        A. cochlea and otolith organs
        B. semicircular canals and cochlea
        C. semicircular canals and otolith organs
        D. cerebellum and sinuses
        (C, p. 201, factual)

89.     The vestibular organ consists of:

        A. three otolith organs.
        B. two semicircular canals.
        C. otolith organs and semicircular canals.
        D. the cochlea and an otolith organ.
        (C, p. 201, factual)

90.     What is the function of the semicircular canals?

        A. to locate the source of low frequency tones
        B. to locate the source of high frequency tones
        C. to detect movement of the head
        D. to establish a sense of direction while traveling
        ("WWW" C, p. 201, factual)

91.     What is the function of the semicircular canals?

        A. to locate the source of low frequency tones
        B. to locate the source of high frequency tones
        C. to help the brain control eye movements
        D. to establish a sense of direction while traveling
        (C, p. 201, factual)

92.     The semicircular canals are filled with a substance that
        resembles:

        A. chalk
        B. string.
        C. jelly.
        D. hot air.
        (C, p. 201, factual)

93.    The otolith organs contain patches of hair cells which:

       A. run horizontally in both organs.
       B. run vertically in both organs.
       C. run horizontally in one organ and run vertically in the other
          organ.
       D. are distributed in a random pattern.
       (C, p. 201, factual)

94.    An acceleration of the head in any plane causes:

       A. the jellylike substance in one of the semicircular canals to
          move to another canal.
       B. the jellylike substance in one of the semicircular canals to
          push against hair cells.
       C. fluid to spill out from the otolith organs into the
          semicircular canals.
       D. hair cells to become stiff and straight.
       (B, p. 201, factual)

**Somatosensation**

95.    The somatosensory system involves sensation of:

       A. sight and sound.
       B. sound and touch.
       C. the body and its movements.
       D. the head and movements of the eyes.
       ("WWW" C, p. 201, factual)

96.    What kind of receptors detect pain, warmth, and cold?

       A. cranial
       B. semicircular
       C. vestibular
       D. somatosensory
       (D, p. 201, factual)

97.    Meissner's corpuscles are:

       A. elaborate neuron endings for touch.
       B. simple, bare neuron endings.
       C. bare endings surrounded by nonneural cells.
       D. important components of the blood.
       (A, p. 202, factual)

98.    Pain receptors of the skin are:

       A. elaborate neuron endings.
       B. also known as Ruffini endings
       C. simple, bare neuron endings.
       D. also known as Meissner's corpuscles.
       (C, p. 202, factual)

99.   To what kind of stimulation does a Pacinian corpuscle respond?

      A. sound waves
      B. temperature
      C. movements of the head
      D. displacement of the skin
      (D, p. 202 factual)

100.  The outer structure of the Pacinian corpuscle resembles an:

      A. onion.
      B. automobile tire.
      C. umbrella.
      D. ice cream cone.
      (A, p. 202, factual)

101.  When mechanical pressure bends the membrane of a Pacinian
      corpuscle:

      A. the membrane's resistance to the flow of sodium ions
         increases.
      B. the membrane's resistance to the flow of sodium ions
         decreases.
      C. the membrane becomes hyperpolarized.
      D. there is a sustained, long-term response to this pressure.
      (B, p. 202, factual)

102.  How many sets of sensory and motor nerves (called spinal nerves)
      does the spinal cord have?

      A. 2
      B. 12
      C. 18
      D. 31
      (D, p. 202, factual)

103.  Each spinal nerve has:

      A. either a sensory or a motor component.
      B. both a sensory and a motor component.
      C. connections to most parts of the body.
      D. connections to each of the major internal organs.
      (B, p. 202, factual)

104.  What is a dermatome?

      A. an area of the skin innervated by a given spinal nerve
    an instrument used to record impulses in the spinal cord
    the point at which sensory nerves make contact with motor
         nerves
      D. an area of the skin that has no touch receptors
      (A, p. 202, factual)

105. Somatosensory information travels from the thalamus to which area of the cortex?

    A. parietal lobe
    B. frontal lobe
    C. hippocampus
    D. limbic cortex
    (A, p. 203, factual)

106. Which of the following is true about various types of somatosensation?

    A. They are produced by varied responses by a single type of receptor.
    B. They involve different receptors, but the spinal cord integrates the information.
    C. They remain separate through the spinal cord, but are interpreted by a single set of cortical neurons.
    D. They are at least partly distinct from the receptors through the cerebral cortex.
    (D, p. 203, factual)

107. Someone who has suffered damage to the sensory component of one spinal nerve would lose sensation from:

    A. the contralateral half of the body.
    B. the ipsilateral half of the body.
    C. one ventricle.
    D. one dermatome.
    (D, p. 204, conceptual)

108. What is necessary for the left hand to know what the right hand is feeling?

    A. contralateral control
    B. ipsilateral control
    C. bilateral control
    D. somatosensory cortex communication across the corpus callosum
    (D, p. 204, factual)

    **Pain**

109. What neurotransmitter is released by axons that carry pain information to the brain?

    A. dopamine
    B. serotonin
    C. substance P
    D. enkephalin
    (C, p. 204, factual)

110.   A mild pain stimulus is associated with a release of:

       A. substance P.
       B. substance P and glutamate.
       C. glutamate.
       D. neuromodulators.
       (C, p. 205, factual)

111.   What would you expect if a researcher injected substance P into
       an animal's spinal cord?

       A. The animal would be paralyzed.
       B. The animal would show indications of pain in the part of the
          body that sends information to that section of the spinal
          cord.
       C. The animal would show indications of pain in the part of the
          spinal cord where the substance was injected.
       D. The animal would show signs of aggression.
       (B, p. 205, factual)

112.   What is the initial effect of an injection of capsaicin?

       A. It blocks all feeling from that point and below.
       B. It blocks pain messages from that point and below.
       C. It blocks the release of substance P.
       D. It increases the release of substance P.
       (D, pp. 205-206, factual)

113.   Initially, an injection of capsaicin would:

       A. block sensation.
       B. block pain messages.
       C. stimulate pain receptors sensitive to cold.
       D. stimulate pain receptors sensitive to moderate heat.
       (D, p. 206, factual)

114.   Initially, an injection of capsaicin would:

       A. induce paralysis.
       B. induce a painful burning sensation.
       C. induce a lack of sensation.
       D. block the release of substance P.
       (B, p. 206, factual)

115.   What are the long-term effects of an injection of capsaicin into
       the spinal cord?

       A. It blocks all feeling from that point and below.
       B. It blocks pain messages from the body area that sends
          information to that part of the spinal cord.
       C. It sends pain messages from the body area that sends
          information to that part of the spinal cord.
       D. It has no long-term effects.
       (B, p. 206, factual)

116.  How does an injection of capsaicin into the spinal cord lead to
      an insensitivity to pain?

      A. It blocks sodium channels.
      B. It stimulates neurotransmitters that compete with pain
         messages.
      C. It depletes substance P from neurons that transmit pain
         messages.
      D. It hyperpolarizes neural membranes.
      (C, p. 206, conceptual)

117.  In what way does capsaicin decrease sensitivity to pain?

      A. by depleting substance P from parts of the nervous system
      B. by mimicking the effects of endorphins at the synapses
      C. by preventing sodium from crossing the membrane
      D. by altering blood flow to various parts of the nervous system
      (A, p. 206, conceptual)

118.  Where is capsaicin commonly found?

      A. in electric eels
      B. in mushrooms
      C. in snake venom
      D. in jalapeno peppers
      (D, p. 206, factual)

119.  Which naturally occurring substance depletes substance P and
      relieves pain when it is rubbed onto a painful part of the body?

      A. capsaicin
      B. miraculin
      C. phenylalanine
      D. pheromone
      (A, p. 206, factual)

120.  PET scans indicate that individuals experiencing pain show:

      A. decreased activity in the somatosensory cortex and increased
         activity in the cingulate cortex.
      B. increased activity in the somatosensory and decreased activity
         in the cingulate cortex.
      C. increased activity in both the somatosensory cortex and
         cingulate cortex.
      D. decreased activity in both the somatosensory cortex and
         cingulate cortex.
      (C, p. 206, factual)

121.  The cingulate cortex traditionally has been linked to:

      A. the inhibition of aggression.
      B. emotional responses.
      C. migraine headaches.
      D. sleep disorders.
      (B, p. 207, factual)

122. During brain surgery, surgeons can directly stimulate the cingulate cortex of the patient and the patient reports:

    A. a painful sensation.
    B. feeling no pain at all.
    C. feeling very emotional.
    D. feeling a sensation, although it can't be described very well.
    (B, p. 207, factual)

123. The gate theory of pain suggests:

    A. the brain can increase, but not decrease, its own exposure to pain information.
    B. the brain can decrease, but not increase, its own exposure to pain information.
    C. the brain can increase or decrease its own exposure to pain information.
    D. that certain areas of the brain respond with a gating mechanism, releasing substance P, thereby inhibiting pain.
    (C, p. 207, factual)

124. What process is predicted by the gate theory of pain?

    A. Pain information grows more intense as it passes each synapse on its way to the brain.
    B. Non-pain information can inhibit pain information.
    C. Intense pain can shut out all other sensory information.
    D. The intensity of pain experience depends entirely on the excitability of pain receptors.
    (B, p. 207, conceptual)

125. Where are opiate receptors concentrated in the brain?

    A. where acetylcholinesterase is concentrated
    B. where substance P is concentrated
    C. in the cerebrospinal fluid
    D. where dopamine receptors are located
    ("WWW" B, p. 207, factual)

126. The brain chemicals known as endorphins and enkephalins produce effects similar to which naturally occurring substance?

    A. vitamin B-1 (thiamine)
    B. substance P
    C. opiates
    D. amphetamine
    (C, p. 207, factual)

127.  Enkephalins:

      A. can interact with the same receptors as morphine.
      B. have chemical structures just like morphine.
      C. increase pain.
      D. are human made drugs which mimic endorphins.
      (A, p. 207, factual)

128.  What is another name for the brain's own morphines?

      A. endorphins
      B. capsaicins
      C. anesthetics
      D. amnesiacs
      (A, p. 207, factual)

129.  Certain painful stimuli activate neurons which release endorphins
      in the:

      A. periaqueductal gray area.
      B. brainstem.
      C. forebrain.
      D. entire hindbrain.
      (A, p. 207, factual)

130.  In what way do morphine and other opiate drugs decrease
      sensitivity to pain?

      A. by depleting substance P from parts of the nervous system
      B. by mimicking the effects of endorphins at the synapses
      C. by preventing sodium from crossing the membrane
      D. by altering blood flow to various parts of the nervous system
      (B, p. 207, conceptual)

131.  What is the current view of how endorphins decrease the
      experience of pain?

      A. They deplete the brain of substance P.
      B. They block the release of substance P.
      C. They block sodium channels in the membrane of certain neurons.
      D. They increase the sensitivity of neurons to dopamine.
      ("WWW " B, p. 207, factual)

132.  Why is morphine NOT used to suppress pain during an operation?

      A. It is only effective while a person is conscious.
      B. Its effects are local.
      C. It inhibits dull pain, but not sharp pain.
      D. Its effects would be too temporary.
      (C, p. 208, factual)

133.  Morphine is effective in relieving:

      A. pain on the skin.
      B. sharp pain.
      C. slow, dull pain.
      D. pain in the interior of the body.
      (C, p. 208, factual)

134.  Large-diameter pain fibers:

      A. carry sharp pain information.
      B. carry dull pain information.
      C. readily respond to endorphins.
      D. are associated with small cell bodies.
      (A, p. 208, factual)

135.  Small-diameter pain fibers:

      A. carry sharp pain information.
      B. carry dull pain information.
      C. do not respond to endorphins.
      D. are associated with large cell bodies.
      (B, p. 208, factual)

136.  Which of the following produces analgesia?

      A. substance P
      B. miraculin
      C. naloxone
      D. endorphins
      (D, p. 208, factual)

137.  Transcutaneous electrical nerve stimulation:

      A. has been unsuccessful in eliciting endorphin release.
      B. supports the gate theory of pain.
      C. has provided relief from pain but only for a very small
         percentage of individuals.
      D. is associated with some harmful side effects.
      (B, p. 208, factual)

138.  What do acupuncture and transcutaneous electrical nerve
      stimulation (TENS) have in common?

      A. Both provide pain relief for virtually all people.
      B. Both involve thin needles placed in the skin.
      C. Both have more side effects than morphine.
      D. Both produce the release of endorphins.
      (D, p. 208, factual)

139. What is the purpose of transcutaneous electrical nerve
     stimulation (TENS)?

     A. reduce the perception of a phantom limb
     B. produce pain sensations in people who normally are insensitive
        to pain
     C. relieve pain
     D. inhibit the release of endorphins
     (C, p. 208, factual)

140. Some physicians hesitate to prescribe morphine because:

     A. even moderate doses can suppress breathing.
     B. even under controlled conditions, many people become addicted.
     C. opiates temporarily weaken the immune system.
     D. it has long-term effects on the body's endorphin supply.
     (C, p. 208, factual)

141. Which of the following is true about the use of morphine to
     control pain in a hospital setting?

     A. There is a high probability of addiction.
     B. It weakens the immune system briefly, but less than prolonged
        pain would.
     C. It weakens the immune system more than prolonged pain would.
     D. It relieves pain without the side effects of nausea.
     (B, p. 208-209, factual)

142. With respect to the immune system, morphine is to _____ as
     prolonged intense pain is to _____.

     A. short-term weakening; long-term weakening
     B. short-term strengthening; long-term weakening
     C. long-term weakening; short-term weakening
     D. long-term weakening; long-term strengthening
     (A, p. 208-209, conceptual)

143. Damaged tissue triggers the release of a number of chemicals
     which:

     A. decrease the number of sodium gates in nearby receptors.
     B. increase the number of potassium gates in nearby receptors.
     C. increase the number of sodium gates in nearby receptors.
     D. inhibit further release of substance P.
     (C, p. 209, factual)

144. What is a possible negative outcome of the body's own attempts to
     repair damaged tissue?

     A. an addiction to endorphins
     B. increased sensitivity to pain
     C. decreased availability of substance P
     D. weakening of the immune system
     (B, p. 209, conceptual)

**Module 7.3: The Chemical Senses**

145.  Most theorists believe that the first sensory system was:

      A. vision.
      B. vestibular.
      C. pain.
      D. chemical.
      (D, p. 211, factual)

      **General Issues About Chemical Coding**

146.  One difference between labeled-line coding and across-fiber
      pattern coding is that labeled-line is:

      A. only found in vertebrates.
      B. less versatile.
      C. more complicated.
      D. slower.
      (B, p. 211, conceptual)

147.  Each receptor responds to a limited range of stimuli and sends a
      direct line to the brain.  This type of coding is referred to as:

      A. across-fiber.
      B. labeled-line.
      C. vestibular.
      D. hierarchical.
      (B, p. 211, factual)

148.  Each receptor responds to a wide range of stimuli and contributes
      to the perception of each of them.  This type of coding is
      referred to as:

      A. across-fiber.
      B. labeled-line.
      C. hierarchical.
      D. reciprocal-excitatory.
      (A, p. 211, factual)

149.  Our ability to see a wide range of colors, despite the presence
      of only three types of receptors, indicates that color vision
      depends on which type of coding?

      A. across-fiber pattern
      B. reciprocal-inhibitory
      C. labeled-line
      D. hierarchical
      (A, p. 211, factual)

**Taste**

150. When people complain that they "no longer taste their food very much," the usual reason is that:

    A. the taste receptors have temporarily depleted their supply of neurotransmitters.
    B. the person actually has an impaired sense of smell.
    C. the taste receptors have been damaged by hot liquid.
    D. the taste receptors have been impaired by capsaicin.
    (B, p. 212, factual)

151. The receptors for taste:

    A. are true neurons.
    B. are covered in myelin.
    C. are modified skin cells.
    D. do not release neurotransmitters.
    ("WWW" C, p. 212, factual)

152. The receptors for taste are not true neurons, but are actually modified skin cells. In what way are these cells like neurons?

    A. Once taste receptors die they are never replaced.
    B. They release neurotransmitters.
    C. They have axons.
    D. They are covered with a myelin sheath.
    (B, p. 212, factual)

153. The receptors for taste are like skin cells in that:

    A. taste receptors are continuously being replaced.
    B. they are covered with a myelin sheath.
    C. they are also sensitive to touch.
    D. they do not release neurotransmitters.
    (A, p. 213, factual)

154. Which of the following is characteristic of the receptors for taste?

    A. They are concentrated near the center of the tongue.
    B. They are replaced every day.
    C. They are replaced approximately every two weeks.
    D. Each receptor is housed in its own taste bud.
    (C, p. 213, factual)

155. What are found in papillae?

    A. olfactory receptors
    B. clusters of neurons
    C. hair cells
    D. taste buds
    (D, p. 212-213, factual)

156.  In adult humans, the taste buds are:

      A. evenly distributed across the front half of the tongue.
      B. evenly distributed across the whole tongue.
      C. concentrated near the center of the tongue.
      D. concentrated along the outside edge of the tongue.
      (D, p. 212-213, factual)

157.  Which of the following is true about taste receptors?

      A. Their dendrites extend outside the taste buds.
      B. They are virtually nonexistent in the center of the tongue.
      C. Each taste bud contains only one receptor cell.
      D. Humans have hundreds of types of taste receptors, each
         sensitive to a different set of chemicals.
      (B, pp. 212-213, factual)

158.  The evidence from research on taste suggests the existence of how
      many types of taste receptors?

      A. just 1
      B. 2 or 3
      C. at least 5
      D. hundreds
      (C, p. 213, factual)

159.  What has been the most frequently used approach in research
      attempting to identify the number of taste receptors in humans?

      A. find out how many different tastes people can distinguish
      B. microscopically analyze the structure of various taste
         receptors
      C. find procedures that can affect one taste without affecting
         others
      D. isolate the various neurotransmitters involved
      (C, p. 213, factual)

160.  After soaking their tongues in a sour solution, what do most
      people experience?

      A. Other sour substances taste less sour.
      B. other sour substances taste more sour.
      C. Other sour substances taste sweet as well as sour.
      D. All substances are perceived as relatively tasteless.
      (A, p. 213, factual)

161.  Exposure to an extremely salty substance decreases sensitivity to
      other salty substances.  What is this phenomenon called?

      A. adaptation
      B. olfaction
      C. umami
      D. analgesia
      (A, p. 213, conceptual)

162. After soaking your tongue in a sour solution you try tasting salty, sweet, and bitter substances. How are these tastes affected?

    A. You will be unable to detect the sweet taste, but the other two will be unaffected.
    B. You will be unable to detect the sweet or salty tastes, but bitter will be unaffected.
    C. You will be unable to reliably detect any of the other tastes.
    D. There will be little or no effect on these three tastes.
    (D, p. 213, conceptual)

163. Reduced response to one taste after exposure to another is referred to as:

    A. adaptation.
    B. cross-adaptation.
    C. umami.
    D. PTC.
    (B, p. 213, factual)

164. Adaptation is to _____ as cross-adaptation is to _____.

    A. sour; sweet
    B. same tastes; different tastes
    C. overstimulation; rebound effects
    D. weak stimulation; strong stimulation
    (B, p. 213, conceptual)

165. A saltiness receptor is special in that:

    A. it is not necessary that sodium ions cross its membrane for excitation to occur.
    B. it does not need a specialized membrane site sensitive to sodium.
    C. it responds to other tastes as well.
    D. it is resistant to adaptation.
    (B, p. 213, factual)

166. Chemicals which prevent sodium from crossing the membrane:

    A. intensify the salty taste.
    B. do not affect taste.
    C. reduce the intensity of salty tastes.
    D. cause an increase in sensitivity to other primary tastes.
    (C, p. 213, factual)

167. What causes excitation of the taste receptors that respond to salty tastes?

    A. a decrease in the activity of adjacent sweet and bitter receptors
    B. sodium ions crossing the membrane of the receptor
    C. a hyperpolarization due to the increased concentration of sodium ions outside the cell
    D. a blockage of the sodium gates
    (B, p. 213, conceptual)

168. What is the effect of a chemical that prevents sodium ions from crossing the membrane of a taste receptor?

    A. an increase in salty tastes
    B. a decrease in salty tastes
    C. a decrease in sweet tastes
    D. an increase in all tastes
    (B, p. 213, factual)

169. Taste receptors which operate by closing potassium channels are those signaling:

    A. bitter tastes.
    B. sour tastes.
    C. sweet tastes.
    D. salty tastes.
    (B, p. 213, factual)

170. Which of the following types of chemicals would increase the taste of salty substances?

    A. one that facilitates the passage of sodium across the membrane
    B. one that alters the saltiness receptor so that it can be excited by acids
    C. one that increases the activity of the sodium-potassium pump
    D. one that blocks the sodium gates in the membrane
    (A, p. 213, conceptual)

171. Which taste would be affected most strongly and most immediately?

    A. salty
    B. sour
    C. sweet
    D. bitter
    (B, p. 213, factual)

172. Which two tastes apparently use similar operations to transmit their information?

    A. sweet and sour
    B. sweet and bitter
    C. bitter and sour
    D. salty and bitter
    (B, p. 213, factual)

173.  Sweetness, bitterness and umami receptors operate by:

      A. closing potassium channels.
      B. depolarizing the membranes.
      C. activating a protein which causes the release of a second
         messenger.
      D. simply permitting sodium ions to cross their membranes.
      (C, p. 213, factual)

      **Individual Differences in Taste**

174.  Chewing "miracle berries" produces what effect?

      A. All the senses become more responsive to stimuli.
      B. Sour substances taste both sour and sweet.
      C. All substances taste sweet.
      D. All substances taste sour.
      (B, p. 214, factual)

175.  Which of the following procedures temporarily causes sour
      substances to taste sweet?

      A. first tasting a bitter substance, then the sour substance
      B. first tasting a capsaicin extract
      C. first tasting a different sour substance
      D. first chewing "miracle berries"
      (D, p. 214, factual)

176.  Why does orange juice taste unpleasant just after one uses
      toothpaste?

      A. Toothpaste contains a chemical that changes certain taste
         receptors.
      B. When the teeth are clean, the acid in the orange juice
         irritates them.
      C. Toothpaste removes a coating that protects the tongue.
      D. Toothpaste enhances the binding of molecules to sweetness
         receptors.
      (A, p. 214, conceptual)

177.  If you are a supertaster:

      A. you require high concentrations of a particular taste to be
         able to identify it.
      B. you have more fungiform papillae in the center of your tongue.
      C. you are more sensitive than the average person to nearly all
         tastes.
      D. your ability to taste makes up for your lack of ability to
         identify odors by smell.
      (C, p. 214, factual)

178.  Which of the following is consistent with the labeled-line theory
     of taste?

      A. Each receptor contributes to the perception of all tastes.
      B. Each receptor also carries information about temperature and
         texture.
      C. Each receptor carries information about just one primary
         taste.
      D. Most people who are insensitive to one taste are insensitive
         to others also.
      (C, p. 214, conceptual)

179.  In the absence of neurons which respond best to sweet substances:

      A. the remaining cells would not be able to distinguish sweetness
         from other tastes.
      B. some remaining cells would become ultrasensitive to sweet
         tastes.
      C. all other tastes would be sensed as increasingly bitter.
      D. sweet substances would now taste sour.
      (A, p. 214, factual)

180.  Information carried to the brain along the chorda tympani comes
     from the:

      A. posterior one-third of the tongue.
      B. posterior two-thirds of the tongue.
      C. center of the tongue.
      D. anterior two-thirds of the tongue.
      (D, p. 214, factual)

181.  If someone anesthetized your chorda tympani, you would:

      A. no longer taste anything.
      B. no longer taste anything in the posterior part of your tongue.
      C. no longer taste anything in the anterior part of your tongue.
      D. not notice any change in your ability to taste.
      (C, p. 214, factual)

182.  If someone anesthetized your chorda tympani, you would:

      A. become more sensitive to bitter tastes than before.
      B. become more sensitive to salt.
      C. become less sensitive to most other tastes.
      D. not notice any change in your ability to taste.
      (A, pp. 214-215, factual)

183.  Forty percent of people with anesthetized chorda tympanis:

      A. experience no noticeable change in their ability to taste.
      B. experience taste "phantoms."
      C. find that bitter substances now taste sweet.
      D. become more sensitive to salt.
      (B, p. 215, factual)

184.  The nucleus of the tractus solitarius in the medulla is known to
      receive information from what source?

      A. tongue
      B. nose
      C. ears
      D. skin of the hands
      (A, p. 215, factual)

185.  The taste nerves initially project to the:

      A. nucleus of the tractus solitarius.
      B. cerebral cortex.
      C. hypothalamus.
      D. orbital prefrontal cortex.
      (A, p. 215, factual)

186.  In rats, an increase or decrease in preference for a particular
      taste involves a corresponding change in the activity of which
      area of the brain?

      A. medulla
      B. fornix
      C. thalamus
      D. basal ganglia
      (A, p. 215, factual)

187.  In rats, an increase or decrease in preference for a particular
      taste involves a corresponding change in the activity of which
      area of the brain?

      A. nucleus of the tractus solitarius.
      B. orbital prefrontal cortex.
      C. corpus callosum.
      D. thalamus.
      (A, p. 215, factual)

**Olfaction**

188.  What is unusual about olfactory receptors compared to most other
      mature mammalian neurons?

      A. They have no dendrites.
      B. They have no axons.
      C. They are replaceable when old neurons die.
      D. They use more than one neurotransmitter.
      (C, p. 215, factual)

189.    In mammals, each olfactory cell has threadlike dendrites:

A. that extend from the cell body into the mucous surface of the nasal passage.
B. that extend from the cell body directly into the brain.
C. that extend from the mucous surface of the nasal passage to the base of the skull.
D. that intermingle with one another to form a weblike structure.
(A, p. 215-216, factual)

190.    Olfactory receptor sites are located:

A. in the brain.
B. on cilia.
C. in the olfactory bulb.
D. on the basilar membrane.
("WWW" B, p. 216, factual)

191.    Why is there a delay between the time a substance is inhaled and the time it is smelled?

A. Olfactory cells are very resistant to changes in permeability to sodium.
B. Axons from olfactory cells follow an indirect route to the brain.
C. Olfactory cells have a resting potential near zero.
D. Molecules in the air must pass through a mucous layer before they reach a receptor.
(D, p. 216, factual)

192.    How many kinds of olfactory receptors do we have?

A. two or three
B. seven
C. twenty
D. hundreds
(D, p. 216, factual)

193.    What is a "specific anosmia"?

A. a strong preference for a particular smell
B. an inability to smell a particular substance
C. an odorous chemical that excites all olfactory receptors
D. a chemical released by one animal that exerts a specific effect on another animal
(B, p. 217, factual)

194.  What is the purpose behind research on specific anosmias?

        A. to determine the minimum number of olfactory receptor types
        B. to determine whether each species is most sensitive to
           different odors
        C. to determine which olfactory nerves send information to which
           parts of the brain
        D. to understand the role of pheromones in behavior
        (A, p. 216, conceptual)

195.  The best way to determine the number of olfactory receptor types
      is to:

        A. take a small number of odors and test whether people can mix
           various proportions of those odors to match all other odors.
        B. study people who have trouble smelling a specific type of
           chemical.
        C. isolate the specific receptor molecules.
        D. further research the vomeronasal organ.
        (C, p. 216, factual)

196.  Researchers, in 1991, identified a family of proteins in
      olfactory receptors.  These receptor proteins are:

        A. seen only in olfactory receptors.
        B. the same type of proteins seen in the cochlea.
        C. the same type of proteins found in cones.
        D. the same type of proteins found in touch receptors.
        (A, p. 217, factual)

197.  How is olfactory information coded in receptor cells?

        A. Each odor produces a different ratio of firing across three
           types of olfactory cells.
        B. Each odor produces a different ratio of firing across six
           types of olfactory cells.
        C. Each olfactory cell has hundreds of types of receptor
           molecules, each responsive to a different chemical.
        D. Each olfactory cell has it sown receptor molecule, and
           different cells have hundreds of different molecules.
        (B, p. 217, factual)

198.  Which of the following is NOT true of olfactory receptors?

        A. Each responds to one, and only one, chemical.
        B. They are proteins in the cell membranes.
        C. There are many different kinds of receptors.
        D. They are covered by a mucous lining.
        (A, p. 217, conceptual)

199.  Based on research done to date, which sensory modality seems to
      have the widest variety of receptor types?

      A. hearing
      B. sight
      C. smell
      D. taste
      (C, p. 217, conceptual)

200.  Why are there so many different olfactory receptors compared to
      other senses?

      A. Other stimuli tend to vary on only a single dimension.
      B. Chemical senses developed first in evolutionary terms.
      C. There are more possible odorous stimuli.
      D. Chemical senses are still the most critical for survival.
      (A, p. 218, conceptual)

**Vomeronasal Sensation and Pheromones**

201.  The vomeronasal organ (VNO) is a set of receptors:

      A. that is part of the olfactory receptors.
      B. located near, but separate from, the olfactory receptors.
      C. that share the amino acid sequences of the olfactory system.
      D. which readily adapt to a continued stimulus.
      (B, p. 218, factual)

202.  The VNO's role in behavior is:

      A. basically the same as that of the olfactory system.
      B. much less limited than that of the olfactory system.
      C. much more limited than that of the olfactory system.
      D. just as important for humans as it is for other mammals.
      (C, p. 218, factual)

203.  What is a pheromone?

      A. an odor released by an animal that affects the behavior of
         other animals
      B. a sound emitted by a female to indicate that she is in estrus
      C. a low frequency noise used by insects to communicate their
         location to other insects
      D. a burst of electrical energy released by an eel.
      (A, p. 218, factual)

204.  Which of the following is characteristic of pheromones?

      A. They are hormones that are also used as neurotransmitters.
      B. They play a part in the sexual behaviors of some species.
      C. They increase aggression in males when released by other
         males.
      D. Even the human olfactory system can easily detect them.
      (B, p. 218, factual)

205.  Researchers have found the VNO in humans.  It compares to other
      species in that it is:

      A. more dependent on practice or training in humans.
      B. a more prominent organ in humans.
      C. a small organ without obvious receptors.
      D. a small organ with many more receptors.
      ("WWW" C, p. 218, factual)

206.  Many women living in a college dormitory will gradually begin to
      synchronize their menstrual cycles.  The research indicates that
      this is, at least in part, based on:

      A. sound.
      B. sight.
      C. odor.
      D. similar activity schedules.
      (C, p. 219, conceptual)

207.  Studies indicate that pheromones may play a role in:

      A. altering the human ability to detect odors.
      B. enhancing the ability to discriminate among similar odors.
      C. human sexual behaviors.
      D. the regulation of menstrual cycles while taking birth-control
         pills.
      (C, p. 219, factual)

## Module 8.1: The Control of Movement

### Muscles and Their Movements

1.   What type of muscle controls movements of internal organs?

     A. smooth
     B. striated
     C. cardiac
     D. antagonistic
     (A, p. 224, factual)

2.   What type of muscle is responsible for the movement of your body
     through the environment?

     A. smooth
     B. striated
     C. cardiac
     D. syncarpous
     (B, p. 224, factual)

3.   Internal organs are to _____ as movement of the body is to _____

     A. smooth muscles; rough muscles
     B. smooth muscles; striated muscles
     C. striated muscles; skeletal muscles
     D. antagonistic muscles; skeletal muscles
     (B, p. 224, conceptual)

4.   Another name for striated muscles is:

     A. smooth.
     B. rough.
     C. skeletal.
     D. cardiac.
     (C, p. 224, factual)

5.   Cardiac muscles have properties:

     A. just like those of smooth muscles.
     B. just like those of skeletal muscles.
     C. just like those of antagonistic muscles.
     D. intermediate between those of smooth and skeletal.
     (D, p. 224, factual)

6.    What is the relationship between the motor neuron axons and
      muscle fibers?

      A. Each axon innervates only one muscle fiber.
      B. The more muscle fibers a single axon innervates, the more
         precise the movements.
      C. The more axons which innervate a single muscle fiber, the more
         precise the movements.
      D. The fewer muscle fibers a single axon innervates, the more
         precise the movements.
      (D, p. 224, conceptual)

7.    Why can the eye muscles be moved with greater precision than the
      biceps muscles?

      A. The biceps have only slow-twitch muscles.
      B. The biceps have only fast-twitch muscles.
      C. The biceps are opposed by an antagonistic muscle; the eye
         muscles are not.
      D. The eye muscles have a lower ratio of muscle fibers to axons.
      (D, p. 224, conceptual)

8.    With a low ratio of muscle fibers to axons, there is:

      A. greater precision of movement.
      B. less precision of movement.
      C. more rapid fatigue of movement.
      D. greater muscle strength.
      (A, p. 224, conceptual)

9.    What is the name given to the synapse where a motor neuron's axon
      meets a muscle fiber?

      A. neuromuscular junction
      B. polar junction
      C. muscle spindle
      D. neurofiber synapse
      (A, p. 224, factual)

10.   A neuromuscular junction is a synapse:

      A. where a sensory axon delivering information from a muscle
         meets a neuron.
      B. where a motor neuron axon meets a muscle fiber.
      C. specific to cardiac muscles.
      D. where a muscle excites or inhibits a neuron.
      ("WWW" B, p. 224, factual)

11.  When an axon releases a transmitter at the nerve-muscle junction,
     what is the response of the muscle?

     A. It always relaxes.
     B. It always contracts.
     C. It relaxes or contracts, depending on the transmitter.
     D. It relaxes or contracts, depending on the duration and amount
        of transmitter.
     (B, p. 224, factual)

12.  Axons release _____ at junctions with skeletal muscles.

     A. many different neurotransmitters
     B. dopamine
     C. norepinephrine
     D. acetylcholine
     (D, p. 224, factual)

13.  What will cause a muscle to relax?

     A. electrical stimulation
     B. absence of acetylcholine
     C. presence of norepinephrine
     D. presence of epinephrine
     (B, p. 224, conceptual)

14.  A flexor muscle _____ an arm.

     A. straightens
     B. limits movement in
     C. raises
     D. is used to both flex and extend
     (C, p. 224, factual)

15.  Which muscle is "antagonistic" to a flexor muscle in the right
     arm?

     A. a flexor muscle in the right arm
     B. an extensor muscle in the left arm
     C. an extensor muscle in the right arm
     D. another flexor muscle in the right arm
     (C, p. 224, conceptual)

16.  What is needed in order to be able to move your ankle in all
     directions?

     A. a high ratio of axons to nerve fibers
     B. a low ratio of axons to nerve fibers
     C. both smooth and striated fibers
     D. an antagonist set of muscles
     (D, p. 224, conceptual)

17.    Myasthenia gravis is caused by:

A. damage to dopamine-containing cells in the substantia nigra.
B. damage to acetylcholine receptors at neuromuscular junctions.
C. loss of cell bodies in the basal ganglia and cerebral cortex.
D. damage to the myelin sheath that covers axons in the spinal
   cord.
(B, p. 224, factual)

18.    Myasthenia gravis is caused by:

A. the immune system attacking dopamine receptors.
B. the immune system attacking acetylcholine receptors.
C. a proliferation of glial cells.
D. damage to the myelin sheath of spinal neurons.
(B, p. 224, factual)

19.    Symptoms of myasthenia gravis include:

A. tremors and inability to start voluntary movements.
B. loss of sensation and motor control in one or more limbs.
C. weakness and rapid fatigue of skeletal movements.
D. unresponsiveness to instructions and inability to organize
   purposeful behaviors.
(C, p. 224, factual)

20.    Symptoms of myasthenia gravis are a result of:

A. a decrease in acetylcholine levels in the brain.
B. a decrease in acetylcholine receptors in the muscles.
C. an increase in acetylcholine levels in the brain.
D. an increase in acetylcholine levels in the muscles.
(B, p. 224, factual)

21.    After motor neurons fire a few times in quick succession,
       subsequent action potentials release:

A. more acetylcholine.
B. less acetylcholine.
C. more glutamate.
D. less glutamate.
(C, p. 224, factual)

22.    An important way to treat myasthenia gravis is to prescribe drugs
       which:

A. inhibit acetylcholine.
B. inhibit acetylcholinesterase.
C. increase acetylcholinesterase production.
D. cause motor neurons to fire in rapid succession for long
   periods of time.
(B, pp. 224-225, factual)

23.   What happens when a fish swims at low temperatures?

      A. Muscle fibers contract more vigorously than at high
         temperatures.
      B. The fish swims more slowly.
      C. The fish swims at its usual speed but fatigues more rapidly.
      D. The fish swims at its usual speed but fatigues more slowly.
      (C, p. 226, factual)

24.   How does a fish adjust to lower water temperatures?

      A. by increasing the speed of its action potentials
      B. by increasing the amplitude of its action potentials
      C. by recruiting different muscle fibers
      D. by increasing its basal metabolic rate
      (C, p. 226, factual)

25.   What are the differences among the three types of skeletal muscle
      found in fish (red, pink, and white)?

      A. speed of contraction
      B. susceptibility to fatigue
      C. both speed of contraction and susceptibility to fatigue
      D. only their color
      (C, p. 226, conceptual)

26.   Of the three types of skeletal muscles found in fish, which ones
      respond almost indefinitely without fatigue?

      A. red
      B. white
      C. blue
      D. pink
      (A, p. 226, factual)

27.   At high temperatures, a fish relies mostly on its:

      A. white muscles.
      B. red muscles.
      C. blue muscles.
      D. pink muscles.
      (B, p. 226, factual)

28.   At cold temperatures, a fish relies mostly on its:

      A. white muscles.
      B. red muscles.
      C. blue muscles.
      D. pink muscles.
      (A, p. 226, factual)

29. Which would be especially important when running up a flight of stairs at full speed?

    A. fast-twitch muscles
    B. slow-twitch muscles
    C. smooth muscles
    D. intermediate muscles
    (A, p. 226, application)

30. Which of the following fatigues rapidly?

    A. smooth muscle
    B. cardiac muscle
    C. slow-twitch muscles
    D. fast-twitch muscles
    (D, p. 226, factual)

31. Compared to the average weekend jogger, a world class marathon runner probably has a higher percentage of which kind of fibers in his legs?

    A. slow-twitch
    B. fast-twitch
    C. smooth muscle
    D. white muscle
    (A, p. 226, conceptual)

32. Compared to a long distance runner, a world class sprinter probably has more of which kind of fibers in her legs?

    A. slow-twitch
    B. fast-twitch
    C. smooth muscle
    D. striated muscle
    (B, p. 226, conceptual)

33. If a new species were found with legs composed almost completely of fast-twitch muscles, what could we infer about its behavior?

    A. It could chase prey over long distances.
    B. It could chase prey only over short distances.
    C. It probably travels constantly.
    D. It probably moves slowly and grazed on vegetation.
    (B, p. 226, conceptual)

34.     A proprioceptor is sensitive to the:

        A. degree of relaxation or contraction of smooth muscle
           tissue.
        B. position and movement of a part of the body.
        C. percentage of fibers that are contracting within a muscle
           bundle.
        D. degree of fatigue in a muscle.
        ("WWW" B, p. 227, factual)

35.     The stretch reflex:

        A. results in a stretch.
        B. is caused by a stretch.
        C. inhibits motor neurons.
        D. sends a message for a muscle to relax.
        (B, p. 227, factual)

36.     Which of the following are two kinds of proprioceptors?

        A. extensors and contractors
        B. contractors and muscle spindles
        C. muscle spindles and Golgi tendon organs
        D. muscle spindles and extensors
        (C, p. 227, factual)

37.     A muscle spindle responds to the:

        A. oxygen level in the muscle.
        B. acetylcholine concentration at the nerve-muscle junction.
        C. fatigue of the muscle.
        D. stretch of the muscle.
        (D, p. 227, factual)

38.     A sudden stretch of a muscle excites a feedback system that
        opposes the stretch.  This message starts in the:

        A. dorsal root ganglion.
        B. cerebellum.
        C. Pacinian corpuscles.
        D. muscle spindles.
        (D, p. 227, conceptual)

39.     What is true about a stretch reflex?

        A. It causes a muscle to stretch.
        B. It is activated when your arm or leg "falls asleep."
        C. It is caused by a stretch.
        D. It is triggered by a muscle cramp.
        (C, p. 227, factual)

40.  When a physician taps you just below the knee, what kind of reflex is being tested?

     A. stretch
     B. Golgi
     C. extensor
     D. vestibular
     (A, p. 227, factual)

41.  A physician taps you just below the knee to check a reflex that is based on information from which kind of receptor?

     A. a Golgi tendon organ
     B. an oscillator
     C. a muscle spindle
     D. a vestibular organ
     (C, p. 227, factual)

42.  Which type of proprioceptor responds to increases in muscle tension?

     A. Golgi tendon organ
     B. fast-twitch fiber
     C. muscle spindle
     D. slow-twitch fiber
     (A, p. 227, factual)

43.  What is the role of the Golgi tendon organs?

     A. to control the intensity of muscle contractions
     B. to guard against fatigue of muscles
     C. to produce rapid repetitive movements such as finger tapping
     D. to regulate blood flow to the tendons and muscles
     (A, p. 227, factual)

44.  Muscle spindles respond to changes in muscle _____; Golgi tendon organs respond to changes in muscle _____.

     A. tension; fatigue
     B. fatigue; tension
     C. stretch; tension
     D. tension; stretch
     (C, p. 227, conceptual)

45.  Activity of a muscle spindle is to _____ as activity of the Golgi tendon organ is to _____.

     A. contraction; inhibition of contraction
     B. inhibition of contraction; contraction
     C. inhibition of contraction; inhibition of contraction
     D. contraction; contraction
     (A, p. 227, conceptual)

46.    What experience is similar to losing proprioception?

A. losing your sense of equilibrium
B. walking on a leg that has "fallen asleep"
C. a phantom limb
D. teeth chattering in the cold
(B, p. 227, factual)

**Units of Movement**

47.    Under what conditions can Parkinson's disease patients, who
usually have trouble walking, walk surprisingly well?

A. when they have their eyes closed
B. when they walk backwards
C. when they count their steps
D. when they are following a parade
(D, p. 228, factual)

48.    If someone marks lines across a floor, Parkinson's patients:

A. can step across each line more easily than simply walk along
an unmarked floor.
B. can better count while walking than if the floor is unmarked.
C. find it more difficult to walk.
D. cannot walk backwards.
(A, p. 228, factual)

49.    What is characteristic of a ballistic movement?

A. It is a rhythmic alternation between two movements.
B. It is guided by feedback during the course of the movement.
C. It proceeds automatically once it has been triggered.
D. It tends to overcorrect itself.
(C, p. 228, conceptual)

50.    Which of the following is an example of a ballistic movement?

A. threading a needle
B. singing a song
C. picking up a newspaper
D. a reflexive knee jerk
(D, p. 228, conceptual)

51.    The rooting reflex and the grasping reflex are characteristic of
which group?

A. infants, but not normal adults
B. adults, but not normal infants
C. humans, but not non-humans
D. non-humans, but not humans
(A, p. 229, factual)

52.   What is the stimulus for the Babinski reflex?

      A. stroking the sole of the foot
      B. placing an object firmly in the palm of the hand
      C. touching the cheek near the mouth
      D. a loud noise
      (A, p. 229, factual)

53.   What is the stimulus for the rooting reflex?

      A. stroking the sole of the foot
      B. placing an object firmly in the palm of the hand
      C. touching the cheek near the mouth
      D. a loud noise
      (C, p. 229, factual)

54.   What happens to the rooting and Babinski reflexes after infancy?

      A. They continue to occur, just as in infancy.
      B. They are completely lost, as the reflexive connections
         disappear.
      C. They are suppressed, but they can return if cortical activity
         decreases.
      D. They are suppressed, but they can return if the person is
         motivated.
      (C, p. 229, factual)

55.   If a neurologist tests an adult patient for infant reflexes, the
      neurologist is probably trying to determine whether the person
      has suffered damage to the:

      A. cerebral cortex.
      B. spinal cord.
      C. peripheral motor system.
      D. cerebellum.
      (A, p. 229, factual)

56.   An adult might produce the Babinski reflex:

      A. during sleep.
      B. under any normal circumstance.
      C. if activity in the cerebral cortex has been suppressed.
      D. if the spinal cord has been damaged.
      (C, p. 229, factual)

57.   What causes sneezing in response to stepping suddenly into bright
      sunlight?

      A. the rooting reflex
      B. an allied reflex
      C. a Babinski reflex
      D. a ballistic movement
      (B, p. 229, factual)

58.   Central pattern generators:

      A. contribute to rhythmic patterns of movement.
      B. generate movement which is unresponsive to environmental
         stimulation.
      C. constrict the pupils in response to bright light.
      D. control all reflexes in adult humans.
      (A, p. 229, factual)

59.   What is the role of a sensory stimulus with respect to a central
      pattern generator?

      A. The stimulus is the trigger.
      B. The stimulus determines the rhythm.
      C. The stimulus is the trigger and determines the rhythm.
      D. The stimulus provides feedback.
      (A, p. 229, conceptual)

60.   With respect to a central pattern generator, a sensory stimulus:

      A. determines the rhythm.
      B. provides feedback.
      C. controls the frequency of repetition of the alternating
         movements.
      D. may be the trigger.
      (D, p. 229, factual)

61.   What is a motor program?

      A. A mechanism that guides movement on the basis of sensory
         feedback.
      B. A mechanism that produces an alternation between two
         movements.
      C. A plan for training a brain-damaged person to walk.
      D. A movement that, once triggered, continues automatically until
         its completion.
      (D, p. 229, conceptual)

62.   What behavior is exhibited by a chicken with featherless wings?

      A. It makes no use of its wings.
      B. It learns to fly by beating its wings faster than a normal
         chicken.
      C. It flaps its wings (uselessly) if it is suddenly dropped.
      D. It uses its wings the way mammals use their paws.
      (C, p. 230, factual)

63.    Which of the following is an example of a motor program in
       chickens with featherless wings?

       A. flapping wings if suddenly dropped
       B. learning to fly
       C. stretching its wings but not flapping them
       D. flapping its wings while eating
       (A, p. 230, factual)

64.    Which of the following is an example of a motor program in a
       human?

       A. yawning
       B. a list of things to do today
       C. a baby's first steps
       D. a teenager learning to drive
       (A, p. 230, conceptual)

## Module 8.2: Brain Mechanisms of Movement

### The Role of the Cerebral Cortex

65.    In order to elicit movement, the motor cortex:

       A. has direct connections to the muscles.
       B. sends axons to the brainstem and spinal cord.
       C. controls isolated movement in a single muscle.
       D. relies on feedback from individual muscle fibers.
       (B, p. 231, factual)

66.    In general, what is the role of the cerebral cortex for movements
       like coughing, laughing, and crying?

       A. It basically has no role as these movements are basically
          controlled by subcortical structures.
       B. It directs most of the individual muscle contractions.
       C. It modifies the muscle movements based on feedback from
          proprioceptors.
       D. It is essential for initiating these movements.
       (A, p. 231, factual)

67.    Each spot in the motor cortex controls:

       A. exactly one body area.
       B. just one muscle.
       C. just one cell.
       D. a population of cells.
       (D, p. 232, factual)

68.    People with posterior parietal damage:

   A. cannot walk toward something they hear.
   B. have trouble converting vision into action.
   C. can walk toward something they see but cannot reach out to
      grasp it.
   D. cannot accurately describe what they see.
   (B, p. 232, conceptual)

69.    Which of the following is characteristic of people with posterior
       parietal damage?

   A. They can see an object, but are unable to describe it.
   B. They have good hand-eye coordination only if they close one
      eye.
   C. They have difficulty accurately locating and approaching a
      sound.
   D. They will not step over an obstacle, although they can
      accurately describe it.
   (D, p. 232, conceptual)

70.    In contrast to people with posterior parietal damage, people with
       damage to certain parts of the occipital cortex outside the
       primary visual cortex:

   A. can describe color but not motion.
   B. can describe motion but not color.
   C. can accurately describe what they see but cannot reach out to
      grasp it.
   D. cannot accurately describe what they see but can reach out to
      grasp it.
   (D, p. 232, conceptual)

71.    Which of the following is characteristic of someone with damage
       to part of the occipital lobe outside the primary visual cortex?

   A. They can see an object, but are unable to describe it.
   B. They have good hand-eye coordination only if they close one
      eye.
   C. They will not step over an obstacle, although they can
      accurately describe it.
   D. They have difficulty accurately locating and approaching a
      sound.
   (A, p. 232, factual)

72.   What is the difference between paraplegia, hemiplegia, and
      quadriplegia?

      A. whether limbs have lost their sensory input, motor output, or
         both
      B. which limbs have lost their sensory and motor connections
      C. whether the sensory and motor connections were lost completely
         or only damaged partially
      D. whether the damage to sensory and motor connections is
         temporary or permanent
      (B, p. 233, conceptual)

73.   Inability to move one part of the body voluntarily, accompanied
      by low muscle tone and weak reflexive movements refers to:

      A. paraplegia
      B. hemiplegia
      C. tabes dorsalis
      D. flaccid paralysis
      (D, p. 233, factual)

74.   Stiff muscles, higher than normal muscle tone, and strong, jerky
      reflexes are characteristic of which disorder?

      A. amyotrophic lateral sclerosis
      B. tabes dorsalis
      C. flaccid paralysis
      D. spastic paralysis
      (D, p. 233, factual)

75.   The part of the cortex which responds mostly to the sensory
      signals that lead to a movement is the:

      A. premotor cortex.
      B. prefrontal cortex.
      C. supplementary motor cortex.
      D. tabes dorsalis.
      ("WWW" B, p. 233, factual)

76.   The part of the cortex which is most active during preparations
      for a movements and less active during the movement itself is
      the:

      A. premotor cortex.
      B. somatosensory cortex.
      C. inferior temporal cortex.
      D. tabes dorsalis.
      (A, p. 233, factual)

77.  When are the cells in the premotor cortex (in contrast to the
     primary motor cortex) most active?

     A. in preparation for movements
     B. during movements
     C. at or after the end of movements
     D. during inhibition of movements
     (A, p. 233, factual)

78.  When monkeys were shown a red or green light signaling whether
     they would later have to touch a red or green pad to get food,
     this provoked activity mostly in the:

     A. premotor cortex.
     B. prefrontal cortex.
     C. supplementary motor cortex.
     D. tabes dorsalis.
     (B, p. 233-234, factual)

79.  Monkeys were shown a red or green light signaling which pad they
     would later have to touch to get food. After a short delay, they
     saw a second light signaling a delay before they could touch the
     correct pad. This second stimulus provoked activity mostly in
     the:

     A. premotor cortex.
     B. prefrontal cortex.
     C. supplementary motor cortex.
     D. tabes dorsalis.
     (B, p. 234, factual)

80.  Which part of the cortex is most active during preparations for a
     rapid series of movements?

     A. the premotor cortex
     B. the prefrontal cortex
     C. the supplementary motor cortex
     D. the tabes dorsalis
     (C, p. 234, factual)

81.  Damage to the _____ impairs the ability to organize smooth
     sequences of activities.

     A. premotor cortex
     B. prefrontal cortex
     C. supplementary motor cortex
     D. tabes dorsalis
     (C, pp. 235, factual)

82.  Which of the areas surrounding the primary motor cortex is
     especially active during the preparation for a rapid series of
     movements?

     A. prefrontal cortex
     B. premotor cortex
     C. supplementary motor cortex
     D. somatosensory cortex
     (C, pp. 234, factual)

83.  From where do most of the axons in the dorsolateral tract
     originate?

     A. primary motor cortex, surrounding areas, and red nucleus
     B. primary somatosensory cortex and areas of the parietal lobe
     C. primary somatosensory cortex and areas of the occipital lobe
     D. red nucleus and reticular formation
     (A, p. 235, factual)

84.  What are the two major pathways from the cerebral cortex for
     controlling movement?

     A. contralateral and ipsilateral
     B. sympathetic and parasympathetic
     C. dorsolateral and ventromedial
     D. basal ganglia and limbic system
     (C, pp. 235-236, conceptual)

85.  Axons of the dorsolateral tract extend to what area?

     A. cerebellum
     B. cerebral cortex
     C. spinal cord
     D. thalamus
     (C, p. 236, factual)

86.  Most of the axons of the dorsolateral tract go to which side of
     the body?

     A. contralateral
     B. ipsilateral
     C. bilateral
     D. neither, they go to the cerebral cortex
     (A, p. 236, conceptual)

87.  The dorsolateral tract cross over point is in the:

     A. pyramids of the medulla.
     B. spinal cord.
     C. reticular formation.
     D. vestibular nucleus.
     (A, p. 236, factual)

88.  Dorsolateral tract axons are responsible for movements in which
     areas of the body?

     A. the periphery
     B. the trunk
     C. the face and head
     D. internal organs
     (A, p. 236, factual)

89.  Which behaviors would most likely be impaired by damage to the
     dorsolateral tract?

     A. writing a check
     B. walking
     C. standing
     D. digesting food
     (A, p. 236, conceptual)

90.  Which tract includes many axons from the primary motor cortex,
     the reticular formation, and the vestibular nucleus?

     A. the pyramids of the medulla
     B. the ventromedial tract
     C. the dorsolateral tract
     D. the cerebellar tract
     (B, p. 236, factual)

91.  Most of the axons of the ventromedial tract go to which side of
     the body?

     A. contralateral
     B. ipsilateral
     C. bilateral
     D. neither, they go to the cerebral cortex
     ("WWW" C, p. 236, factual)

92.  Movements near the midline of the body, such as bending and
     turning of the trunk, are controlled by which motor system?

     A. dorsolateral tract
     B. ventromedial tract
     C. supplementary
     D. hippocampal
     (B, p. 236, conceptual)

93. What is the relationship between the dorsolateral tract and the ventromedial tract?

    A. most movements are controlled by one or the other, but not both
    B. most movements rely on both, which work in a cooperative fashion
    C. most movements that are initiated by one are terminated by the other
    D. one is excitatory while the other is inhibitory
    (B, p. 237, factual)

**The Role of the Cerebellum**

94. If you have trouble with rapid, ballistic movement sequences that require accurate timing, you probably have suffered damage to the:

    A. reticular formation.
    B. cerebellum.
    C. hippocampus.
    D. hypothalamus.
    (B, p. 237, factual)

95. Speaking, piano playing, athletic skills, and other rapid movements would be most impaired by damage to which structure?

    A. the reticular formation
    B. the cerebellum
    C. the ventromedial hypothalamus
    D. the parasympathetic nervous system
    (B, p. 237, conceptual)

96. Damage to the cerebellum is most likely to interfere with which of the following?

    A. lifting weights
    B. the ability to remember a series of events
    C. rapid movements that require timing
    D. chewing and swallowing
    (C, p. 237, factual)

97. Which of the following is characteristic of people who have suffered damage to the cerebellum?

    A. They have to plan their movements one at a time.
    B. They lose feedback from proprioceptors.
    C. They become paralyzed in certain parts of the body.
    D. They can move normally except that they fatigue quickly.
    ("WWW" A, p. 237, conceptual)

98.   In which species would damage to the cerebellum be LEAST
      noticeable?

      A. cat
      B. human
      C. sloth
      D. hawk
      (C, p. 237, factual)

99.   Saccades refer to:

      A. rapid eye movements during sleep.
      B. rapid eye movements when someone moves the eyes from one focus
         point to another.
      C. rapid, ballistic movements of the finger.
      D. the clumsy bodily movements of someone with an impaired
         cerebellum.
      (B, p. 237, factual)

100.  What is the name of the rapid eye movement occurring when a
      person moves his or her eyes from one focus point to another?

      A. gyration
      B. sclerosis
      C. occiput
      D. saccade
      (D, p. 237, factual)

101.  What is a saccade?

      A. a reflex controlled by the spinal cord
      B. a tic that results from damage to the cerebellum
      C. an impairment of all rapid, ballistic movements
      D. a ballistic eye movement from one fixation point to another
      (D, p. 237, factual)

102.  A saccade is initiated by impulses from the:

      A. spinal cord.
      B. hypothalamus.
      C. cerebellum.
      D. hippocampus.
      (C, p. 237, conceptual)

103.  The finger-to-nose test is a common way of testing for possible
      damage to what structure?

      A. spinal cord
      B. basal ganglia
      C. medulla
      D. cerebellum
      (D, p. 237, factual)

104. After damage to the cerebellum, an individual has trouble with
     which part of the finger-to-nose test?

     A. the initial rapid movement to the nose
     B. the second step involving the hold function
     C. the third step which involves the finger moving to the nose by
        a slow movement
     D. both the second and third steps
     (A, p. 237, factual)

105. After damage to the cerebellum, an individual has trouble with
     the initial rapid movement of bringing a finger to the nose. A
     problem is that the individual:

     A. may not stop the finger soon enough.
     B. cannot move the finger in any direction but up.
     C. cannot move the finger in any direction but down.
     D. can move the finger in any direction except to the nose.
     (A, p. 237, factual)

106. The nuclei of the cerebellum (as opposed to the cerebellar
     cortex) are most important in:

     A. moving a finger rapidly toward a target.
     B. holding a finger in a steady position.
     C. using the hands to lift heavy weights.
     D. coordinating the left hand with the right hand.
     (B, p. 237, factual)

107. A man who has suffered from damage to the cerebellar cortex is
     given the finger-to-nose test.  He is most likely to have trouble
     with which part of the task?

     A. understanding the instructions
     B. controlling the initial, rapid movement
     C. holding his finger steady following the initial, rapid
        movement
     D. moving his finger to his nose following the brief hold
     function
     (B, p. 237, factual)

108. The symptoms of cerebellar damage resemble those of:

     A. a heart attack.
     B. Parkinson's disease.
     C. intoxication.
     D. mental illness.
     ("WWW" C, p. 237, factual)

109.  Tests for alcoholic intoxication resemble the tests for damage to
      which structure?

      A. temporal lobe
      B. cerebellum
      C. spinal cord
      D. basal ganglia
      (B, p. 237, factual)

110.  What is one of the temporary effects of alcohol intoxication?

      A. symptoms resembling cerebellar damage
      B. interference with infant reflexes
      C. loss of reflexive responses
      D. anosmia
      (A, p. 237, factual)

111.  What other condition resembles the symptoms of damage to the
      cerebellum?

      A. the third stage of syphilis
      B. damage to the hypothalamus
      C. alcoholic intoxication
      D. calcium deficiency
      (C, p. 237, factual)

112.  Which of the following would be most disrupted by damage to the
      cerebellum?

      A. following directions
      B. playing ping-pong
      C. playing chess
      D. lifting weights
      (B, p. 237, conceptual)

113.  Which of the following would be least affected by damage to the
      cerebellum?

      A. lifting weights
      B. playing the drums
      C. completing crossword puzzles
      D. driving a car
      (C, p. 237, conceptual)

114.  In a study, functional MRI measured cerebellar activity.  It was
      found that the cerebellum was quite active when individuals:

      A. lifted objects.
      B. performed tasks that did not require precise timing.
      C. performed tasks that did not require a precise aim.
      D. felt objects with both hands to decide whether they were the
         same.
      (D, p. 237-238, factual)

115. The cerebellum appears to be critical for:

    A. motor behaviors only.
    B. certain aspects of attention.
    C. judging which tone is louder.
    D. controlling the force of a movement.
    (B, p. 238, factual)

116. Which widely branching cells are responsible for all of the output from the cerebellar cortex to the nuclei of the cerebellum?

    A. Parallel fibers
    B. Purkinje cells
    C. Putamen cells
    D. Saccade cells
    (B, p. 238, factual)

117. What effect do Purkinje cells have on target cells within the cerebellum?

    A. excitation
    B. inhibition
    C. excitation of some cells, inhibition of others
    D. increase blood flow without exciting or inhibiting
    (B, p. 238, factual)

118. Purkinje cells receive most of their input from:

    A. proprioceptors.
    B. the basal ganglia.
    C. nuclei in the central cerebellum.
    D. parallel fibers on the cerebellar cortex.
    (D, p. 238, factual)

119. The greater the number of Purkinje cells activated, the:

    A. less the collective duration of the response.
    B. greater the collective duration of the response.
    C. greater the strength of the response.
    D. less the strength of the response.
    (B, p. 238, factual)

120. The number of Purkinje cells activated determines the _____ of the resulting movement.

    A. speed
    B. power
    C. duration
    D. accuracy
    ("WWW" C, p. 238, factual)

### The Role of the Basal Ganglia

121.   Which structure is composed of the caudate nucleus, putamen, and globus pallidus?

A. the basal ganglia
B. the limbic system
C. the cerebellum
D. the sympathetic nervous system
(A, p. 240, factual)

122.   The basal ganglia are structures of the:

A. hindbrain
B. midbrain
C. forebrain
D. medulla
(C, p. 240, factual)

123.   Which basal ganglia structure(s) is(are) important for receiving input from sensory areas of the thalamus and the cerebral cortex?

A. globus pallidus and putamen
B. globus pallidus and caudate nucleus
C. caudate nucleus and putamen
D. globus pallidus
(C, p. 240, factual)

124.   The basal ganglia are particularly important for which components of movement?

A. initiation
B. organization
C. only for movements in response to a stimulus
D. only for habitual movements
("WWW" B, p. 240, factual)

125.   Cerebellar damage is to _____ as basal ganglia impairments are to _____.

A. clumsy; paralysis
B. initiation; stopping
C. gross muscle function; fine motor coordination
D. timing; force
(D, pp. 240-241, conceptual)

**Module 8.3: Disorders of Movement**

**Parkinson's Disease**

126.   What is one of the main symptoms of Parkinson's disease?

A. rapid fatigue of the muscles
B. loss of saccadic eye movements
C. difficulty initiating movements
D. inability to coordinate speech with movements
("WWW" C, p. 242, factual)

127.   Most Parkinson's patients suffer depression:

A. only during the late stages of the disease.
B. as a reaction to the muscle failure they suffer.
C. as one of the symptoms of the disease.
D. if they are under 50 years of age when the disease strikes.
(C, p. 242, factual)

128.   Which of the following is NOT common in people with Parkinson's disease?

A. difficulty initiating voluntary movements
B. slowness of movements
C. rigidity and tremors
D. outbursts of emotions
(D, p. 242, factual)

129.   Parkinson's disease is caused by degeneration of a pathway of neurons that releases which neurotransmitter?

A. acetylcholine
B. substance P
C. serotonin
D. dopamine
(D, p. 242, factual)

130.   The immediate cause of Parkinson's disease is the:

A. net increase in the excitatory output from the globus pallidus.
B. gradual, progressive death of neurons.
C. immediate, mass death of neurons releasing acetylcholine.
D. accumulation of amyloid-beta in neurons.
(B, p. 242, factual)

131.   Most research on Parkinson's disease has focused on which part of the brain?

A. globus pallidus
B. substantia nigra
C. thalamus
D. cortex
(B, p. 242, factual)

132.  People with Parkinson's lose:

      A. serotonin-releasing axons.
      B. glutamate-releasing axons.
      C. dopamine-releasing axons.
      D. substance-P releasing axons.
      (C, p. 242, factual)

133.  The neurological result of Parkinson's disease is:

      A. a net decrease in the excitatory output from the hippocampus
         to the prefrontal cortex.
      B. a net increase in the inhibitory output from the globus
         pallidus to the thalamus.
      C. an increase in the excitation from the thalamus to the cortex.
      D. a decrease in the inhibitory output from the cerebellum to the
         medulla.
      (B, p. 242, factual)

134.  In Parkinson's disease, which pathway in the brain degenerates?

      A. basal ganglia to cerebellum
      B. substantia nigra to caudate nucleus and putamen
      C. cerebellum to spinal cord
      D. cerebral cortex to spinal cord
      (B, p. 242, factual)

135.  Many of the symptoms of Parkinson's disease apparently relate to:

      A. an imbalance between activity in the left and right
         hemispheres.
      B. a decrease in metabolic activity in the cerebellum.
      C. loss of arousal in the cortex.
      D. increased excitation of neurons in the substantia nigra.
      (C, p. 243, factual)

136.  Symptoms of Parkinson's disease emerge only after the number of
      neurons in the substantia nigra decreases to what level?

      A. to the point where there are no cells remaining
      B. less than 20% of the original total
      C. less than 50% of the original total
      D. less than 90% of the original total
      (B, p. 243, factual)

137.  Having an identical twin with Parkinson's disease greatly
      increases the other twin's likelihood of also getting Parkinson's
      disease if:

      A. the first twin had late-onset Parkinson's disease.
      B. the first twin had early-onset Parkinson's disease.
      C. the twins are male.
      D. the twins are female.
      (B, p. 243, conceptual)

138.  The role of heredity in late-onset Parkinson's disease:

      A. equals that of early onset Parkinson's disease.
      B. is probably not as great as with early onset Parkinson's
         disease.
      C. is greater for DZ twins that MZ twins.
      D. is greater for females than males.
      (B, p. 243, factual)

139.  At least some cases of Parkinson's disease are apparently linked
      to what cause?

      A. a recessive gene on chromosome 4
      B. the accumulation of aluminum in the cerebral cortex and
         hypothalamus
      C. a chronic lack of vitamin B-1
      D. a toxic substance found in a heroin substitute
      (D, p. 243, factual)

140.  Although Parkinson's disease is usually limited to old people, it
      has occurred in a small number of young people.  What did many of
      them have in common?

      A. They used a designer drug.
      B. They used cocaine.
      C. They lived near a nuclear power plant.
      D. They were on low-protein diets.
      (A, p. 243, conceptual)

141.  What is the effect of MPTP?

      A. It kills the neurons that release dopamine.
      B. It suppresses activity of the immune system.
      C. It is converted in the brain to dopamine.
      D. It inhibits the enzyme acetylcholinesterase.
      (A, p. 243, factual)

142.  The brains of Parkinson's patients may compensate for the
      dopamine loss by:

      A. synthesizing more neurotransmitter other than dopamine.
      B. increasing postsynaptic neuron receptors.
      C. converting MPTP to MPP.
      D. converting some of the remaining dopamine to MPP.
      (B, p. 243, factual)

143.  Spraying herbicides and pesticides on plants intended for human
      consumption may increase the risk of:

      A. Huntington's disease.
      B. myasthenia gravis.
      C. Parkinson's disease.
      D. tabes dorsalis.
      (C, p. 244, conceptual)

144.  What is believed about exposure to herbicides and pesticides?

A. It is the primary cause of Parkinson's disease.
B. It is a contributing factor in some cases of Huntington's disease.
C. It is the primary cause of myasthenia gravis.
D. It is a contributing factor in some cases of Parkinson's disease.
(D, p. 244, conceptual)

145.  If Parkinson's disease were caused primarily by exposure to herbicides and pesticides, we should expect to find:

A. near epidemics in some geographical regions.
B. greater incidence in people under 50 than in older people.
C. greater incidence in women than in men.
D. greater incidence in left-handers than in right-handers.
(A, p. 244, factual)

146.  One explanation for the correlation between low rates of Parkinson's disease and heavy cigarette smoking is that:

A. nicotine acts as a neurotrophin.
B. nicotine's chemical structure is similar to MPTP.
C. nicotine's chemical structure is similar to dopamine.
D. nicotine only affects neurons in the substantia nigra.
(A, p. 244, factual)

147.  What is the most common drug in the treatment for Parkinson's disease?

A. haloperidol
B. physostigmine
C. Dilantin
D. L-dopa
(D, p. 244, factual)

148.  What characteristic of L-dopa makes it an effective treatment for Parkinson's disease?

A. L-dopa has a negative ionic charge.
B. L-dopa dissolves readily in water but poorly in fats.
C. L-dopa binds tightly to both glutamate and GABA synapses.
D. L-dopa can cross the blood-brain barrier.
(D, p. 244, factual)

149.  L-dopa is most effective:

A. in the early to intermediate stages of Parkinson's disease.
B. in the late stages of Parkinson's disease.
C. for females.
D. for either the very young or the very old.
(A, p. 245, factual)

150. One hypothesis suggests that the symptoms of Parkinson's disease
depend partly on neurons which:

   A. lack their usual connections.
   B. develop abnormally thick myelin sheaths.
   C. leak serotonin at odd times.
   D. remain developmentally immature.
   (A, p. 245, factual)

151. Parkinsonian symptoms may arise because dopamine:

   A. reaches the synapses too quickly.
   B. quickly decomposes into inactive fragments.
   C. competes with neurons usually sensitive to serotonin.
   D. may not reach the correct synapses at the correct times.
   (D, p. 245, factual)

152. Which of the following is NOT a potential treatment for
Parkinson's disease?

   A. L-dopa
   B. MPTP
   C. nicotine
   D. antioxidant drugs
   (B, p. 245, factual)

153. Drugs that block glutamate may prove to be an effective treatment
for Parkinson's disease because:

   A. glutamate dominates in the left hemisphere, whereas dopamine
      dominates in the right hemisphere.
   B. glutamate destroys dopamine neurons.
   C. glutamate increases apoptosis.
   D. a deficit of dopamine leads to excess glutamate activity.
   (D, p. 245, factual)

154. A common treatment for Parkinson's disease is a drug that has
what effect?

   A. inhibits activity of the immune system
   B. increases the brain's production of dopamine
   C. blocks the enzyme acetylcholinesterase
   D. facilitates the passage of sodium across neuron membranes
   (B, p. 245, factual)

155. Of the following, which is considered LEAST promising as a
treatment for Parkinson's disease?

   A. high-frequency electrical stimulation of the globus pallidus.
   B. adrenal gland transplants.
   C. antioxidants.
   D. neurotrophins.
   (B, p. 246, factual)

156.    Transplanted brain tissue from aborted fetuses has proven to be:

        A. the most successful treatment for Parkinson's to date.
        B. more successful in treating Parkinson's in humans than
           animals.
        C. more successful in treating Parkinson's in older humans than
           younger humans.
        D. more successful in treating Parkinson's in young rats than
           aging rats.
        (D, p. 246, factual)

157.    Injecting neurotrophins into the brain:

        A. enhances the growth of the cerebral ventricles.
        B. impairs the growth of the cerebral ventricles.
        C. enhances the growth of axons and dendrites.
        D. impairs the growth of axons and dendrites.
        (C, p. 246, factual)

**Huntington's Disease**

158.    Early symptoms of Huntington's disease usually include:

        A. paralysis.
        B. jerky arm movements and body tremors.
        C. rapid fatigue.
        D. difficulty coordinating the left hand with the right hand.
        (B, p. 246, factual)

159.    What is a common symptom of Huntington's disease?

        A. rapid fatigue of the muscles
        B. loss of both sensation and motor control in certain limbs
        C. tremors that interfere with voluntary movement
        D. impairment of saccadic eye movements and rapid alternating
           movements
        ("WWW" C, p. 247, factual)

160.    What is especially limited in a patient with Huntington's
        disease?

        A. the ability to learn and improve new movements
        B. controlling aim and duration of eye movements.
        C. reflexes
        D. short-term memory
        (A, p. 247, factual)

161.    Which parts of the brain deteriorate most strongly in
        Huntington's disease?

        A. pathways of neurons containing the neurotransmitter dopamine
        B. the cerebellum and medulla
        C. the caudate nucleus, putamen, and globus pallidus
        D. the hippocampus and amygdala
        (C, p. 247, factual)

162.   Of the following brain areas, which is LEAST impaired in
       Huntington's disease?

       A. the caudate nucleus
       B. the cerebral cortex
       C. the globus pallidus
       D. the reticular formation
       (D, p. 247, factual)

163.   Which disorder is associated with a loss of 15-20% of overall
       brain weight?

       A. posttraumatic stress disorder
       B. myasthenia gravis
       C. dsylexia
       D. Huntington's disease
       (D, p. 247, factual)

164.   What is the usual age of onset for Huntington's disease?

       A. 5-7 years old
       B. 12-20 years old
       C. 30-50 years old
       D. 65 years or older
       (C, p. 247, factual)

165.   Which of the following is NOT true of Huntington's disease?

       A. It is controlled by a gene on chromosome 4.
       B. It is possible to predict with nearly 100% accuracy who will
          get the disease.
       C. It is generally treated with L-dopa.
       D. The average age of onset is around 40 years.
       (C, p. 247, factual)

166.   What is the relationship of genetics to Huntington's disease?

       A. It is caused by a dominant gene on the X chromosome.
       B. It is caused by a dominant gene on chromosome 4.
       C. It is caused by a recessive gene on one of the autosomal
          chromosomes.
       D. There is no evidence linking Huntington's disease to any gene.
       (B, p. 247, factual)

167.   How do current presymptomatic tests for Huntington's disease
       differ from those used prior to 1993?

       A. The new tests are now accurate about 50% of the time.
       B. The new tests require testing most of the person's relatives.
       C. The new tests require examining the person's chromosomes.
       D. The new tests only work when the cause of the disease is
          environmental.
       (C, p. 247, factual)

168.   Which of the following can be used as a presymptomatic test for
       Huntington's disease?

       A. differences in blood flow between the left and right
          hemispheres
       B. examination of chromosome 4
       C. a blood test that measures the concentration of phenylalanine
       D. tests of the P300 component of an evoked potential
       (B, p. 247, factual)

169.   What is examined in a presymptomatic test to identify which
       people are likely to get Huntington's disease?

       A. their dopamine levels
       B. their neuromuscular junctions
       C. the glutamate level in their blood
       D. their chromosomes
       (D, p. 247, factual)

170.   Whose chromosomes need to be examined with the new presymptomatic
       test for Huntington's disease?

       A. the person at risk
       B. only the person's relatives
       C. both the person at risk and his or her relatives
       D. both the person at risk and his or her spouse
       (A, p. 247, factual)

171.   In its normal form, part of the gene which controls Huntington's
       disease repeats its sequence of bases:

       A. under ten times.
       B. between approximately 11-24 times.
       C. at least 36 times.
       D. approximately 75 or 80 times.
       (B, p. 247, factual)

172.   The presymptomatic test for Huntington's disease enables one to
       predict not only who will get the disease but also:

       A. the approximate age of onset.
       B. what other diseases the person will get.
       C. which drugs will best alleviate the disease.
       D. which symptoms will become prominent first, and which ones
          later.
       (A, p. 247, factual)

173.   The gene for Huntington's disease codes for a protein called:

       A. huntingtin.
       B. chorea.
       C. protein #4
       D. C-A-G.
       (A, p. 247, factual)

174.  The huntingtin protein is located:

   A. outside neurons.
   B. both on neuron membranes and inside neurons.
   C. on neuron membranes.
   D. inside neurons.
   (D, p. 248, factual)

**Module 9.1: Rhythms of Waking and Sleeping**

1.   Psychologists in the early to mid part of the 20<sup>th</sup> century had
     difficulty with the notion that wake and sleep cycles were
     generated from within the body because:

     A. there was no scientific evidence to support this notion.
     B. all species operate on the same cycle.
     C. at that time there were no recorded sleep disorders.
     D. they accepted the theory that all behaviors were responses to
        stimuli.
     (D, p. 254, factual)

**Endogenous Cycles**

2.   If a migratory bird is kept in a laboratory room with constant
     temperature and 12 hours of light each day, when does it show
     migratory restlessness?

     A. steadily at all times
     B. never
     C. at approximately the correct time of year for migration
     D. at random intervals throughout the year
     (C, p. 254, conceptual)

3.   If a migratory bird is kept in a laboratory without any cues to
     the season, it will become:

     A. more active in the spring.
     B. less active in the spring.
     C. more active in the summer.
     D. more active in the winter.
     (A, p. 254, factual)

4.   If a migratory bird is released during spring from an environment
     without seasonal cues, it will fly:

     A. north.
     B. south.
     C. east.
     D. west.
     (A, p. 254, factual)

5.   What does "endogenous" mean?

     A. occurring at regular intervals
     B. learned
     C. sensitive to light/dark patterns
     D. generated from within
     (D, p. 254, factual)

6.    Endogenous circannual rhythms:

    A. influence when animals eat throughout the day.
    B. influence when animals go to sleep and awaken.
    C. are internal mechanisms which prepare birds for seasonal
       changes.
    D  are external mechanisms which prepare birds for seasonal
       changes.
    (C, p. 254, conceptual)

7.    Which of the following is most clearly under the control of a
      circadian rhythm in most animals?

    A. sleep
    B. storage of body fat
    C. migration
    D. mating
    ("WWW" A, p. 254, conceptual)

8.    Circadian cycles are to _____ as circannual cycles are to _____

    A. light-dark; temperature
    B. endogenous; exogenous
    C. mating; hibernating
    D. daily; yearly
    (D, p. 254, conceptual)

9.    Which of the following is true concerning the duration of a self-
      generated sleep/activity cycle?

    A. It is unreliable in most species, and dependably close to 24
       hours only in primates.
    B. It is longer if the organism is normally active in the dark.
    C. There is little or no variability from one individual to
       another.
    D. It is highly consistent in a given individual in a given
       environment.
    (D, p. 254, factual)

10.   Mammals have circadian rhythms:

    A. only for their sleep/activity cycle.
    B. only for frequency of eating and drinking
    C. for sleep and body temperature only.
    D. for a variety of activities, including sleep.
    (D, p. 254, factual)

11. What ordinarily happens to human body temperature over the course of 24 hours?

    A. It is about 1 Celsius degree higher in the afternoon
       than in the middle of the night.
    B. It is about 1 Celsius degree higher in the middle of the night
       than in the afternoon.
    C. At irregular intervals it varies about 2 Celsius degrees.
    D. It is constant throughout the day.
    (A, p. 254-255, conceptual)

12. A human's body temperature over the course of 24 hours is
    usually highest:

    A. about the time of awakening.
    B. mid-morning.
    C. mid to late afternoon.
    D. in the middle of the night.
    (C, p. 255, conceptual)

13. What is a "free-running rhythm"?

    A. the activity level of an animal that does not have a
       biological clock.
    B. the sleep pattern of a sleep-deprived person allowed to sleep
       without restrictions
    C. a pattern of activity that varies unpredictably from one day
       to the next
    D. the activity cycle generated by a biological clock that is not
       reset
    (D, p. 255, factual)

14. An activity cycle generated by a biological clock that is not
    reset is called:

    A. an endogenous circannual rhythm.
    B. a ring cycle.
    C. a free-running rhythm.
    D. a zeitgeber.
    (C, p. 255, factual)

15. What is a "Zeitgeber"?

    A. a biological clock
    B. an animal that does not have a biological clock
    C. an environmental cue that resets a biological clock
    D. a body activity that is controlled by a biological clock
    (C, p. 255, factual)

16.    What is the principal Zeitgeber for land animals?

       A. light
       B. the tides
       C. temperature
       D. barometric pressure
       (A, p. 255, factual)

17.    If you want to stay awake and alert longer than usual, you
       should:

       A. spend a period of time away from the sunlight.
       B. expose yourself to exercise in the morning.
       C. take melatonin in the afternoon.
       D. expose yourself to heavy exercise and loud noises in the
          evening.
       (D, p. 255, conceptual)

18.    Under what circumstances is a person's circadian activity cycle
       most likely to drift out of phase with the activity of other
       people?

       A. if the person spends a period of time in the wilderness, away
          from clocks
       B. if the person habitually eats a big meal just before bedtime
       C. if the person spends a period of time in seclusion, away from
          sunlight
       D. if the person lives near the equator, where the seasons do not
          vary
       (C, p. 255, conceptual)

19.    What happens if people are put in an environment that is
       constantly light?

       A. It does not affect them in any way.
       B. They complain that they cannot sleep.
       C. They complain that they have difficulty waking up.
       D. They follow a cycle closer to 28 hours than to 24 hours.
       ("WWW" B, p. 255, factual)

20.    What happens if people are put in an environment that is
       constantly dark?

       A. It does not affect them in any way.
       B. They complain that they cannot sleep.
       C. They complain that they have difficulty waking up.
       D. They follow a cycle closer to 28 hours than to 24 hours.
       (C, p. 255, factual)

21.  What happens if people live in an environment in which the cycle
     of light and dark is other than 24 hours?

     A. Within a few days they adjust to waking and sleeping on the
        new schedule, whatever it is.
     B. They adjust better if the cycle is some multiple of 24 (e.g.
        48).
     C. They adjust better if the cycle is close to 24 (e.g. 25).
     D. They fail to adjust at all.
     (C, p. 255, conceptual)

22.  Based on research, it has been determined that the human
     circadian rhythm appears:

     A. to be shorter than 24 hours.
     B. to be exactly 24 hours.
     C. to be just over 24 hours.
     D. to be closer to 28 hours.
     (C, p. 255, factual))

**Resetting the Biological Clock**

23.  What is a biological reason why people tend to stay up late on
     weekends and have trouble waking up on Monday? ·

     A. Over the course of evolution, the biological clock has become
        weaker.
     B. The human biological clock generates a rhythm longer than 24
        hours.
     C. The human biological clock generates a rhythm shorter than 24
        hours.
     D. In a temperature-controlled environment, the biological clock
        stops operating.
     (B, p. 256, factual)

24.  When traveling across time zones, adjustments are easier when
     traveling which direction?

     A. to the east
     B. to the west
     C. there is no difference
     D. it varies greatly from person to person
     (B, p. 256, factual)

25.  Research shows that traveling baseball teams seem to play more
     poorly when traveling from the:

     A. east to the west.
     B. west to the east.
     C. north to the south.
     D. south to the north.
     (B, p. 256, factual)

26. What was found in a study of the effects of traveling on the performance of the visiting team in major-league baseball?

    A. Traveling south decreased performance compared to traveling north.
    B. Traveling west improved performance compared to not traveling.
    C. Traveling east improved performance compared to not traveling.
    D. Traveling east decreased performance compared to not traveling.
    (D, p. 256, conceptual)

27. If a company sends a representative to an important meeting two or more time zones east from home, it is best to send this individual:

    A. as the meeting begins.
    B. for as short a time as possible.
    C. a day or two before the meeting.
    D. in the middle of the night.
    (C, p. 256, conceptual)

28. Given our biological clock, which of the following is easiest to adjust to?

    A. going on daylight savings time in the spring
    B. going off daylight savings time in the fall
    C. traveling three time zones west
    D. traveling three time zones east
    (B, p. 256, application)

29. Under what conditions do shift workers (who go to sleep at a variety of times of day) find that they sleep longest?

    A. if they go to sleep when the sun is either about to rise or about to set
    B. if they go to sleep when body temperature is lower than room temperature
    C. if they go to sleep immediately after working a full shift
    D. if they go to sleep when body temperature is decreasing
    (D, p. 257, conceptual)

30. Successfully shifting one's circadian rhythm for night work:

    A. is impossible because one's biological rhythm cannot be reset.
    B. is difficult with ordinary lighting.
    C. is more easily done with ordinary lighting than bright outdoor light.
    D. can easily be accomplished within a week or two.
    (B, p. 257, conceptual)

31.    What most reliably produces a shift in the circadian rhythm?

       A. exposure to loud noise
       B. exposure to bright lights
       C. working at night on a regular basis
       D. eating a big meal before going to sleep
       (B, p. 257, factual)

32.    What has research on circadian rhythms shown to be one of the
       best ways to increase the alertness and efficiency of workers on
       night shifts?

       A. expose them to bright lights while they work
       B. keep the environmental temperature constant from night to day
       C. have them eat a big meal before going to sleep
       D. allow them to catnap
       (A, p. 257, factual)

33.    In humans, which of the following is most effective in shifting
       the biological clock?

       A. lighting
       B. temperature
       C. activity
       D. barometric pressure
       (A, p. 257, conceptual)

34.    People adjust best to night work if they:

       A. can sleep in a very dark room during the day.
       B. can sleep in a light room during the day.
       C. can work in light that is not too bright.
       D. take catnaps at night.
       (A, p. 257, factual)

**The Mechanisms of the Biological Clock**

35.    When studying disruptions to the biological clock in animals,
       what did Curt Richter find?

       A. Blinding animals strongly disrupted their clock.
       B. Rendering animals deaf strongly disrupted their clock.
       C. Long periods of forced activity strongly disrupted the clock.
       D. The biological clock is insensitive to most forms of
          interference.
       (D, p. 257, factual)

36.    Blind or deaf animals generate:

       A. abnormal circadian rhythms.
       B. nearly normal circadian rhythms.
       C. circadian rhythms in phase with the external world.
       D. zeitgebers.
       (A, p. 257, factual)

37.    What happens after damage to the suprachiasmatic nucleus itself?

    A. Light no longer resets the biological clock, but the animal
       continues generating a 24-hour rhythm.
    B. Animals' activity patterns becomes less consistent and no
       longer respond to light and dark cycles.
    C. Animals lose their biological rhythms of temperature, but keep
       other circadian rhythms.
    D. Animals begin to maintain a constant level of activity
       throughout the 24-hour day.
    (B, p. 257, factual)

38.    The surest way to disrupt the biological clock is to damage what
      area of the brain?

    A. the substantia nigra
    B. the caudate nucleus
    C. the lateral hypothalamus
    D. the suprachiasmatic nucleus
    ("WWW" D, p. 257, factual)

39.    A key area of the hypothalamus, particularly important in the
      regulation of the biological clock, is the:

    A. substantia nigra.
    B. caudate nucleus.
    C. lateral hypothalamus.
    D. suprachiasmatic nucleus.
    (D, p. 257, factual)

40.    The suprachiasmatic nucleus is located:

    A. inside the optic chiasm.
    B. just above the optic chiasm.
    C. below the optic chiasm.
    D. in the occipital lobe.
    (B, p. 257, factual)

41.    After damage to the suprachiasmatic nucleus, the body:

    A. cannot generate biological rhythms.
    B. still has rhythms in synchrony with environmental patterns of
       light and dark.
    C. still has rhythms, but they are less consistent.
    D. still has rhythms, but they can only be reset by artificial
       light.
    (C, p. 257, factual)

42.   If suprachiasmatic nucleus neurons are disconnected from the rest
      of the brain, they:

      A. no longer produce any activity.
      B. continue to produce activity that follows a circadian rhythm.
      C. produce a 20-hour rhythm.
      D. produce spontaneous bursts of activity, but on no rhythmic
         pattern.
      (B, p. 257, factual)

43.   What is a strong piece of evidence that the suprachiasmatic
      nucleus (SCN) generates the circadian rhythm?

      A. Stimulation of the SCN awakens an individual.
      B. SCN neurons generate a circadian rhythm of impulses even after
         removal from the brain.
      C. Different groups of SCN neurons reach their peak of activity
         at different times of day.
      D. Certain animals that are born without an SCN are inactive
         throughout the day.
      (B, p. 257, conceptual)

44.   What is the role of the suprachiasmatic nucleus in circadian
      rhythms?

      A. Its neurons generate a 24-hour rhythm by themselves.
      B. Its neurons can reset the biological clock, but they do not
         generate it.
      C. It relays visual information to the biological clock.
      D. It relays information from the biological clock to areas that
         control temperature and activity.
      (A, p. 257, factual)

45.   What is the role of the suprachiasmatic nucleus (SCN) in the
      regulation of biological rhythms?

      A. The SCN coordinates several biological clocks.
      B. The SCN feeds visual information to the biological clock.
      C. The SCN generates the circadian rhythm.
      D. The SCN generates circannual rhythms.
      (C, p. 257, factual)

46.   When fetal hamster SCN tissue was transplanted, the adult
      recipients' biological clocks:

      A. no longer functioned.
      B. shifted by one hour.
      C. began producing a rhythm consistent with that of the donor.
      D. were unaffected by the donor SCN tissue.
      (C, p. 257, factual)

47.     Researchers removed the SCN from adult hamsters that had a 20-
        hour rhythm (the result of a mutant gene) and transplanted SCN
        tissue from hamster fetuses with either 20-hour or 24-hour
        rhythms.  What did they find?

        A. The adult hamsters continued on their previous cycle.
        B. The adult hamsters continued a cycle, but drifted out of
           phase.
        C. The adult hamsters adopted the rhythm of the transplanted
           tissue.
        D. All indications of a cycle disappeared.
        (C, p. 257, factual)

48.     The SCN produces circadian rhythms by altering:

        A. blood pressure.
        B. production of proteins.
        C. action potential velocity.
        D. axon myelination.
        (B, p. 257, factual)

49.     The SCN produces circadian rhythms through the action of two
        genes which produce proteins that are present in:

        A. large amounts early in the morning.
        B. large amounts in the middle of the night.
        C. large amounts by evening.
        D. constant concentrations through the day and night.
        (C, p. 257, factual)

50.     Researchers have demonstrated that the expression of the SCN
        genes can be changed through:

        A. exposure of the eyes to light.
        B. barometric pressure.
        C. the diet.
        D. morning exercise.
        (A, p. 257, factual)

51.     A small branch of the optic nerve which extends directly from the
        retina to the SCN in the hypothalamus is called the:

        A. retinohypothalamic path.
        B. SCN-hypothalamus path.
        C. fimbria.
        D. fornix.
        (A, pp. 257-258, factual)

52.     The retinohypothalamic path extends directly from the:

        A. SCN to the hypothalamus.
        B. retina to the SCN.
        C. hypothalamus to the SCN.
        D. retina to the cortex.
        (B, p. 258, factual)

53.  Mice with genetic defects can reset their biological clocks in
     synchrony with light even though their:

     A. rods, but not their cones, are destroyed.
     B. cones, but not their rods, are destroyed.
     C. rods and cones are destroyed.
     D. suprachiasmatic nucleus is destroyed.
     (C, p. 258, factual)

54.  Blind mole rats have neither eye muscles nor a lens with which to
     focus an image.  This translates into:

     A. an inability to reset their circadian rhythms.
     B. unusual circadian rhythms.
     C. a circadian rhythm which is unresponsive to light.
     D. a circadian rhythm which is still capable of being reset by
        light.
     (D, p. 258, factual)

55.  Participants who were kept in the dark for a number of days:

     A. had to have light they could see, even if for a short period
        of time, in order to reset their biological clocks.
     B. found that they could reset their biological clocks without
        any exposure to light.
     C. were able to reset their biological clocks when light was
        focused on a part of the body even if it was hidden from view.
     D. lost their ability to reset their biological clocks for about
        24 hours.
     (C, pp. 258-259, factual)

56.  What effect does melatonin have on sleep?

     A. It increases sleepiness.
     B. It decreases sleepiness.
     C. It increases narcolepsy.
     D. It increases sleep apnea.
     (A, p. 259, factual)

57.  When do the secretions of melatonin begin?

     A. Just before a person awakens.
     B. When body temperature is at its lowest.
     C. When body temperature is at its highest.
     D. A couple of hours before a person naturally falls asleep.
     (D, p. 259, factual)

58.  What is the effect of taking melatonin pills in the late evening?

     A. It phase-advances the biological clock.
     B. It phase-delays the biological clock.
     C. It increases sleepiness.
     D. It has no noticeable effects.
     ("WWW" D, p. 259, factual)

59.   Why will taking a melatonin pill in the evening have little
      effect on sleepiness?

      A. Body temperature is too low.
      B. Body temperature is too high.
      C. The pineal gland is only active in the morning.
      D. The pineal gland produces melatonin at that time anyway.
      (D, p. 259, factual)

60.   If you take a melatonin pill at any time other than evening, you
      will:

      A. become very active.
      B. be wide awake in a very short period of time.
      C. become sleepy within 2 hours.
      D. not sleep well that night.
      (C, p. 259, factual)

61.   You can put melatonin to good use:

      A. one hour before you are ready for bed.
      B. when you travel to a different time zone.
      C. in the morning when you take your vitamins.
      D. when you mix it with dairy products.
      (B, p. 259, factual)

62.   What are the side effects of melatonin pills?

      A. irritability
      B. addiction
      C. insomnia
      D. unknown
      (D, p.259, factual)

## Module 9.2: Stages of Sleep and Brain Mechanisms

### The Stages of Sleep

63.   What device can be used to measure stages of sleep?

      A. GSR
      B. EEG
      C. ACTH
      D. FSH
      (B, p. 261, factual)

64.   What does an electroencephalograph measure?

      A. action potentials in an individual neuron
      B. the electrical resistance of the scalp
      C. the rate of glucose uptake in active regions of the brain
      D. the average of the electrical potentials of the cells in a
         given region of the brain
      (D, p. 261, factual)

65.    What is the best way to objectively determine if someone is
       asleep?

       A. monitor breathing rates
       B. measure muscle tension
       C. monitor brain waves
       D. use self-report measures
       (C, p. 261, factual)

66.    An electroencephalograph displays:

       A. action potentials of individual neurons.
       B. a net average of all the neurons' potentials.
       C. the rate of glucose uptake in active regions of the brain.
       D. the electrical resistance of the scalp.
       (B, p. 261, factual)

67.    Alpha waves are characteristic of what type of activity?

       A. NREM sleep
       B. nightmares
       C. relaxed wakefulness
       D. periods of great excitement
       (C, p. 261, factual)

68.    What do the EEG waves look like when brain activity is
       "desynchronized"?

       A. long, slow waves of large amplitude
       B. short, rapid waves of large amplitude
       C. regular alternation between waves of large amplitude and waves
          of small amplitude
       D. irregular waves with low amplitude
       ("WWW" D, p. 261, conceptual)

69.    Sleep spindles and K-complexes are most characteristic of which
       sleep stage?

       A. stage 1
       B. stage 2
       C. stage 3
       D. stage 4
       (B, p. 261 factual)

70.    A sleep spindle consists of:

       A. 2-4 Hz waves during a burst that lasts at least half a second.
       B. 2-4 Hz waves during a burst that lasts at least 2-4 seconds.
       C. 12-14 Hz waves during a burst that lasts at least half a
          second.
       D. 12-14 Hz waves during a burst that lasts at least 12-14
          seconds.
       (C, p. 261, factual)

71.  A sharp high-amplitude negative wave followed by a smaller,
     slower, positive wave is called:

     A. a sleep spindle.
     B. a K-complex.
     C. a slow-wave.
     D. REM.
     (B, p. 261, factual)

72.  What is also known as slow-wave sleep?

     A. alpha wave sleep
     B. stages 1 and 2
     C. stages 3 and 4
     D. REM sleep
     (C, p. 261, factual)

73.  How do stages 2, 3, and 4 differ?

     A. body position
     B. percentage of REM
     C. percentage of serotonin that is released
     D. percentage of slow, low amplitude waves
     (D, p. 261, factual)

74.  With each succeeding stage of sleep (from 1 to 4):

     A. breathing and heart rates increase.
     B. brain activity increases.
     C. slow, large-amplitude waves increase in number.
     D. brain waves become smaller.
     (C, p. 261, factual)

75.  Why are EEG waves larger when brain activity decreases?

     A. because the EEG measures muscle tension, which also decreases
     B. because neurons are becoming more synchronized
     C. because neurons are becoming more desynchronized
     D. because blood flow is increasing
     (B, p. 261, conceptual)

76.  In which stage of sleep is the cortex LEAST responsive to sensory
     input?

     A. stage 1
     B. stage 2
     C. stage 3
     D. stage 4
     (D, p. 261, factual)

77.   After entering stage 4 for the first time each evening, the
      sleeper typically:

      A. returns immediately to stage 1.
      B. enters REM
      C. cycles back through stages 3 and 2.
      D. wakes up.
      (C, pp. 261, factual)

**Paradoxical or REM Sleep**

78.   What is one of the contradictions in "paradoxical" sleep?

      A. The frequency of the brain waves is low, while the amplitude
         is high.
      B. The brain is very active, while many of the muscles are deeply
         relaxed.
      C. Subcortical structures are very active, while the cerebral
         cortex is inactive.
      D. Postural muscles are tense, while heart rate and breathing
         rate are very low.
      (B, p. 262-263, conceptual)

79.   What is paradoxical about paradoxical sleep?

      A. It serves restorative functions, and yet the body has no
         apparent need for it.
      B. It is light sleep in some ways and deep sleep in other ways.
      C. It depends on serotonin for its onset and acetylcholine for
         its offset.
      D. It is associated with dreaming although brain activity is low.
      (B, pp. 262-263, factual)

80.   What is synonymous with paradoxical sleep?

      A. alpha waves
      B. stages 1 and 2
      C. stages 3 and 4
      D. REM sleep
      (D, p. 263, factual)

81.   Researchers use the term REM sleep when referring to:

      A. sleep without dreams.
      B. sleep in nonhumans.
      C. a state of sleep in humans, but not animals.
      D. sleep when the EEG shows regular, high-voltage slow waves.
      (C, p. 263, factual)

82.    During REM sleep, the EEG shows:

       A. regular, high-voltage slow waves.
       B. irregular, high-voltage slow waves.
       C. regular, low-voltage slow waves.
       D. irregular, low-voltage fast waves.
       (D, p. 263, factual)

83.    It is possible to determine a person's stage of sleep through
       which kinds of monitoring?

       A. EEG and GSR
       B. GSR and eye movements
       C. EEG and eye movements
       D. body position and carbon dioxide level in the blood
       (C, p. 263, conceptual)

84.    Facial and finger twitches are most characteristic of which stage
       of sleep?

       A. stage 2
       B. stage 3
       C. stage 4
       D. REM
       ("WWW" D, p. 263, factual)

85.    Which of the following is NOT associated with REM sleep?

       A. increased probability of dreaming
       B. facial and finger twitches
       C. EEG pattern resembling wakefulness
       D. tense and active postural muscles
       (D, p. 263, factual)

86.    Which of the following is associated with REM sleep?

       A. decreased probability of dreaming
       B. facial and finger twitches
       C. EEG pattern suggesting very little brain activity
       D. tense and active postural muscles
       (B, p. 263, factual)

87.    REM sleep is characterized by which of the following?

       A. tension and activity of the postural muscles
       B. low and steady heart and breathing rates
       C. a high level of brain activity
       D. a highly synchronized EEG pattern
       (C, p. 263, factual)

88.    The EEG record for REM sleep is most similar to which other sleep
       stage?

       A. stage 1
       B. stage 2
       C. stage 3
       D. stage 4
       (A, p. 263, factual)

89.    For a normal person, about how long does a cycle of sleep (from
       stage 1 to stage 4 and back again) last?

       A. 5-10 minutes
       B. 90-100 minutes
       C. 4 hours
       D. 7-8 hours
       (B, p. 263, factual)

90.    For a normal person, which part of a night's sleep contains the
       largest percentage of stage 4 sleep?

       A. early in the night
       B. the middle of the night
       C. toward the end of the night
       D. all parts equally
       (A, p. 263, factual)

91.    Typically, a person falls asleep and enters:

       A. stage 1 sleep.
       B. stage 2 sleep.
       C. stage 3 sleep.
       D. stage 4 sleep.
       (A, p. 263, factual)

92.    Typically, a person who falls asleep enters:

       A. stage 4 and slowly progresses through the stages 3, 2, 1 and
          then REM.
       B. REM and then slowly progresses from stage 4, to 3, then 2, and
          lastly 1.
       C. stage 1 and slowly progresses through stages 2, 3 and 4, but
          not necessarily in order.
       D. stage 1 and slowly progresses through stages 2, 3 and 4 in
          order.
       (D, p. 263, factual)

93.    How does the later part of a night's sleep compare to the early
       part?

       A. It includes a larger percentage of REM sleep.
       B. It includes a lower percentage of REM sleep.
       C. It is characterized by declining body temperature.
       D. It has more rapid cycles through the stages of sleep.
       (A, p. 263, conceptual)

94.    Which of the following occurs as a normal night's sleep
       progresses?

       A. Stage 4 and REM both increase
       B. Stage 4 and REM both decrease
       C. Stage 4 increases, while REM decreases
       D. Stage 4 decreases, while REM increases
       (D, p. 263, factual)

95.    What is the relationship between sleep stage and dreaming?

       A. Dreams occur only in REM sleep.
       B. Dreams occur only in NREM sleep.
       C. Dreams are more frequent and more vivid in REM sleep.
       D. Dreams are more frequent and more vivid in NREM sleep.
       ("WWW" C, p. 263, conceptual)

96.    How do REM dreams differ from NREM dreams?

       A. REM dreams are less likely to include striking visual imagery.
       B. REM dreams are more likely to include complicated plots.
       C. REM dreams do not contain violence.
       D. REM dreams are almost always less than 5 minutes.
       (B, p. 263, factual)

97.    What is the best way to determine if an individual who claims to
       never dream does, in fact, have dreams?

       A. Ask them about their dreams immediately after they wake up in
          the morning.
       B. Wake them up during REM sleep and ask them if they have been
          dreaming.
       C. Wake them up during NREM sleep and ask them if they have been
          dreaming.
       D. Ask them under hypnosis if they have had any dreams recently.
       (B, p. 263, conceptual)

98.    Which of these statements about dreaming is FALSE?

       A. It appears that nearly all humans dream.
       B. Most dreams last only a second or two, although they seem to
          last longer.
       C. People are more likely to report a dream when awakened from
          REM sleep than from NREM sleep.
       D. People dream in color.
       (B, p. 263, factual)

99.    A brain awakened from REM:

       A. is immediately alert.
       B. shows NREM characteristics.
       C. continues to show some REM characteristics.
       D. shuts down.
       (C, p. 264, factual)

### Brain Mechanisms of Wakefulness and Arousal

100. After a cut through the midbrain separates the forebrain and part of the midbrain from all the lower structures, an animal:

    A. stops sleeping.
    B. sleeps a normal amount per day, but lacks REM sleep.
    C. enters a prolonged state of sleep.
    D. alternates rapidly between sleep and wakefulness.
    (C, p. 264, factual)

101. After cutting each of the individual tracts that enter the medulla and spinal cord, depriving the brain of almost all sensory input, an animal:

    A. continues to have periods of wakefulness and sleep.
    B. stops sleeping.
    C. goes into a coma.
    D. enters a prolonged state of sleep.
    (A, p. 264, factual)

102. What is most disruptive to wakefulness?

    A. injecting acetylcholine into the forebrain
    B. cutting through the midbrain
    C. cutting tracts that enter the medulla
    D. cutting tracts that enter the spinal cord
    (B, pp. 264-265, factual)

103. What is most disruptive to arousal and wakefulness?

    A. cutting through the spinal cord
    B. cutting tracts that enter the medulla
    C. cutting through the reticular formation
    D. cutting tracts that enter the spinal cord
    (C, p. 265, factual)

104. What is the result of electrical stimulation to the reticular formation?

    A. sudden onset of sleep
    B. increased alertness
    C. coma
    D. hallucinations
    (B, p. 265, factual)

105. What correctly characterizes the role of the reticular formation in arousal?

    A. It is the single, critical system in arousing the cortex.
    B. It is only one of several systems involved in arousal.
    C. It is activated only by external stimuli.
    D. It is activated only by internal stimuli.
    (B, p. 265, factual)

106.  What is activated by the reticular formation?

      A. the spinal cord
      B. only those portions of the cerebral cortex involved in
         processing sensory information
      C. only subcortical structures in the brain stem and midbrain
      D. wide regions of the entire cerebral cortex
      (D, p. 265, conceptual)

107.  Stimulation of the pontomesencephalon:

      A. awakens a sleeping individual.
      B. decreases alertness in someone already awake.
      C. shifts the EEG from short waves to long, slow waves.
      D. delays the onset of the next REM period.
      (A, p. 265, factual)

108.  The locus coeruleus is believed to be important in which kind of
      activity?

      A. storage of memories
      B. sexual arousal
      C. aggression
      D. fight or flight
      (A, p. 265, factual)

109.  What is the role of the locus coeruleus with regard to sleep and
      arousal?

      A. It is very active during sleep.
      B. It is active when the pontomesencephalon is not.
      C. It is almost completely inactive during sleep.
      D. It is instrumental in waking us up.
      (C, p. 265, factual)

110.  What is one possible explanation for why most dreams are not
      remembered?

      A. There is little brain activity of any kind during REM sleep.
      B. The reticular formation is active during REM sleep.
      C. The locus coeruleus is inactive during REM sleep.
      D. Dreams are unconscious.
      (C, p. 265, factual)

111.  What part of the arousal system is often severely damaged in
      Alzheimer's disease?

      A. reticular formation
      B. locus coeruleus
      C. basal forebrain
      D. spinal cord
      (C, p. 265, factual)

112.   In response to meaningful events, the locus coeruleus releases:

       A. norepinephrine.
       B. acetylcholine.
       C. dopamine.
       D. serotonin.
       (A, p. 265, factual)

113.   The output from the locus coeruleus causes recipient cells to:

       A. activate genes important for storing information.
       B. degenerate and eventually die.
       C. release dopamine.
       D. inhibit dreaming.
       (A, p. 265, factual)

114.   Cells in the basal forebrain increase arousal and wakefulness by
       releasing:

       A. norepinephrine.
       B. acetylcholine.
       C. dopamine.
       D. serotonin.
       (B, p. 265, factual)

115.   Damage to the basal forebrain leads to:

       A. increased arousal.
       B. decreased time spent in NREM sleep.
       C. increased time spent in NREM sleep
       D. increased time spent in REM sleep
       (C, p. 265, factual)

116.   A couple of paths from the hypothalamus release histamine,
       thereby:

       A. increasing arousal.
       B. initiating sleep.
       C. shifting sleep from REM to NREM.
       D. slowing the circadian rhythm.
       (A, p. 265, factual)

117.   An important step toward decreasing arousal and therefore
       entering sleep is to decrease:

       A. temperature in the extremities, such as hands and feet.
       B. temperature of the brain.
       C. parasympathetic nervous activity.
       D. action potential velocity in the thalamus.
       (B, p. 265, factual)

118.  What is one of the best predictors of how quickly people can fall
      asleep?

      A. if they shift their blood flow so less flows to the periphery
      B. if the body core cools quickly.
      C. if the body core stays warm.
      D. if blood flow slows down.
      (B, p. 265, factual)

119.  Which of the following is instrumental in facilitating sleep?

      A. increasing the temperature of the brain and body
      B. adenosine levels
      C. dopamine levels
      D. activating the basal forebrain
      (B, p. 265, factual)

120.  Adenosine levels generally increase during periods of:

      A. wakefulness.
      B. REM sleep.
      C. NREM sleep.
      D. transition from wakefulness to sleep or sleep to wakefulness.
      (A, p. 265, factual)

121.  Caffeine increases arousal by:

      A. exciting adenosine.
      B. causing the release of prostoglandins.
      C. inhibiting adenosine.
      D. inhibiting the release of prostoglandins.
      (C, p. 265, factual)

122.  Prostoglandins promote sleep by _____ a cluster of neurons that
      _____ hypothalamic cells.

      A. stimulating; inhibit
      B. inhibiting; stimulate
      C. stimulating; stimulate
      D. inhibiting; inhibit
      (A, p. 266, factual)

123.  Drugs which inhibit GABA:

      A. promote sleep.
      B. promote prolonged wakefulness.
      C. inhibit dreaming in REM.
      D. inhibit dreaming in NREM.
      (B, p. 266, factual)

124. During a fever the preoptic and anterior hypothalamus:

    A. inhibit GABA output.
    B. inhibit dreaming in NREM.
    C. increase their output to the basal forebrain sleep-related
       cells.
    D. decrease their output to the basal forebrain sleep-related
       cells.
    (C, p. 266-267, factual)

125. Serotonin is released by the:

    A. locus coeruleus.
    B. basal forebrain.
    C. hypothalamus.
    D. dorsal raphe.
    (D, p. 267, factual)

126. Histamine is released by the:

    A. locus coeruleus.
    B. basal forebrain.
    C. hypothalamus.
    D. dorsal raphe.
    (C, p. 267, factual)

127. Different sets of cells in the basal forebrain release which
     two neurotransmitters?

    A. acetylcholine and GABA
    B. histamine and norepinephrine
    C. serotonin and substance P
    D. CCK and neuropeptide Y
    (A, p. 267, factual)

**Brain Functions in REM Sleep**

128. Research found that during REM sleep, activity:

    A. decreased in the pons, while it increased in the limbic
       system.
    B. increased in the pons, while it decreased in the limbic
       system.
    C. decreased in both the pons and the limbic system.
    D. increased in both the pons and the limbic system.
    (D, p. 267, factual)

129. During REM sleep, neuronal activity DECREASES in:

    A. the entire brain.
    B. the pons.
    C. the limbic system.
    D. the primary visual cortex and the motor cortex.
    (D, p. 267, factual)

130.  Activity in the pons:

      A. triggers the onset of REM sleep.
      B. triggers the onset of NREM sleep.
      C. disrupts REM sleep.
      D. stimulates arousal.
      (A, p. 267, factual)

131.  PGO (waves) is an abbreviation for which of the following?

      A. paradoxical gradual onset
      B. psycho-galvanic oscillation
      C. pons geniculate occipital
      D. psychasthenia glyceric onomatopoeia
      (C, p. 267, factual)

132.  PGO waves are associated with which of the following?

      A. NREM sleep
      B. REM sleep
      C. relaxation during wakefulness
      D. being awakened from REM sleep
      (B, p. 267, factual)

133.  REM sleep is associated with which of the following?

      A. tension and activity of the postural muscles
      B. PGO waves in the brain
      C. a highly synchronized EEG pattern
      D. decreased heart rate
      (B, p. 267, factual)

134.  The sequence of neural activity, from the first area it is
      detected until last, is as follows:

      A. first lateral geniculate nucleus, then the pons and lastly the
         occipital cortex
      B. first the occipital cortex, then the pons and lastly the
         lateral geniculate nucleus
      C. first the pons, then the lateral geniculate nucleus and lastly
         the occipital cortex
      D. first the pons, then the occipital lobe and lastly the lateral
         geniculate nucleus
      (C, p. 267, factual)

135.  Where does the pons send inhibitory messages during REM sleep?

      A. to the spinal cord
      B. to the occipital lobe
      C. to the vestibular system
      D. to the cerebral cortex
      (A, p. 267, factual)

136.  Which saying reflects the inhibitory message sent out by the pons
      during REM sleep?

      A. "look but don't touch"
      B. "don't believe everything you see"
      C. "don't believe everything you hear"
      D. "act first, ask questions later"
      (A, p. 267, conceptual)

137.  After damage to the floor of the pons, what happens to a cat's
      REM sleep?

      A. The eyes move vertically instead of horizontally.
      B. Heart rate becomes steadier.
      C. Breathing rate decreases.
      D. The muscles are not relaxed.
      (D, p. 267-268, factual)

138.  It appears from research with cats that one function of the
      messages from the pons to the spinal cord is to prevent us from:

      A. dreaming.
      B. sleeping too soundly.
      C. acting out our dreams.
      D. having difficulty falling asleep.
      (C, p. 268, factual)

**Abnormalities of Sleep**

139.  What is a defining criterion for insomnia?

      A. a person who consistently feels sleepy during the day
      B. consistently less than 6 hours of sleep per night
      C. at least 50% less REM sleep than normal
      D. more time spent in NREM sleep than in REM sleep
      (A, p. 268, factual)

140.  Which disorder involves difficulty falling asleep?

      A. narcolepsy
      B. onset insomnia
      C. termination insomnia
      D. sleep apnea
      (B, p. 269, factual)

141.  In which of these disorders does the person awaken repeatedly
      during the night?

      A. narcolepsy
      B. REM behavior disorder
      C. maintenance insomnia
      D. termination insomnia
      (C, p. 269, factual)

142.    A phase-advanced temperature rhythm is to _____ as a phase-
        delayed temperature rhythm is to _____.

        A. maintenance insomnia; onset insomnia
        B. sleep apnea; narcolepsy
        C. termination insomnia; onset insomnia
        D. onset insomnia; termination insomnia
        (C, p. 269, conceptual)

143.    What is a possible cause of sleep-onset insomnia and sleep-
        termination insomnia?

        A. damage to the SCN
        B. a shift of the biological rhythm involving temperature
        C. spontaneous activity in the locus coeruleus
        D. inadequate production of the neurotransmitter glutamate
        (B, p. 269, conceptual)

144.    What is a likely consequence if someone's body temperature cycle
        is phase delayed?

        A. narcolepsy
        B. sleep apnea
        C. onset insomnia
        D. termination insomnia
        (C, p. 269, factual)

145.    What is a likely consequence if someone's body temperature cycle
        is phase advanced?

        A. narcolepsy
        B. sleep apnea
        C. onset insomnia
        D. termination insomnia
        (D, p. 269, factual)

146.    What is a likely consequence if someone falls asleep after the
        temperature cycle has already passed its minimum and started to
        rise again?

        A. rapid entry into REM sleep
        B. a night without any REM sleep
        C. more sleep than usual that night
        D. REM sleep periods without dreams
        (A, p. 269, factual)

147.  What is one disadvantage in using tranquilizers as sleeping
      pills?

      A. They may cause narcolepsy.
      B. They may decrease body temperature during the second half of
         the night.
      C. They may cause sleeplessness on later nights.
      D. They may prevent the brain from inhibiting movements during
         sleep.
      (C, p. 269, conceptual)

148.  Most sleeping pills operate partly by:

      A. blocking the activity of neurotransmitters that increase
         arousal.
      B. increasing the activity of norepinephrine.
      C. increasing the activity of histamine.
      D. preventing the brain from inhibiting movements during sleep.
      (A, p. 269, factual)

149.  Short-acting tranquilizers, when used as sleeping pills, have the
      advantage that they do not leave the person sleepy the next
      morning.  What is their disadvantage?

      A. The person takes a long time to get to sleep in spite of the
         pills.
      B. The person may wake up early and be unable to get back to
         sleep.
      C. The person has unpleasant dreams.
      D. The person may experience apnea.
      (B, p. 269, factual)

150.  Why might a person who takes a short-acting tranquilizer as a
      sleeping pill be likely to wake up early?

      A. The need for sleep was satisfied more quickly than usual.
      B. REM periods occur early in the night, not at their usual time.
      C. The person experiences withdrawal effects from the drug.
      D. The nightmares associated with the drug interfere with sleep.
      (C, p. 269, conceptual)

151.  A long-lasting tranquilizer, when used as a sleeping aid, may
      have the disadvantage of:

      A. causing unpleasant dreams.
      B. causing apnea.
      C. leaving the person sleepy during the day.
      D. wearing off during the night.
      (C, p. 269, factual)

152.  What is involved in sleep apnea?

    A. involuntary movements of the arms and legs during sleep
    B. inability to breathe while sleeping
    C. tendency to fall asleep suddenly during the day
    D. sleep-talking
    (B, p. 269, factual)

153.  Which of the following physical conditions is related to apnea?

    A. puberty
    B. being female
    C. being obese
    D. having asthma
    (C, p. 269, factual)

154.  One of the possible causes of sudden infant death syndrome is:

    A. onset insomnia.
    B. termination insomnia.
    C. sleep apnea.
    D. narcolepsy.
    (C, p. 269, factual)

155.  It has been suggested that sleep apnea may be related to which of
      the following?

    A. schizophrenia
    B. sudden infant death syndrome
    C. infant autism
    D. hippocampal damage
    (B, p. 269, factual)

156.  The probability of sleep apnea is increased among which group of
      people?

    A. college students during finals week
    B. those who are addicted to tranquilizers
    C. overweight men
    D. people who work on swing shifts
    (C, pp. 269, conceptual)

157.  Among which group is sleep apnea, resulting when brain mechanisms
      for respiration cease functioning during sleep, most common?

    A. college students
    B. men
    C. women
    D. elderly
    (D, p. 270, factual)

158.  What is narcolepsy?

      A. sleepwalking
      B. the inability to breathe while sleeping
      C. involuntary movements of the limbs while sleeping
      D. sudden periods of sleepiness during the day
      (D, p. 270, factual)

159.  Which of the following is NOT a common characteristic of
      narcolepsy?

      A. attacks of sleepiness during the day
      B. attacks of muscle weakness during the day
      C. involuntary movements of the limbs during sleep
      D. dreamlike experiences that are hard to distinguish from
         reality
      (C, p. 270, conceptual)

160.  Which of the following has often been interpreted as an intrusion
      of REM sleep into wakefulness?

      A. narcolepsy
      B. sleep apnea
      C. REM behavior disorder
      D. somnambulism
      (A, p. 270, factual)

161.  What does cataplexy involve?

      A. dreamlike experiences that the person has trouble
         distinguishing from reality
      B. an attack of muscle weakness while awake
      C. a lack of inhibition of movement during REM sleep
      D. repeated involuntary movement of the legs or arms during sleep
      (B, p. 270, factual)

162.  What are the dreamlike experiences at the onset of sleep that are
      difficult to distinguish from reality?

      A. hypnagogic hallucinations
      B. idiopathic hallucinations
      C. occipital illusions
      D. pseudo-psychedelic visions
      (A, p. 270, factual)

163.  One explanation for narcolepsy is that it results from:

      A. underactive acetylcholine synapses.
      B. overactive acetylcholine synapses.
      C. insufficient REM sleep.
      D. obesity.
      (B, p. 270, factual)

164.  Drugs that are used to control narcolepsy also tend to produce
      what other effects?

      A. uncontrollable hand tremors and facial tics
      B. increased wakefulness
      C. reduction of sympathetic arousal
      D. relief from the symptoms of schizophrenia
      (B, p. 270, conceptual)

165.  Periodic involuntary movements of the legs and arms during sleep
      are most often seen in which group?

      A. infants
      B. adolescents
      C. middle-aged adults
      D. narcoleptics who have just fallen asleep or are just waking up
      (C, p. 270, conceptual)

166.  Which of the following is characteristic of people with REM
      behavior disorder?

      A. They show intrusions of REM sleep into wakefulness.
      B. They show bizarre behaviors while awake due to REM deprivation
         at night.
      C. They enter REM sleep at unusual and unpredictable times.
      D. They move vigorously during REM, apparently acting out their
         dreams.
      (D, p. 270, factual)

167.  People who move around vigorously during dreams, apparently
      acting out those dreams, have which of the following conditions?

      A. narcolepsy
      B. REM behavior disorder
      C. hypnagogic hallucinations
      D. periodic limb movement disorder
      ("WWW" B, p. 270, factual)

168.  One study of people with REM sleep disorder found:

      A. damage in the pons and midbrain.
      B. damage to areas of the brain that normally produce movements
         during REM.
      C. restricted oxygen intake during sleep due to factors
         associated with obesity.
      D. abnormally high levels of serotonin in the brain.
      (A, p. 270, factual)

169.  A night terror is most common in _____ during _____.

      A. adults; NREM sleep
      B. adults; REM sleep
      C. children; NREM sleep
      D. children; REM sleep
      (C, p. 271, factual)

170.   Nightmares are to _____ as night terrors are to _____.

       A. children; adults
       B. REM; NREM
       C. narcolepsy; cataplexy
       D. dopamine; serotonin
       (B, p. 271, conceptual)

171.   Night terrors can be distinguished from nightmares in that night
       terrors:

       A. occur during REM sleep.
       B. occur during NREM sleep.
       C. are far more common in adults than children.
       D. usually involve sleep talking.
       (B, p. 271, factual)

172.   Which of the following is more common during REM sleep than
       during NREM sleep?

       A. sleep talking
       B. sleepwalking
       C. nightmares
       D. night terrors
       (C, p. 271, conceptual)

173.   When does sleep talking occur?

       A. mostly during REM sleep
       B. mostly during NREM sleep
       C. during both REM sleep and NREM sleep with about equal
          probability
       D. during the brief transition period between REM sleep and non-
          REM sleep
       (C, p. 271, factual)

174.   Which of the following is NOT true about sleepwalking?

       A. It occurs mostly in children.
       B. It is dangerous to awaken a sleepwalker.
       C. It runs in families.
       D. It occurs most often during stages 3 and 4.
       (B, p. 271, factual)

175.   Which of the following is true about sleepwalking?

       A. It occurs mostly in adults.
       B. It is most common early in the night.
       C. It occurs during REM.
       D. It is dangerous to awaken a sleepwalker.
       (B, p. 271, factual)

**Module 9.3: Why Sleep?  Why REM?  Why Dreams?**

### The Functions of Sleep

176.  The repair and restoration theory of sleep suggests that the part of the body most in need of the restorative functions of sleep is/are the:

A. muscles
B. heart
C. blood
D. brain
(D, p. 273, factual)

177.  How does prolonged sleep deprivation affect human volunteers?

A. It produces death.
B. It decreases later need for sleep.
C. Brain activity increases.
D. It impairs concentration.
(D, p. 273, factual)

178.  How does prolonged sleep deprivation affect human volunteers compared to rats?

A. Sleep deprivation produces more severe consequences in rats.
B. Sleep deprivation produces more severe consequences in humans.
C. Both humans and rats show equal levels of consequences.
(A, p. 273, factual)

179.  What effects are generally produced during prolonged sleep deprivation in laboratory animals?

A. continuous seizures
B. few noticeable adverse effects
C. similar effects to sleep deprivation studies with humans
D. more severe effects than in sleep deprivation studies with humans
(D, p. 273, factual)

180.  One reason given for any differences in sleep-deprivation consequences between rats and humans is differences in:

A. metabolism.
B. the amount of sleep normally required.
C. the brain structures controlling circadian rhythms.
D. the degree to which the sleep deprivation procedures are stressful.
(D, p. 273, conceptual)

181. In rats, after a number of days of sleep deprivation:

     A. the immune system begins to fail.
     B. brain activity increases dramatically.
     C. brain areas responsible for sleep initiation die out.
     D. body temperature decreases.
     (A, p. 273, factual)

182. A day involving greater than usual mental and physical exertion has what effect on sleep?

     A. People sleep only slightly more than normal that night.
     B. People sleep significantly less than normal that night.
     C. People sleep significantly more than normal that night.
     D. People sleep the normal amount but get less REM sleep.
     (A, p. 273, factual)

183. What is a line of evidence AGAINST the repair and restoration theory of sleep?

     A. People sleep about as long after an inactive day as after a vigorous day.
     B. Digestion and protein synthesis take place during sleep.
     C. Prolonged sleep deprivation leads to irritability and impaired concentration.
     D. Certain stimulant drugs can interfere with sleep.
     (A, p. 273, conceptual)

184. Which of the following claims would be made by the evolutionary theory of sleep?

     A. The function of sleep is similar to that of hibernation.
     B. More highly evolved species, such as humans, need more sleep than other species.
     C. During sleep, we relive the experiences of past generations.
     D. Sleep enables the body to repair and restore itself to promote survival.
     (A, p. 273, factual)

185. According to the evolutionary theory of sleep, what is the primary function of sleep?

     A. to conserve energy
     B. to promote brain development
     C. to restore body functions that were exhausted during wakefulness
     D. to enable the person to reexperience, in dreams, the events of the past
     (A, p. 273, factual)

186. According to the evolutionary theory, which species would be expected to sleep the most?

    A. horses and other grazing species
    B. wolves and other predatory species
    C. relatively primitive species such as hedgehogs
    D. those with the most highly developed brains
    (B, p. 274, conceptual)

187. According to the evolutionary theory, which species would be expected to sleep the least?

    A. horses and other grazing species
    B. wolves and other predatory species
    C. relatively primitive species such as hedgehogs
    D. those with the most highly developed brains
    (A, p. 274, conceptual)

188. According to the evolutionary theory of sleep, why do bats sleep more hours per day than horses?

    A. Bats are more vigorous when awake.
    B. Bats are safer from predators while they sleep.
    C. Bats are a relatively more primitive species.
    D. Bats are a more highly evolved species.
    (B, p. 274, factual)

189. Which of the following is NOT true about hibernation?

    A. The longer an animal spends in hibernation, the shorter its life expectancy.
    B. During hibernation, an animal's body temperature drops.
    C. Pet hamsters sometimes hibernate.
    D. An extract from the brain of a hibernating animal can cause another animal to lower its body temperature.
    (A, p. 274, factual)

190. Which animals do not lower their body temperature while sleeping during the winter, so it is debatable whether or not they actually hibernate?

    A. ground squirrels
    B. bats
    C. hamsters
    D. bears
    (D, p. 274, factual)

191. What do animals do when they periodically come out of their hibernation every few days?

    A. mate
    B. eat
    C. drink
    D. sleep
    (D, p. 274, factual)

**The Functions of REM Sleep**

192.  For which species does REM sleep compose the largest percentage
      of total sleep?

      A. species that get a great deal of sleep
      B. species that sleep very little
      C. humans, dolphins, and others with a large brain
      D. the aged members of any species
      (A, p. 274, factual)

193.  If we compare either different species or different ages, what
      trend emerges?

      A. the less total sleep, the higher the percentage of REM sleep
      B. the more total sleep, the higher the percentage of REM sleep
      C. the more activity during wakefulness, the higher the
         percentage of REM sleep
      D. the more activity during wakefulness, the lower the percentage
         of REM sleep
      (B, p. 274, factual)

194.  If a person is awakened every time she enters REM sleep for a few
      days, and is then permitted to sleep without interruptions:

      A. she will spend about 50 percent more time in REM sleep than
         usual.
      B. she will get nothing but REM sleep the next night.
      C. she will get little or no REM sleep for the next several
         nights.
      D. she will spend about the same time in REM sleep as usual.
      (A, p. 276, conceptual)

195.  What do most people report if they are awakened every time they
      enter REM sleep over a period of a few days?

      A. quite drastic personality changes
      B. decreased appetite
      C. irritability and impaired concentration
      D. no changes in personality or sleep patterns
      (C, p. 276, factual)

196.  What often is reported by human subjects deprived of REM sleep
      for several consecutive days?

      A. no noticeable negative effects
      B. anxiety, irritability, and impaired concentration
      C. elation, euphoria, and improved concentration
      D. the same effects as control subjects awakened at random times
      (B, p. 276, factual)

197. Which of the following is true about NREM sleep?

    A. It contains the most vivid dreams.
    B. Its length varies more from one species to another than REM
       does.
    C. It dominates the time just before awaking.
    D. Time spent in NREM remains fairly constant over an
       individual's life.
    (D, p. 276, conceptual)

198. If over the course of seven nights experimenters awaken subjects
    every time they enter a REM stage of sleep, what happens by the
    seventh night?

    A. The experimenters will have to awaken the subjects much more
       frequently than they did on the first night.
    B. REM sleep will have pretty much disappeared, and the subjects
       will be able to sleep uninterrupted.
    C. Subjects will make the same number of attempts to enter REM as
       they did the first night.
    D. Subjects will begin to display REM cycles while awake.
    (A, p. 276, conceptual)

199. If a cat is awakened every time it starts to enter REM sleep,
    what happens to the number of attempts to enter REM sleep?

    A. It remains steady over days.
    B. It gradually decreases to zero.
    C. It gradually increases.
    D. It increases or decreases, depending on the cat's sex and age.
    (C, p. 276, factual)

200. Following a new learning experience:

    A. REM increases in humans, but not nonhumans.
    B. REM increases in nonhumans, as well as humans.
    C. REM decreases in humans, but not nonhumans.
    D. REM decreases in nonhumans, as well as humans.
    (B, p. 276, factual)

201. Research suggests that REM is:

    A. important for all types of memory.
    B. most important for strengthening memories of motor skills.
    C. most important for strengthening memories lists of words.
    D. not important for strengthening memories of any kind.
    (B, pp. 277, factual)

202. As compared to REM, research suggests that NREM is:

    A. important for all types of memory.
    B. important for strengthening memories of motor skills.
    C. important for strengthening memories of lists of words.
    D. not important for strengthening memories of any kind.
    ("WWW" C, p. 277, factual)

203. Paradoxical sleep has been shown to have which effects?

    A. It inhibits sexual arousal.
    B. It interferes with new learning.
    C. It strengthens the formation of new motor skills.
    D. It strengthens memories for new facts.
    (C, p. 277, conceptual)

204. Memories are strengthened during:

    A. REM sleep only.
    B. NREM sleep only.
    C. both REM and NREM.
    D. NREM and REM, although it is minimal during REM.
    (C, p. 277, factual)

205. A recent hypothesis proposed that the role of REM is:

    A. to shake the eyeballs back and forth in order to get
       sufficient oxygen to the corneas of the eyes.
    B. to shake the eyeballs back and forth so the individual moves
       from REM to NREM.
    C. no different than the role of NREM.
    D. to bring to the surface the individual's unconscious wishes.
    (A, p. 277, factual)

206. Whereas most theorists have proposed that REM serves functions in
     memory and brain development, according to one newer hypothesis,
     the role of REM is merely to:

    A. rest the muscles.
    B. increase oxygen flow to the cornea.
    C. keep the person from waking up.
    D. synchronize activity between the left and right hemispheres.
    (B, p. 277, factual)

**Biological Perspectives on Dreaming**

207. What was Freud's explanation for dreams?

    A. They are the id's attempt to make sense of spontaneous neural
       activity.
    B. They reflect the superego's dominance over the id.
    C. They reflect a reliving of the evolution of the species.
    D. They are unconscious motivations and desires.
    (D, p. 277, conceptual)

208.  According to the activation-synthesis hypothesis, what do dreams
      reflect?

      A. the brain's attempt to make sense of spontaneous neural
         activity
      B. unconscious motivations and emotions
      C. experiences that have been part of the species' evolutionary
         history
      D. an imbalance among hormone levels
      ("WWW" A, p. 277, factual)

209.  According to the activation-synthesis hypothesis, it should be
      possible to predict (with better than chance accuracy) the
      content of a person's dreams if we know what information about
      the person?

      A. concentration of serotonin and acetylcholine in the cerebral
         cortex
      B. number and type of emotional experiences during the day
      C. stimuli currently acting on the body and areas of spontaneous
         brain activity
      D. time the person went to sleep and the current time
      (C, p. 277, conceptual)

210.  Occasional bursts of vestibular sensation are common during REM
      sleep according to which hypothesis/theory?

      A. Freud's theory of dreams
      B. the repair and restoration theory
      C. a clinico-anatomical hypothesis
      D. the activation-synthesis hypothesis
      (D, p. 277, factual)

211.  Dreams begin with arousing stimuli, whether generated from the
      external or internal environment, according to which
      hypothesis/theory?

      A. Freud's theory of dreams
      B. the repair and restoration theory
      C. a clinico-anatomical hypothesis
      D. the evolutionary theory
      (C, p. 278, factual)

212.  Which hypothesis/theory suggests that the primary motor
      cortex is suppressed so arousal during sleep cannot lead to
      action?

      A. Freud's theory of dreams
      B. the repair and restoration theory
      C. a clinico-anatomical hypothesis
      D. the activation-synthesis hypothesis
      (C, p. 278, factual)

213.  Patients with damage here report no dreams.

A. the upper part of the parietal cortex
B. the lower part of the parietal cortex
C. all layers of the occipital lobe
D. the nonvisual areas of the temporal lobe
(B, p. 278, factual)

214.  One advantage of the clinico-anatomical hypothesis of dreams, in contrast to the activation-synthesis hypothesis, is that the clinico-anatomical hypothesis is based on:

A. Freud's theory of dreams.
B. careful comparisons of several animal species.
C. studies of brain-damaged people.
D. mathematical models of the nervous system.
(C, p. 278, factual)

**Module 10.1: Temperature Regulation**

1.  Humans expend most of their energy on what activity?

    A. walking, running, and other forms of locomotion
    B. in the beating of their hearts and blood circulation
    C. propagating action potentials in the billions of neurons in
       the nervous system
    D. maintaining basal metabolism
    (D, p. 282, factual)

2.  Humans expend most of their energy on what activity?

    A. forms of locomotion
    B. beating of their hearts and blood circulation
    C. mental activity
    D. maintaining a constant body temperature
    (D, p. 282, factual)

**Homeostasis**

3.  Walter B. Cannon introduced what term?

    A. homeostasis
    B. poikilothermic
    C. synergism
    D. homeothermic
    (A, p. 282, factual)

4.  What defines a homeostatic process?

    A. the regulation of blood flow
    B. any process governed by hormones
    C. the maintenance of certain body variables within a fixed range
    D. reproduction involving distinct male and female genders in a
       species
    (C, p. 282, factual)

5.  When the range maintained by homeostatic processes is very
    narrow, what is it called?

    A. a set point
    B. a match point
    C. idiopathic
    D. band specific
    (A, p. 282, factual)

6.  A set point refers to:

    A. a variable that the body works to maintain at a stable level.
    B. the regulation of blood flow.
    C. the release of hormones at a set point in time.
    D. initiating a change in body temperature at a set point in
       time.
    (A, p. 282, factual)

7.    How is the mechanism that controls human body temperature
      different than the thermostat that controls the temperature of a
      house?

      A. It maintains a set range.
      B. It anticipates future needs.
      C. It can heat as well as cool.
      D. The more extreme the conditions, the more energy is required.
      (B, p. 282, conceptual)

8.    Why is the mechanism that controls human body temperature *NOT*
      *exactly* homeostatic?

      A. The maintenance range is narrow.
      B. It can initiate a change before it's needed.
      C. It makes changes in one direction but not the other.
      D. The set range can change over time.
      (B, p. 282, conceptual)

9.    Set points for temperature and body fat:

      A. are fixed.
      B. change with time of year only.
      C. only change due to varying internal conditions.
      D. change depending on many conditions.
      (D, p. 282, factual)

10.   What is true regarding the body temperature set point in mammals?

      A. The body has a lower limit but no upper limit for temperature.
      B. The body has an upper limit but no lower limit for
         temperature.
      C. In general, the larger the animal, the higher the body
         temperature.
      D. Most mammals have a body temperature close to that of humans.
      (D, p. 282, factual)

**Controlling Body Temperature**

11.   Poikilothermic organisms include:

      A. humans.
      B. most mammals.
      C. amphibians and reptiles.
      D. all mammals and all fish.
      (C, p. 282, factual)

12.   Poikilothermic organisms have body temperatures which:

      A. remain relatively constant no matter what changes the external
         environment subjects them to.
      B. are the same as the temperatures of their environments.
      C. are nearly constant, although the brain temperature varies.
      D. allow them to survive in very warm climates only.
      (B, p. 282, factual)

13.   What is it called if an animal's body temperature stays the same
      as that of the environment?

      A. homeostatic
      B. homeothermic
      C. poikilothermic
      D. hypovolemic
      (C, p. 282, factual)

14.   How do reptiles control their body temperature?

      A. They dilate or constrict blood vessels.
      B. They move to different locations in their environment.
      C. They adjust their activity levels.
      D. There is nothing they can do.
      (B, p. 282, conceptual)

15.   Homeothermic organisms include:

      A. amphibians
      B. reptiles
      C. fish
      D. mammals
      (D, p. 282, factual)

16.   Homeothermic organisms include:

      A. amphibians
      B. reptiles
      C. fish
      D. birds
      (D, p. 282, factual)

17.   Homeothermic organisms include:

      A. amphibians and reptiles
      B. reptiles and fish
      C. amphibians and fish
      D. mammals and birds.
      (D, p. 282, factual)

18.   Homeothermic organisms can maintain an almost constant body
      temperature:

      A. but only in the summer.
      B. despite large variations in the environmental temperature.
      C. without much effort.
      D. without much fuel.
      ("WWW" B, p. 282, factual)

19.   Which of the following would require the most energy per gram to
      maintain homeothermy?

      A. a bear
      B. a rabbit
      C. a wolf
      D. a cow
      (B, p. 282, conceptual)

20.   Generating heat is to _____ as radiating heat is to _____.

      A. surface area; temperature of the set point
      B. total body mass; surface area
      C. raising the set point; lowering the set point
      D. sweating; shivering
      (B, p. 282, factual)

21.   Some insects, frogs and fish survive extreme cold by:

      A. generating vast amounts of heat through their blood.
      B. stocking their blood with large amounts of glycerol at the
         start of the winter.
      C. allowing ice crystals to expand in their blood vessels and
         cells.
      D. decreasing their surface to volume ratio.
      (B, p. 283, factual)

22.   What is one advantage of being homeothermic?

      A. It reduces the fuel requirements of the body.
      B. It prevents excessive reliance on a single sensory system.
      C. It enables the individual to stay active when the environment
         is cool.
      D. It decreases the need for shivering and sweating.
      (C, p. 283, factual)

23.   What is an advantage of maintaining a constant body temperature?

      A. It enables an animal to stay equally active at all
         environmental temperatures.
      B. It enables an animal to survive on a wider variety of diets.
      C. It minimizes the energy that must be expended on basal
         metabolism.
      D. It enables an animal to detect changes in the temperature of
         the environment.
      ("WWW" A, p. 283, conceptual)

24.  Why did mammals evolve a body temperature of 37 degrees Celsius?

     A. They benefit from a high temperature because they seldom need
        to cool themselves by much.
     B. Most protein bonds begin to break at this temperature.
     C. Their body proteins are stable only at 37 degrees Celsius or
        above.
     D. It is the only way they can detect changes in the temperature
        of the environment.
     (A, pp. 283-284, factual)

25.  What is the benefit of maintaining a body temperature of 37
     degrees Celsius?

     A. warmer muscles
     B. more protein
     C. more blood
     D. more body water
     (A, p. 283, factual)

26.  In part, the enzymatic properties of proteins depend on:

     A. a rigid structure.
     B. a flexible structure.
     C. very high temperatures.
     D. blood vessel construction.
     (B, p. 284, factual)

27.  What kind of temperature is required by reproductive cells of
     birds and most mammals?

     A. One that is higher than the rest of the body.
     B. One that is lower than the rest of the body.
     C. One that is the same as the internal organs of the body.
     D. One that fluctuates in direct opposition to changes in body
        temperature.
     (B, p. 285, factual)

**Brain Mechanisms**

28.  Blood vessel constriction, shivering, and sweating are controlled
     by which area of the brain?

     A. pineal body
     B. preoptic area of the hypothalamus
     C. parietal cortex
     D. cerebellum
     (B, p. 285, factual)

29.     If an experimenter heats the preoptic area of an animal in a cool environment, the animal will:

       A. shiver.
       B. pant or sweat.
       C. increase its preference for salty tastes.
       D. decrease its preference for salty tastes.
       (B, p. 285, factual)

30.     If an experimenter cools the preoptic area of an animal in a warm environment, the animal will:

       A. shiver.
       B. pant or sweat.
       C. increase its preference for salty tastes.
       D. decrease its preference for salty tastes.
       (A, p. 285, factual)

31.     What evidence do we have that the preoptic area controls body temperature?

       A. After damage to the preoptic area, an animal will simultaneously sweat and shiver.
       B. Each cell in the preoptic area has a temperature at which it is most active.
       C. Removed cells maintain a constant temperature even in a cell culture.
       D. Heating or cooling the preoptic area leads to sweating or shivering.
       (D, p. 285, factual)

32.     Cells in the preoptic area of the hypothalamus monitor which temperatures?

       A. internal organs
       B. their own and the skin
       C. differences between the arteries and veins
       D. differences between internal organs and the skin
       (B, p. 286, factual)

33.     When is a person most likely to shiver?

       A. when the skin is cold, but the preoptic area is at normal temperature
       B. when the temperature difference between the skin and the preoptic area is large
       C. when the skin and the preoptic area are both hot
       D. when the skin and the preoptic area are both cold
       (D, p. 286, factual)

34.    What happens to an animal after damage to the preoptic area?

   A. It eats a great deal and gains weight.
   B. It stops eating.
   C. It fails to sweat when overheating, but still shivers when
      cold.
   D. It fails to shiver and sweat sufficiently.
   (D, p. 286, factual)

35.    What happens to an animal after damage to the preoptic area?

   A. It can no longer shiver.
   B. It can no longer sweat.
   C. It fails to shiver and sweat sufficiently.
   D. Its internal body temperature will fluctuate wildly,
      irrespective of the environmental temperature.
   (C, p. 286, factual)

36.    How do amphibians and reptiles control their body temperature?

   A. they can not
   B. by shivering and sweating
   C. by changing the reflectivity of their skin
   D. by choosing an appropriate area of the environment
   (D, p. 286, conceptual)

37.    Which organisms, if any, use behavioral means to regulate their
       body temperature?

   A. poikilothermic, but not homeothermic
   B. homeothermic, but not poikilothermic
   C. both poikilothermic and homeothermic
   D. neither poikilothermic nor homeothermic
   (C, p. 286, factual)

38.    How do adult mammals with damage to the preoptic area regulate
       their body temperature?

   A. physiologically
   B. pharmacologically
   C. behaviorally
   D. not at all
   (C, p. 286, factual)

39.    The way that mammals with damage to their preoptic area regulate
       their body temperature is similar to what other group?

   A. birds
   B. reptiles
   C. normal mammals
   D. inanimate objects
   (B, p. 286, factual)

40.    Leukocytes release a protein called:

       A. leptin.
       B. cholecystokinin.
       C. interleukin-1.
       D. insulin.
       (C, p. 286, factual)

41.    What is the function of the chemicals prostaglandin E1 and E2?

       A. It causes the biological clock for temperature to be phase-
          advanced.
       B. It causes an increase in body temperature.
       C. It leads to hypovolemic thirst.
       D. It increases the preference for fluids containing sodium.
       (B, p. 286, factual)

42.    Which of these chemicals is responsible for producing fevers?

       A. 6-hydroxy-dopamine
       B. aldosterone
       C. CCK
       D. prostaglandin E1
       (D, p. 286, conceptual)

43.    Interleukin-1 and prostaglandin E1 work together to create what
       effect?

       A. weight loss
       B. sex drive
       C. fever
       D. long-term memory
       (C, p. 286, conceptual)

44.    If an animal which lacks physiological mechanisms of temperature
       control gets an infection, it:

       A. gets cold instead of feverish.
       B. gets hot only at the point where the infection began.
       C. chooses a hotter environment.
       D. recovers faster than animals that can control body
          temperature.
       (C, p. 286, factual)

45.    Which of the following is true about a fever?

       A. It develops independently of the preoptic area.
       B. It is part of the body's defense against an illness.
       C. It is an indication that the body is not yet fighting the
          infection.
       D. It serves to keep an animal warm during periods of reduced
          activity.
       (B, p. 286, factual)

46.     An animal which would have the best chance of surviving a
        bacterial infection would be one:

        A. whose temperature dropped slightly.
        B. whose temperature remained normal.
        C. with a slight or moderate temperature increase.
        D. with an extreme temperature increase.
        (C, p. 286, conceptual)

47.     How do newborn rabbits regulate their body temperature?

        A. more physiologically, than behaviorally
        B. more behaviorally, than physiologically
        C. by shivering and licking themselves, like adult rats
        D. by varying the thickness of their fur
        (B, p. 286, conceptual)

**Temperature Regulation and Behavior**

48.     Until recently, psychologists believed that infant rats were
        incapable of many behaviors during the first three weeks of life.
        What did experimenters do which changed this belief?

        A. tested the infant rats in an environment that was warmer
        B. used different reinforcers
        C. used females as well as males
        D. tested the young with their mothers present
        (A, pp. 286-287, factual)

49.     When a chick or other baby bird is grabbed by a predator its
        first response is usually to become limp and motionless.  What is
        this behavior called?

        A. tonic immobility
        B. phasic paralysis
        C. hyper-immobilization
        D. hypoactive defense
        (A, p. 287, factual)

50.     A predator grabs a baby bird, causing the bird to go limp and
        motionless.  Assuming the bird has not been harmed, how long will
        this immobile state last?

        A. until the bird's blood sugar rises to a certain level
        B. until the bird's blood salt concentration rises to a certain
           level
        C. until the body temperature of the bird lowers to a certain
           point
        D. until the body temperature of the bird rises to a certain
           point
        (D, p. 287, factual)

51.  A predator grabs a baby chick, causing the chick to go limp and
     motionless.  Assuming the chick has not been harmed, how long
     will this immobile state last?

     A. until the chick's blood sugar rises to a certain level
     B. until the chick's blood salt concentration rises to a certain
        level
     C. until the body temperature of the chick lowers to a certain
        point
     D. until the body temperature of the chick reaches the normal
        body temperature of an adult chicken
     (D, p. 287, factual)

52.  When would you expect to see tonic immobility last longest in a
     chick?

     A. when it is in a cool environment
     B. when it is in a warm environment
     C. when it has just eaten
     D. when it is hungry
     (A, p. 287, conceptual)

**Module 10.2: Thirst**

53.  Approximately what percent of the mammalian body is composed of
     water?

     A. 10%
     B. 20%
     C. 50%
     D. 70%
     (D, p. 289, factual)

**Mechanisms of Water Regulation**

54.  Which species is most likely to produce highly concentrated urine
     in its natural habitat?

     A. fish
     B. beaver
     C. sea gull
     D. gerbil
     (D, p. 289, factual)

55.  Which species is least likely to produce highly concentrated
     urine in its natural habitat?

     A. beaver
     B. gerbil
     C. a desert animal
     D. camel
     (A, p. 289, conceptual)

56.    Your posterior pituitary is most likely to release antidiuretic
       hormone (ADH):

       A. if you are very thirsty.
       B. shortly after drinking a large glass of water.
       C. if you are very hungry.
       D. shortly after eating a large meal.
       (A, p. 289, conceptual)

57.    What is the hormone released by the posterior pituitary that
       causes your kidneys to reabsorb and conserve water?

       A. antidiuretic hormone
       B. insulin
       C. luteinizing hormone
       D. oxytocin
       (A, p. 289, factual)

58.    Which hormone, released by the posterior pituitary, both raises
       blood pressure and enables the kidneys to reabsorb water?

       A. vasopressin
       B. prolactin
       C. thymosin
       D. ACTH
       (A, p. 289, factual)

59.    Vasopressin raises blood pressure:

       A. by causing the blood vessels to dilate.
       B. by constricting the blood vessels.
       C. by increasing the blood's salt concentration.
       D. by decreasing the blood's salt concentration.
       ("WWW" B, p. 289, factual)

**Osmotic Thirst**

60.    After an increase in the solute concentrations in the body, you
       will experience:

       A. a set point.
       B. osmotic thirst.
       C. hypovolemic thirst.
       D. hunger.
       (B, p. 289, factual)

61.    A concentration of 1.0 M has a number of grams of solute equal to
       the:

       A. set point.
       B. molecular weight of that solute dissolved in 1 liter of
          solution.
       C. osmotic pressure
       D. hypovolemic pressure.
       (B, pp. 289-290, factual)

62.    When does osmotic pressure of the body fluids increase?

       A. after drinking a large glass of water
       B. after excreting highly concentrated urine
       C. after gaining solutes
       D. after donating blood
       (C, p. 290, conceptual)

63.    What produces an osmotic pressure?

       A. dryness of the throat
       B. the availability of salty fluids
       C. increased solute concentration in the body fluids
       D. low blood volume
       (C, p. 290, factual)

64.    What is the cause of osmotic thirst?

       A. dryness of the throat
       B. the availability of tasty fluids
       C. low blood volume
       D. increased concentration of solutes in the blood
       (D, p. 290, factual)

65.    The tendency of water to flow across a semipermeable membrane
       from the area of low solute concentration to the area of higher
       concentration is termed:

       A. hypovolemic pressure.
       B. hypovolemic thirst.
       C. osmotic pressure.
       D. OVLT.
       (C, p. 290, factual)

66.    What is caused by a high concentration of solutes outside the
       cells?

       A. increase in blood pressure
       B. water flow into cells
       C. water flow out of cells
       D. excretion of diluted urine
       (C, p. 290, factual)

67.    When solutes in the extracellular spaces are more concentrated
       than the intracellular fluid, what causes water to leave the
       cells?

       A. sodium ions
       B. osmotic pressure
       C. receptors in the blood
       D. hypovolemic pressure
       (B, p. 290, factual)

68.    What kind of thirst is produced by an increased concentration of
       solutes in the blood?

       A. postprandial
       B. hypovolemic
       C. non-homeostatic
       D. osmotic
       (D, p. 290, factual)

69.    When the osmotic pressure is higher outside a cell than inside
       it, what will flow out of the cell?

       A. sodium
       B. potassium
       C. calcium
       D. water
       (D, p. 290, conceptual)

70.    The brain gets part of its information regarding low osmotic
       pressure from:

       A. receptors around the third ventricle.
       B. the blood-brain barrier.
       C. the subfornical organ
       D. thalamus
       (A, p. 290, factual)

71.    Specialized neurons for detecting osmotic pressure are found in
       the brain areas surrounding which structure?

       A. the third ventricle
       B. the nucleus dorsalis
       C. the pituitary gland
       D. the hypothalamus
       (A, p. 290, factual)

72.    The areas around the third ventricle can detect chemicals
       circulating in the blood because:

       A. these areas are not protected by a blood-brain barrier.
       B. these areas have low concentrations of solutes themselves.
       C. there is so much more blood here than anywhere else in the
          brain.
       D. these cells maintain a higher internal temperature than the
          rest of the body.
       (A, p. 290, factual)

73.    What area of the brain is largely responsible for detecting
       osmotic pressure?

       A. the substantia nigra
       B. the red nucleus
       C. the ventromedial hypothalamus
       D. the organum vasculosum laminae terminalis
       (D, p. 290, factual)

74.    The brain can anticipate an osmotic need before the rest of the
       body actually experiences it:

       A. because of the change in blood pressure.
       B. because the stomach can detect high levels of sodium.
       C. through detection of highly concentrated urine.
       D. because of the rate of vasopressin release.
       (B, p. 290, factual)

75.    The rate at which the posterior pituitary releases vasopressin is
       under the control of the:

       A. lateral preoptic area of the hypothalamus.
       B. supraoptic and paraventricular nuclei.
       C. subfornical organ.
       D. thalamus.
       (B, p. 290, factual)

76.    After a lesion to the lateral preoptic area, how would a rat
       react to an increase in sodium levels?

       A. by drinking less and excreting highly concentrated urine
       B. by drinking more and excreting a great deal of dilute urine
       A. by increasing its activity level without changing the amount
          it drinks
       D. by sweating profusely, but not drinking much
       (A, p. 290, application)

77.    What happens to a rat with damage to its lateral preoptic area?

       A. It is incapable of drinking.
       B. It is no longer thirsty.
       C. Osmotic thirst is impaired.
       D. It drinks saltier fluids than normal.
       (C, p. 290, factual)

78.    What happens to a rat with damage to its lateral preoptic area?

       A. It is incapable of drinking.
       B. It drinks only to wash down its food.
       C. It has normal osmotic thirst but impaired hypovolemic thirst.
       D. It has impaired osmotic thirst.
       (D, p. 290, conceptual)

**Hypovolemic Thirst**

79.    What causes hypovolemic thirst?

       A. dryness of the throat
       B. low blood volume
       C. increased concentration of solutes in the blood
       D. too much salt in the diet
       (B, p. 291, factual)

80.    A loss of blood will lead to what kind of thirst?

    A. osmotic
    B. non-homeostatic
    C. hypovolemic
    D. postprandial
    (C, p. 291, factual)

81.    After a loss of blood volume, an animal will:

    A. drink whatever it can find, indiscriminately.
    B. drink a great deal of pure water.
    C. drink excessively concentrated saltwater.
    D. alternately drink pure water and excessively concentrated
       saltwater.
    (D, p. 291, factual)

82.    An animal with hypovolemic thirst will drink

    A. a large volume of pure water.
    B. only enough to moisten its throat.
    C. mildly salty water rather than pure water.
    D. only water with a low pH.
    (C, p. 291, factual)

83.    Hypovolemic thirst:

    A. depends mostly on the lateral preoptic area.
    B. can be satisfied better by salt water than by pure water.
    C. is stimulated by an increased concentration of solutes in the
       blood.
    D. can only be satisfied by drinking a great deal of pure water.
    (B, p. 291, conceptual)

84.    Baroreceptors attached to large veins detect:

    A. the hormone renin.
    B. angiotensin II.
    C. the pressure of blood returning to the heart.
    D. how much salt is in water which is being ingested.
    (C, p. 291, factual)

85.    Hypovolemia induces thirst partly by stimulating which receptors?

    A. autoreceptors
    B. thermoreceptors
    C. glucoreceptors
    D. baroreceptors
    (D, p. 291, factual)

86.    The kidneys release renin:

       A. everytime you are thirsty.
       B. while drinking.
       C. if blood volume drops.
       D. If blood volume increases too quickly.
       ("WWW" C, p. 291, factual)

87.    The kidneys release the hormone renin in response to what
       stimulus?

       A. the presence of food in the small intestine
       B. an increased concentration of carbohydrates in the blood
       C. a decrease in blood volume
       D. increased periods of light during the day
       (C, p. 291, factual)

88.    Which neurons are stimulated when angiotensin, a hormone involved
       in hypovolemic thirst, reaches the brain?

       A. those in the subfornical organ
       B. those in the olfactory bulbs
       C. those in the suprachiasmatic nucleus
       D. those in the lateral preoptic area
       (A, p. 291, factual)

89.    What is caused by the hormone angiotensin II?

       A. increased storage of food as fat
       B. constriction of blood vessels
       C. decreased emptying of the stomach
       D. increased growth of the gonads
       (B, p. 291, factual)

90.    Hypovolemia induces thirst by inducing release of which hormone?

       A. CCK
       B. insulin
       C. prolactin
       D. angiotensin
       (D, p. 291, factual)

91.    Injecting angiotensin near the subfornical organ:

       A. decreases drinking initially, but then drinking increases.
       B. increases drinking.
       C. does not affect drinking behavior initially.
       D. causes the blood-brain barrier to break down.
       (B, p. 291, factual)

92.   What is the effect of an injection of a drug that blocks
      angiotensin II receptors?

      A. It decreases hunger.
      B. It inhibits drinking.
      C. It increases drinking.
      D. It causes blood pressure to rise.
      (B, p. 291, factual)

93.   The subfornical organ is well suited to monitor the blood
      Because it:

      A. is near the hypothalamus.
      B. has numerous synergistic effects.
      C. lies outside of the blood-brain barrier.
      D. releases angiotensin.
      (C, p. 291, factual)

94.   What is the evidence suggesting that angiotensin II stimulates
      hypovolemic thirst?

      A. renin causes a drop in angiotensin levels
      B. injection of a drug that blocks its receptors inhibits
         drinking
      C. injections of angiotensin into the lateral preoptic area
         produce drinking
      D. injections of a drug that blocks angiotensin II receptors
         initiates drinking
      (B, p. 291, factual)

95.   If two effects are synergistic:

      A. they are independent of each other.
      B. they act in opposite directions.
      C. together they produce less effect than either one acting
         alone.
      D. together they produce more than twice the effect of either
         alone.
      (D, p. 291, conceptual)

96.   Receptors for osmotic thirst adjoin the _____; receptors for
      hypovolemic thirst adjoin the _____.

      A. third ventricle; third ventricle
      B. third ventricle; lateral ventricles
      C. lateral ventricles; third ventricle
      D. lateral ventricles; lateral ventricles
      (A, p. 291, factual)

97.    Osmotic thirst is to _____ as hypovolemic thirst is to _____.

A. the OVLT; both baroreceptors and the subfornical organ
B. both baroreceptors and the subfornical organ; the OVLT
C. both baroreceptors and the OVLT; the subfornical organ
D. the subfornical organ; both baroreceptors and the OVLT
(A, p. 291, conceptual)

98.    Individuals who have lost sodium and other solutes:

A. may experience a craving for salty tastes.
B. must learn by trial and error to replace the correct amount.
C. will often experience a craving for vitamins
D. will produce a hormone to excrete less watery fluids than
   usual.
(A, p. 291, factual)

99.    An automatic, unlearned increase in preference occurs in response
to a deficiency in which substance?

A. thiamine
B. fats
C. calcium
D. sodium
(D, p. 291, factual)

100.   The adrenal gland hormone aldosterone:

A. increases the storage of food as fat.
B. causes the kidneys to conserve sodium.
C. decreases the emptying of the stomach.
D. increases sweating.
(B, p. 292, factual)

101.   The hormone aldosterone results in the:

A. conservation of water.
B. excretion of sodium.
C. conservation of sodium.
D. decreased preference for salty tastes.
(C, p. 292, factual)

102.   Aldosterone triggers:

A. conservation of water.
B. an increased preference for salty tastes.
C. exertion of sodium
D. a decreased preference for salty tastes.
(B, p. 292, factual)

103.  A combination of the hormones aldosterone and angiotensin leads
      to an increase in preference for _____ tastes.

      A. sweet
      B. sour
      C. salty
      D. bitter
      (C, p. 292, factual)

104.  The hormones angiotensin and aldosterone synergistically
      increase:

      A. shivering and temperature conservation.
      B. hunger.
      C. sex drive.
      D. a preference for sodium.
      (D, p. 292, factual)

105.  Initial research on the subfornical organ (SFO) indicated that
      this area was important for control of:

      A. salt cravings.
      B. temperature regulation.
      C. alcohol avoidance.
      D. protein metabolism.
      (A, p. 292, factual)

106.  Based on recent research on the subfornical organ (SFO), it was
      determined that if the SFO was lesioned:

      A. animals had trouble displaying their salt cravings.
      B. animals still could drink normally.
      C. aldosterone could no longer affect thirst.
      D. angiotensin II could no longer affect thirst.
      (A, p. 292, factual)

**Module 10.3: Hunger**

107.  Bears eat as much as they can at one time because:

      A. they do not regulate body temperature.
      B. they do not need a constant supply of energy.
      C. their main foods are available in large quantities for short
         times.
      D. their food is always difficult to find.
      (C, p. 294, factual)

108.  Small birds generally eat:

      A. as much as they can at one time.
      B. only what they need at the moment.
      C. three discrete meals per day.
      D. mostly during the night.
      (B, p. 294, factual)

**How the Digestive System Influences Food Selection**

109.  What is the first point in the digestive system where enzymes
      begin to break down food?

      A. mouth
      B. esophagus
      C. stomach
      D. small intestine
      ("WWW" A, p. 295, factual)

110.  The esophagus brings food from the:

      A. mouth to the stomach.
      B. stomach to the sphincter.
      C. sphincter to the intestines.
      D. stomach to the intestines.
      (A, p. 295, factual)

111.  What anatomical structure stores and digests food:

      A. the sphincter
      B. the stomach
      C. the large intestine
      D. the esophagus
      (B, p. 295, factual)

112.  What is the main site for absorption of digested food into the
      bloodstream?

      A. esophagus
      B. stomach
      C. small intestine
      D. large intestine
      (C, p. 295, factual)

113.  When needed, fat reserves can be converted into:

      A. proteins.
      B. glucose.
      C. cholesterol.
      D. insulin.
      (B, p. 295, factual)

114.  The large intestine:

      A. absorbs water and minerals.
      B. digests proteins, fats, and carbohydrates.
      C. is the main site for the absorption of digested foodstuffs
         into the bloodstream.
      D. stores excess nutrients as glycogen, protein, or fat.
      (A, p. 295, factual)

115. Most young mammals stop nursing, at least partly, due to the loss of what ability?

    A. metabolizing the sugar in milk
    B. sucking sufficiently
    C. the Babinski reflex
    D. digesting the fat in milk
    (A, p. 295, factual)

116. After a certain age, most mammals lose their ability to metabolize lactose because:

    A. levels of the enzyme lactase decline.
    B. it competes with other nutrients in other food types.
    C. eating meat is not compatible with drinking milk.
    D. they no longer need the nutrients found in milk.
    (A, p. 295, factual)

117. What do many human adults consume in their diets that differs significantly from most other adult mammals?

    A. milk
    B. proteins
    C. raw foods
    D. carbohydrates
    ("WWW" A, p. 295, conceptual)

118. What best explains the absence of the use of dairy products in many Asian cuisines?

    A. cultural bias
    B. digestive limitations
    C. religious taboos
    D. the geographic region's incapability of supporting dairy
       animals
    (B, p. 295, conceptual)

119. What is the name for an animal that eats both meat and plants?

    A. herbivore
    B. carnivore
    C. omnivore
    D. glutton
    (C, p. 295, factual)

120. What is the name for an animal that eats only meat?

    A. herbivore
    B. carnivore
    C. omnivore
    D. glutton
    (B, p. 295, factual)

121.  What is the name for an animal that eats only plants?

A. herbivore
B. carnivore
C. omnivore
D. glutton
(A, p. 295, factual)

122.  What is the most likely reason that many people consider eating
insects "disgusting"?

A. their bad taste
B. a conditioned taste aversion
C. a culturally learned preference
D. an innate aversion
(C, pp. 295-296, conceptual)

123.  A shipwrecked sailor lands on a deserted island that has no
familiar foods.  During the first few days he would be most
likely to choose what kind of foods?

A. salty
B. sweet
C. bitter
D. sour
(B, p. 296, factual)

124.  Innate preferences are to _____ as innate dislikes are to _____.

A. sweet; bitter
B. sour; salty
C. salty; sweet
D. sweet; sour
(A, p. 296, factual)

125.  If an animal eats a new food and shortly thereafter becomes ill,
it will probably avoid the food subsequently because the:

A. aftereffects of the illness will block the salivary glands.
B. stomach will be unable to digest the food.
C. animal will understand the relationship between the food and
   the illness.
D. food will no longer taste good to the animal.
(D, p. 296, factual)

126. An animal that eats an unfamiliar food and then becomes ill
     develops a conditioned taste aversion.  One feature of this type
     of learning that sets it apart from many other examples of
     learning is that:

     A. the conditioning occurs even if the illness comes hours after
        the food.
     B. the conditioning requires many repetitions of food with
        illness.
     C. the conditioning occurs only if the animal understands the
        relationship between food and illness.
     D. Only carnivores are capable of this type of learning.
     (A, p. 296, factual)

**How Taste and Digestion Control Hunger and Satiety**

127. When college students consumed lunch five days a week by pumping
     it into their stomachs:

     A. they pumped too much and steadily gained weight.
     B. they failed to pump enough and steadily lost weight.
     C. they did not gain or lose weight but reported feeling
        unsatisfied.
     D. the amount they pumped varied significantly from day to day.
     (C, p. 296, factual)

128. In sham-feeding, animals are:

     A. allowed to chew but not swallow.
     B. allowed to chew and swallow, but the food never enters the
        stomach.
     C. only allowed to eat a mixture devoid of nutrients.
     D. only allowed to eat an artificial substance.
     (B, p. 296, factual)

129. How do the eating behaviors of the animal change in sham-feeding
     experiments?

     A. They eat much less than usual.
     B. They eat more protein and less fat.
     C. They eat far more than they normally eat.
     D. They eat less protein and more fat.
     (C, p. 296, factual)

130. Why do the eating behaviors of animals change in sham-feeding
     experiments?

     A. the animals are denied nutrition
     B. the animals get nutrition without tasting the food
     C. the animals get carbohydrates without vitamins
     D. the animals are not allowed to chew the food
     (A, p. 296, factual)

131.  Which of the following is probably the most important mechanism for ending a meal?

    A. the number of calories consumed
    B. levels of the hormone angiotensin II circulating in the blood
    C. oral monitoring of how much food has been swallowed
    D. sensations from the stomach
    (D, p. 296, conceptual)

132.  By what means does the brain find out about the degree of stretch of the stomach?

    A. from visual feedback
    B. from the hormone angiotensin
    C. from sensory receptors on the skin of the abdomen
    D. from activity of the vagus nerve
    (D, p. 297, factual)

133.  By what means does the brain find out about the nutrient contents of the stomach?

    A. from hormones
    B. from activity of the vagus nerve
    C. from activity of the splanchnic nerves
    D. from the duodenum
    (C, p. 297, factual)

134.  The nutrient content of food in the stomach is monitored and is conveyed from the stomach to the brain via which nerves?

    A. splanchnic
    B. vagus
    C. sciatic
    D. thoracic
    ("WWW" A, p. 297, factual)

135.  The vagus nerve is to _____ as the splanchnic nerves are to _____.

    A. stomach fullness; nutrient contents of the stomach
    B. the taste of food; the texture of food
    C. nutrient contents of the stomach; water contents of the stomach
    D. oral factors (such as chewing and taste); stomach fullness
    (A, p. 297, factual)

136.  Under normal circumstances, the _____ nerve is more important for satiety.

    A. sciatic
    B. vagus
    C. splanchnic
    D. angiotensin
    (B, p. 297, factual)

137.  The first digestive site that absorbs a significant amount of
      nutrients is the:

      A. mouth
      B. stomach
      C. duodenum
      D. vagus
      (C, p. 297, factual)

138.  If the duodenum is partly distended and the stomach in not full,
      rats will:

      A. continue to eat.
      B. eat larger meals.
      C. stop eating.
      D. drink more.
      (C, p. 297, factual)

139.  When food is infused directly to the duodenum of human
      volunteers, they report feelings of:

      A. hunger.
      B. discomfort.
      C. satiety.
      D. thirst.
      (C, p. 297, factual)

140.  When food is infused directly to the duodenum of rats, there is a
      decrease in responsiveness by certain neurons to:

      A. bitter tastes
      B. sweet tastes
      C. CCK
      D. insulin
      (B, p. 297, factual)

141.  When food distends the duodenum, the duodenum releases which
      hormone?

      A. CCK
      B. aldosterone
      C. angiotensin II
      D. prolactin
      (A, p. 297, factual)

142.  One way by which food in the duodenum inhibits appetite is by:

      A. inhibiting the release of CCK.
      B. releasing CCK.
      C. breaking down CCK into inactive components.
      D. releasing glucagon.
      (B, p. 297, factual)

143.   Injections of CCK will:

   A. delay a meal.
   B. decrease the size of a meal.
   C. increase the size of a meal.
   D. decrease the delay before the next meal.
   (B, p. 297, factual)

144.   What is the effect of an injection of CCK?

   A. It increases sodium preferences.
   B. It leads to a preference for fatty foods.
   C. It decreases the size of the next meal.
   D. It causes increased storage of food as fats.
   (C, p. 297, factual)

145.   What is one interpretation of how the hormone CCK promotes
       satiety?

   A. It speeds up the digestive processes in the intestines.
   B. It increases the rate at which glucose enters the cells of the
      body.
   C. It causes the stomach to fill more quickly.
   D. It facilitates the emptying of the stomach.
   (C, p. 297, conceptual)

146.   A neuromodulator in the brain related to appetite is:

   A. substance P.
   B. melatonin.
   C. glucose.
   D. CCK.
   (D, p. 297, factual)

147.   The blood's glucose level ordinarily remains relatively constant
       because of the activity of:

   A. CCK.
   B. the liver.
   C. the thyroid gland.
   D. the gall bladder.
   ("WWW" B, p. 297, factual)

148.   Why does the level of glucose in the blood vary so little under
       normal circumstances?

   A. Manufacturing glucose is a lengthy process, so the body uses
      it slowly.
   B. Glucose does not leave the blood to enter the cells of the
      body.
   C. Mammals learn to eat only foods that contain glucose.
   D. The liver can convert stored nutrients into glucose.
   (D, p. 297, factual)

149.    Which hormone controls the rate at which glucose leaves the blood
        and enters the cells?

        A. CCK
        B. aldosterone
        C. glucagon
        D. insulin
        (D, pp. 297-298, factual)

150.    Glucagon stimulates the liver to:

        A. convert glucose to glycogen.
        B. store glucose.
        C. convert glycogen to glucose.
        D. decrease blood glucose levels.
        (C, p. 298, factual)

151.    What happens when insulin levels are high?

        A. Fat supplies are converted to glucose, which enters the blood.
        B. Fat supplies are depleted.
        C. Glucose entry into the cells increases.
        D. The sphincter muscle between the stomach and the duodenum
           opens.
        (C, p. 298, conceptual)

152.    What happens when insulin levels are high upon completing a meal?

        A. Fat supplies are converted to glucose which enters the blood.
        B. Glucose entry into the cells decreases.
        C. Blood glucose levels increase.
        D. The individual feels hungry again soon after the meal.
        (D, p. 298, factual)

153.    How does a chronically high insulin level lead to increased
        appetite?

        A. It lowers body temperature, increasing the need for nutrition.
        B. It prevents glucose from entering the cells.
        C. It causes a high percentage of available glucose to be stored
           as fat.
        D. It directly alters the responses of the taste buds.
        (C, p. 298, conceptual)

154.    What insulin levels would we expect to find when an animal is
        putting on extra fat in preparation for migration or hibernation?

        A. very low, as in diabetes
        B. intermediate
        C. high
        D. unstable and rapidly fluctuating
        (C, p. 298, factual)

155. What happens when blood levels of insulin are extremely low?

    A. Glucose leaves the blood to be stored as fat.
    B. Appetite is low.
    C. There is excess glucose in the blood, but it cannot enter the
       cells.
    D. The brain shifts to proteins as its main source of fuel.
    (C, p. 298, factual)

156. What happens when blood insulin levels are extremely low?

    A. Appetite is low.
    B. Appetite is unaffected.
    C. Individuals feel satiated at the beginning of the meal.
    D. Individuals will eat more than normal.
    (D, p. 298, factual)

157. What is the hormone imbalance associated with diabetes?

    A. too little insulin
    B. too much insulin
    C. too little glucagon
    D. too much glucagon
    (A, p. 298, factual)

158. Why do both high levels and very low levels of insulin lead to
    increased eating?

    A. Glucose leaves the blood to be stored as fat.
    B. Fat supplies are being rapidly converted to glucose.
    C. Little glucose is reaching the cells to be used as fuel.
    D. Activity of the taste buds is directly enhanced.
    (C, p. 298, conceptual)

159. Variations in insulin level alter hunger by changing the:

    A. rate of emptying by the stomach.
    B. availability of glucose to the cells.
    C. sensitivity of the taste buds.
    D. ability of CCK to cross the blood-brain barrier.
    (B, p. 298, conceptual)

160. Which hormonal levels fluctuate when people are eating, or
    getting ready to eat?

    A. insulin levels fall
    B. insulin levels rise
    C. CCK levels rise
    D. CCK levels fall
    (B, p. 298, factual)

161.    Some obese people produce:

        A. more insulin than people of normal weight.
        B. too little insulin at the beginning of a meal.
        C. too little insulin during a meal.
        D. too little insulin after a meal.
        (A, p. 298, factual)

162.    The appetite of an obese person returns soon after a meal because
        (in many cases):

        A. their levels of insulin are too low.
        B. high levels of insulin result in a increase of fat storage.
        C. their metabolic rate is unusually high.
        D. their satiety set points are too low.
        (B, p. 298, factual)

163.    When obese people eat, what happens to their release of insulin?

        A. They release no insulin.
        B. They release some insulin, but less than people of normal
           weight.
        C. They release more insulin than people of normal weight.
        D. They release a normal amount of insulin, but do not respond to
           it.
        (C, p. 298, factual)

164.    Which of the following is NOT a plausible explanation for why
        certain people become obese?

        A. Their stomachs empty faster than normal.
        B. They produce less than normal amounts of the hormone CCK.
        C. For genetic reasons they maintain low levels of basal
           metabolism.
        D. They produce low levels of insulin in response to eating.
        (D, p. 298, conceptual)

**The Hypothalamus and Feeding Regulation**

165.    An animal refuses food and loses weight after damage to which
        structure?

        A. the preoptic area
        B. the ventromedial hypothalamus
        C. the lateral hypothalamus
        D. the baroreceptors
        (C, p. 299, factual)

166. What behavioral change is seen in animals after damage to the lateral hypothalamus?

    A. They show normal osmotic thirst but not hypovolemic thirst.
    B. They show normal hypovolemic thirst but not osmotic thirst.
    C. They eat less.
    D. They eat more.
    (C, p. 299, factual)

167. What can be done to prevent an animal from starving to death after damage to the lateral hypothalamus?

    A. Force-feed it until it recovers some of its ability to eat.
    B. Give it injections to decrease insulin secretions.
    C. Provide food extremely high in carbohydrates.
    D. Provide food extremely high in fat.
    (A, p. 299, factual)

168. Stimulation of a rat's lateral hypothalamus results in:

    A. an increase in food seeking behaviors.
    B. a decrease in food seeking behaviors.
    C. a decrease in chewing and other reflexes associated with eating.
    D. damage to dopamine-containing axons passing through it.
    ("WWW" A, p. 299, factual)

169. If you damage a rat's dopamine-containing axons passing through the lateral hypothalamus, the rat will:

    A. not chew when food is placed in its mouth.
    B. increase its food seeking behaviors.
    C. become chronically inactive.
    D. increase its activity.
    (C, p. 299, factual)

170. If you damage a rat's dopamine-containing axons passing through the lateral hypothalamus, the rat will:

    A. never again eat large amounts of food.
    B. not chew when food is placed in its mouth.
    C. eat normally once it has food in its mouth.
    D. starve to death, no matter what the researcher does.
    (C, p. 299, factual)

171.  Feeding behavior is to _____ as overall arousal is to _____.

    A. cell bodies of the ventromedial hypothalamus; cell bodies of
       the lateral hypothalamus
    B. cell bodies of the lateral hypothalamus; axons passing through
       the lateral hypothalamus
    C. cell bodies of the ventromedial hypothalamus; axons passing
       through the ventromedial hypothalamus
    D. axons passing through the lateral hypothalamus; axons passing
       through the ventromedial hypothalamus
    (B, p. 300, conceptual)

172.  In the lateral hypothalamus, cell bodies are to _____ as axons
passing through are to _____.

    A. feeding; overall arousal
    B. feeding; drinking
    C. overall arousal; feeding
    D. drinking; feeding
    (A, pp. 300, conceptual)

173.  Axons from the lateral hypothalamus extend to the:

    A. mouth.
    B. stomach.
    C. liver.
    D. nucleus of the tractus solitarius (NTS).
    (D, p. 300, factual)

174.  Axons from the lateral hypothalamus extend to the:

    A. mouth
    B. stomach.
    C. liver.
    D. spinal cord.
    (D, p. 300, factual)

175.  An animal has trouble digesting its food after damage to the:

    A. occipital cortex.
    B. lateral hypothalamus.
    C. medial part of the hypothalamus.
    D. pineal gland.
    (B, p. 300, factual)

176.  What is one reason why animals with a lesion in the lateral
      hypothalamus eat so little?

      A. They are constantly active and over-responsive to sensory
         stimuli.
      B. All the food they eat is immediately converted into fat
         storage.
      C. They experience a decreased cortical response to the smell and
         sight of food.
      D. They have low levels of blood sugar.
      (C, p. 300, factual)

177.  What is one reason why animals with a lesion in the lateral
      hypothalamus eat so little?

      A. They are too busy in other activities.
      B. They produce low levels of the hormone CCK.
      C. They are over-responsive to sensory stimuli.
      D. They do not produce sufficient digestive juices.
      (D, p. 300, factual)

178.  An animal is likely to eat great amounts and gain weight after
      damage to which structure?

      A. the preoptic area
      B. the areas surrounding the third ventricle
      C. the ventromedial hypothalamus
      D. the lateral hypothalamus
      (C, pp. 300-301, factual)

179.  What behavioral change is seen in animals after damage in and
      around the ventromedial hypothalamus?

      A. They overeat and gain weight.
      B. They refuse food and lose weight.
      C. They produce low levels of the hormone CCK.
      D. They do not produce sufficient digestive juices.
      (A, pp. 301, factual)

180.  Damage to the ventromedial hypothalamus leads to what changes in
      eating behaviors?

      A. Animals eat the same, but drink less than normal amounts.
      B. Animals eat the same large amount each meal, regardless of the
         taste.
      C. Animals are less finicky about what they eat than are normal
         animals.
      D. Animals eat normal size meals, but eat them very frequently.
      (D, p. 302, factual)

181.  Damage to the ventromedial hypothalamus leads to what changes in
      eating behaviors?

      A. Animals eat the same; there are no changes.
      B. Animals will eat less.
      C. Animals will overeat when presented with a normal or sweetened
         diet.
      D. Animals become less finicky about what they eat.
      (C, p. 302, factual)

182.  Damage to the ventromedial hypothalamus leads to what changes in
      eating behaviors?

      A. Animals show an overall increase in hunger.
      B. Animals eat much more at any given meal.
      C. Animals overeat when presented with a sweetened diet.
      D. Animals only undereat when presented with a very sweet food.
      (C, p. 302, factual)

183.  What are two reasons why animals with ventromedial hypothalamic
      damage overeat?

      A. rapid stomach emptying and high insulin levels
      B. high CCK levels and under-responsiveness to tastes
      C. decreased thirst and lack of facial muscle fatigue
      D. decreased body temperature and increased levels of digestive
         juices
      (A, p. 302, factual)

184.  What is one reason why animals with damage in or near the
      ventromedial hypothalamus overeat?

      A. They have low levels of insulin.
      B. Their stomach emptying rate is slow compared to other animals.
      C. They have excessively high levels of the hormone CCK.
      D. They store too much of each meal as fat.
      (D, p. 302, factual)

185.  Animals with damage in or near the ventromedial hypothalamus gain
      weight:

      A. even if they eat the same amount as a normal animal.
      B. only if they have access to food that tastes unusually good.
      C. only if they have access to unlimited water supplies.
      D. only if they eat a small number of very large meals per day.
      (A, p. 302, factual)

186.  In what way is a rat with damage to the ventromedial hypothalamus
      similar to a starving animal?

      A. Both will eat a large amount of whatever food is available,
         regardless of its taste.
      B. Both empty food out of their stomachs at a rate that is slower
         than normal.
      C. Both have low levels of fuel available to its cells.
      D. Both go through long periods of refusing to eat.
      (C, p. 302, conceptual)

187.  How do rats with damage to the paraventricular nucleus (PVN) eat
      compared to rats with damage in and around the ventromedial
      hypothalamus?

      A. They eat larger meals.
      B. They eat more frequent meals.
      D. They eat more if the food tastes good and less if it tastes
         bad.
      D. They eat smaller meals.
      (A, p. 302, factual)

188.  Which area of the hypothalamus seems to be critical for the
      ending of meals?

      A. the lateral hypothalamus
      B. the ventromedial hypothalamus
      C. the preoptic area
      D. the paraventricular nucleus
      ·  (D, p. 302, conceptual)

189.  An increase in the size of meals is most likely to occur
      following damage to which area of the hypothalamus?

      A. paraventricular
      B. lateral
      C. preoptic
      D. ventromedial
      (A, p. 302, conceptual)

**Satiety Chemicals and Eating Disorders**

190.  Researchers have found that many obese rats lack the protein
      leptin, and its injections lead to weight loss.  What leptin
      levels have researchers found in obese humans?

      A. the same as normal weight adults
      B. much higher than normal weight adults
      C. much lower than normal weight adults
      D. leptin levels are absent in all humans
      (B, p. 303, factual)

191.  Leptin directly activates receptors in the part of the
      hypothalamus known as the:

      A. paraventricular nucleus.
      B. ventromedial hypothalamus.
      C. arcuate nucleus.
      D. lateral preoptic area.
      (C, p. 303, factual)

192.  What is the result of inhibition of the paraventricular nucleus
      (PVN) by the transmitter neuropeptide Y?

      A. increased meal size
      B. decreased meal size
      C. finicky food selection
      D. cessation of drinking during meals
      (A, p. 303, factual)

193.  Leptin is produced by:

      A. the paraventricular nucleus.
      B. body fat.
      C. neuropeptide Y.
      D. orexin A.
      (B, p. 303, factual)

194.  When neuropeptide Y inhibits the paraventricular nucleus, it:

      A. leads to extreme undereating.
      B. produces extreme overeating.
      C. depletes fat stores.
      D. interferes with digestion.
      (B, p. 303-304, factual)

195.  What is the purpose of microdialysis?

      A. to extract small amounts of chemicals from the brain
      B. to stain active brain tissue in a living organism
      C. to implant computer chips into the brains of living animals
      D. to treat rats and other small animals with kidney failure
      (A, p. 304, factual)

196.  The peptide bombesin occurs in:

      A. amphibians and mammals.
      B. only mammals.
      C. only amphibians.
      D. all species.
      (C, p. 304, factual)

197.  A neuromodular in the brain, GLP-1, acts to:

      A. increase eating.
      B. decrease eating.
      C. increase stomach distension.
      D. decrease stomach distension.
      (B, p. 304, factual)

198.  Research has found that mice become obese during middle age if
      they have a mutation of:

      A. a specific serotonin receptor.
      B. dopamine receptors.
      C. norepinephrine receptors.
      D. GLP-1 receptors.
      (A, p. 304, factual)

199.  Most of the diet drugs developed to date act by:

      A. inhibiting dopamine receptors.
      B. stimulating dopamine receptors.
      C. stimulating specific serotonin receptors.
      D. inhibiting norepinephrine receptors.
      (C, p. 305, factual)

**Genetics, Metabolic Rate, and Body Weight**

200.  A Danish study correlating the weights of 540 adopted children
      with various adoptive and biological relatives found:

      A. a higher correlation with biological relatives than adoptive
         relatives.
      B. a higher correlation with adoptive siblings than with
         biological siblings.
      C. the same correlation with biological relatives and adoptive
         relatives.
      D. a higher correlation with biological relatives during
         childhood but a higher correlation with adoptive relatives in
         adulthood.
      (A, p. 305, factual)

201.  If two people eat the same amount of food, the person with the
      lower metabolism will:

      A. release less CCK.
      B. release more CCK.
      C. gain less weight.
      D. gain more weight.
      (D, p. 305, factual)

202.    Lower metabolic rate is to _____ as higher metabolic rate is to
        _____ .

        A. lower weights; higher weights
        B. radiating little heat; radiating lots of heat
        C. lower body temperature; higher body temperature
        D. releasing less CCK; releasing more CCK
        (B, p. 305, conceptual)

203.    Research suggests that genes:

        A. control how fat an individual gets.
        B. have very little influence over how fat an individual gets.
        C. determine how fat one will get, in conjunction with one's
           environment.
        D. do not exert control over one's metabolism.
        (C, p. 306, factual)

204.    Sibutramine affects weight gain by:

        A. stimulating dopamine release.
        B. inhibiting dopamine release.
        C. blocking reuptake of serotonin and norepinephrine.
        D. inhibiting serotonin and norepinephrine.
        (C, p. 306, factual)

205.    Anorexia nervosa is to _____ as bulimia nervosa is to _____ .

        A. disinterest in food; over-interest in food
        B. under-eating; variably over-eating and under-eating
        C. eating; exercising
        D. depression; mania
        (B, p. 306, conceptual)

206.    The majority of people with _____ are _____ :

        A. bulimia; men.
        B. anorexia; men.
        C. anorexia; women.
        D. bulimia; middle-aged women.
        (C, p. 306, factual)

207.    What disorder is common among the relatives of people with
        anorexia?

        A. obsessive-compulsive disorder.
        B. bulimia.
        C. depression.
        D. obesity.
        (A, p. 306, factual)

208.  Many anorexics' cortisol levels:

    A. are very low.
    B. are elevated.
    C. fluctuate drastically.
    D. are very high before the disease but low while suffering from
       anorexia.
    (B, p. 306, factual)

209.  Abnormal levels of which neurotransmitter often have been found
      in bulimics?

    A. higher-than-normal levels of peptide YY
    B. higher-than-normal levels of CCK
    C. higher-than-normal levels of serotonin
    D. lower-than-normal levels of peptide YY
    ("WWW" A, p. 307, factual)

210.  Abnormal levels of which neurotransmitter often have been found
      in bulimics?

    A. lower-than-normal levels of peptide YY
    B. lower-than-normal levels of CCK
    C. higher-than-normal levels of serotonin
    D. increased receptor sensitivity for serotonin
    (B, p. 307, factual)

211.  A recent study gave a tryptophan-deficient diet to women who had
      recovered from bulimia.  The diet was associated with:

    A. anorexic symptoms for most of the women.
    B. bulimic symptoms for most of the women.
    C. mild depression.
    D. an increase in serotonin production.
    (C, p. 307, factual)

**Module 11.1 The Effects of Sex Hormones**

1.    "Male hormones" are referred to as:

      A. activating hormones.
      B. SRY.
      C. androgens.
      D. estrogens.
      (C, p. 312, factual)

2.    "Female hormones" are referred to as:

      A. activating hormones.
      B. SRY.
      C. androgens.
      D. estrogens.
      (D, p. 312, factual)

3.    Which hormones are likely to be found more abundantly in males
      than in females?

      A. peptide hormones
      B. androgens
      C. progesterones
      D. estrogens
      (B, p. 312, factual)

4.    Which is true of androgens and estrogens?

      A. Only males have androgens; only females have estrogens.
      B. Only males have estrogens; only females have androgens.
      C. Males and females have androgens and estrogens in similar
         amounts.
      D. Males and females both have androgens and estrogens, but in
         different proportions.
      ("WWW" D, p. 312, conceptual)

**Organizing Effects of Sex Hormones**

5.    When do the organizing effects of sex hormones occur in humans?

      A. well before birth
      B. shortly before and after birth
      C. during childhood
      D. during adolescence
      (A, p. 312, factual)

6.    When do the organizing effects of sex hormones occur in rats?

      A. well before birth
      B. shortly before and after birth
      C. during their juvenile period
      D. at approximately two months of age
      (B, p. 312, factual)

7.    In general, when do hormones produce "organizing effects"?

      A. whenever the levels of some other hormone have decreased
      B. during early stages in development
      C. during infancy
      D. temporarily at any time in life
      (B, p. 312, conceptual)

8.    An organizing effect differs from an activating effect of a
      hormone in that an organizing effect:

      A. inhibits the effects of another hormone.
      B. lasts only briefly.
      C. more directly affects behaviors rather than structures.
      D. more directly affects structures rather than behaviors.
      (D, p. 312, conceptual)

9.    An organizing effect differs from an activating effect of a
      hormone in that an organizing effect:

      A. magnifies the effects of other hormones.
      B. is more long lasting.
      C. takes place only in the brain, not in the body.
      D. takes place only in the body, not in the brain.
      (B, p. 312, conceptual)

10.   What is one important difference between organizing and
      activating effects of hormones?

      A. Organizing effects take place mostly during an early sensitive
         period.
      B. Activating effects are more permanent.
      C. Organizing effects take place only in the gonads.
      D. Activating effects take place only in the brain.
      ("WWW" A, p. 312, ·factual)

11.   What is one important difference between organizing effects and
      activating effects of hormones?  Activating effects

      A. are shorter-term.
      B. take place mostly during an early sensitive period.
      C. cause the pituitary gland to release another hormone.
      D. control only the peripheral nervous system.
      (A, p. 312, factual)

12.   In comparison to activating effects, organizing effects of
      hormones take place:

      A. later in life and produce more long-lasting effects.
      B. later in life and produce more temporary effects.
      C. earlier in life and produce more long-lasting effects.
      D. earlier in life and produce more temporary effects.
      (C, p. 312, conceptual)

13.  What are the temporary effects of hormones, which result in a
     particular response?

     A. activating effects
     B. organizing effects
     C. aromatization effects
     D. disinhibition effects
     (A, p. 312, conceptual)

14.  Which of the following depends on an organizing effect of
     hormones?

     A. whether an organism develops as male or female
     B. the degree of sexual activity at any time
     C. the timing of migration or hibernation
     D. current metabolic rate
     (A, p. 312, factual)

15.  A female mammal is represented chromosomally by the pattern:

     A. XX.
     B. XY.
     C. YY.
     D. XYY.
     (A, p. 312, factual)

16.  A male mammal is represented chromosomally by the pattern:

     A. XO.
     B. XX.
     C. XY.
     D. YY.
     (C, p. 312, factual)

17.  Mullerian ducts are specific to:

     A. genetic female fetuses only.
     B. genetic male fetuses only.
     C. female and male fetuses early in development.
     D. female and male fetuses until shortly before birth.
     (C, p. 312, factual)

18.  Wolffian ducts are specific to:

     A. genetic female fetuses only.
     B. genetic male fetuses only.
     C. female and male fetuses early in development.
     D. female and male fetuses until shortly before birth.
     (C, p. 312, factual)

19.    What causes the primitive gonads to develop into masculine
       structures?

       A. the X chromosome
       B. the sex region Y (SRY) gene
       C. the sexually dimorphic nucleus
       D. Mullerian inhibiting hormone
       (B, p. 312, factual)

20.    What develops from the Wolffian ducts?

       A. the bladder and urethra
       B. peripheral nerves controlling the genitals
       C. female reproductive structures
       D. male reproductive structures
       (D, p. 312, conceptual)

21.    In mammals, whether the anatomy develops in the male or female
       pattern depends:

       A. mostly upon the presence of estradiol.
       B. mostly upon the presence of testosterone.
       C. on the presence of estradiol and testosterone equally.
       D. on neither estradiol nor testosterone.
       ("WWW" B, p. 312, factual)

22.    The Wolffian ducts are precursors to:

       A. ovaries.
       B. the sexually dimorphic nucleus.
       C. male reproductive structures.
       D. male and female reproductive structures.
       (C, p. 312, factual)

23.    A duct which leads from the testes into the penis is called the:

       A. MIH.
       B. vas deferens.
       C. seminal vesicle.
       D. SRY.
       (B, p. 312, factual)

24.    What would cause a genetic female mammal to develop an anatomical
       appearance resembling a male's?

       A. a lack of estradiol
       B. moderate levels of estradiol during an early stage of
          development
       C. a high level of testosterone during an early stage of
          development
       D. a high level of testosterone during the late part of puberty
       (C, p. 312, factual)

25.    What develops from the Mullerian ducts?

       A. the bladder and urethra
       B. peripheral nerves controlling the genitals
       C. female reproductive structures
       D. male reproductive structures
       (C, p. 312, conceptual)

26.    Why is it impossible for an individual to develop a complete,
       normal set of external female genitalia AND a complete, normal
       set of external male genitalia?

       A. An individual has either estradiol or testosterone, but not
          both.
       B. Both types of external genitalia develop from the same fetal
          structure.
       C. Development of the external genitalia is not influenced by
          early hormonal levels.
       D. The female genitals reach maturity earlier than the male
          genitals.
       (B, p. 312, conceptual)

27.    How does the development of external genitalia differ from the
       development of the internal reproductive structures?

       A. Reproductive structures are influenced by hormone levels;
          genitals are not.
       B. Reproductive structures for males and females develop from a
          single unisex structure; genitals develop from separate
          Wolffian and Mullerian structures.
       C. Genitals for males and females develop from a single unisex
          structure; reproductive structures develop from separate
          Wolffian and Mullerian structures.
       D. Genital development is controlled by estrogen; the
          reproductive structures are controlled by androgen.
       (C, p. 312, conceptual)

28.    Genitals for males and females develop from _____; reproductive
       structures develop from _____.

       A. a single unisex structure; separate structures
       B. separate structures; a single unisex structure
       C. a single unisex structure; a single unisex structure
       D. separate structures; separate structures
       (A, p. 312, conceptual)

29.    The sexually dimorphic nucleus is part of the:

       A. thalamus.
       B. lateral hypothalamus.
       C. medial preoptic hypothalamus.
       D. male brain, only.
       (C, p. 312, factual)

30.     The sexually dimorphic nucleus is:

        A. larger in males.
        B. smaller in males.
        C. equal in size in both males and females.
        D. smaller in females until adolescence; then the female's
           becomes larger.
        (A, p. 312, factual)

31.     How is the sexually dimorphic nucleus related to sex differences?

        A. It is larger in males than in females.
        B. It is larger in females than in males.
        C. It is present in males, absent in females.
        D. It is present in females, absent in males.
        ("WWW" A, p. 312, factual)

32.     Parts of the hypothalamus can generate a cyclic pattern of
        hormone release in:

        A. females only.
        B. males only.
        C. females and males.
        D. females during childhood and males during adolescence.
        (A, p. 312, factual)

33.     If you expose a female to testosterone early in life, it will
        cause her hypothalamus to:

        A. decrease in size.
        B. develop a cyclic pattern of hormone release.
        C. develop more like a typical male hypothalamus.
        D. become inactive.
        (C, 312, factual)

34.     What anatomical difference, other than sex organs, is reliably
        seen between males and females, even at an early age?

        A. differences in the complexity of the cerebral cortex
        B. differences in the size of the pituitary
        C. differences in the organization of the brain stem
        D. differences in the size of parts of the hypothalamus
        (D, p. 312, factual)

35.     A sensitive period is:

        A. any time in an organism's life when it is sensitive to
           hormones released by the sexually dimorphic nucleus.
        B. an early period when a hormone has a long lasting effect.
        C. an early period when a hormone has an intense, but brief,
           effect.
        D. a period of time, usually once a month, when hormones are
           released.
        (B, p. 312, factual)

36.    The sensitive period for human genital formation is
       approximately:

       A. the first three weeks of gestation.
       B. the third and fourth months of gestation.
       C. the last trimester of gestation.
       D. shortly after birth.
       (B, p. 312, factual)

37.    If a female rat is injected with testosterone during the last few
       days before being born or the first few days afterward, the
       injection will:

       A. have no effect.
       B. partly masculinize her.
       C. behaviorally masculinize her, but will not affect her
          physically.
       D. physically masculine her, but her behavior is still like that
          of a typical female.
       (B, pp. 312-313, conceptual)

38.    If a female rat is injected with testosterone during the last few
       days before being born or the first few days afterward, the
       injection will:

       A. sterilize her without changing her behavior or appearance.
       B. cause her reproductive structures to look like those
          intermediate between female and male.
       C. affect her behaviorally, but not structurally.
       D. affect her structurally, but not behaviorally.
       (B, p. 313, factual)

39.    If a female rat is injected with testosterone during the last few
       days before being born or the first few days afterward, at
       maturity her:

       A. pituitary and ovaries will not produce their hormones.
       B. ovaries will no longer produce hormones, although her
          pituitary will.
       C. pituitary and ovaries will produce steady levels of hormones
          instead of cyclic levels of hormones.
       D. pituitary and ovaries will produce cyclic levels of hormones
          instead of steady levels.
       (C, p. 313, factual)

40.    If a female rat is injected with testosterone during the last few
       days before being born or the first few days afterward, at
       maturity:

       A. her brain, but not her behavior, will be masculinized.
       B. her behavior, but not her brain, will be masculinized.
       C. certain parts of her hypothalamus would appear anatomically
          more male than female.
       D. she will eat excessively and become obese.
       (C, p. 313, factual)

41.   What would cause a young mammal to develop an appearance
      intermediate between a male and a female?

      A. A genetic female develops without normal levels of estrogen.
      B. A genetic male develops with high levels of both testosterone
         and estrogen.
      C. A genetic female develops with more testosterone than other
         females.
      D. A genetic male is totally insensitive to the effects of
         testosterone.
      (C, p. 313, conceptual)

42.   A female rat injected with testosterone during the first 10 days
      after birth will be at least partly masculinized.  What areas
      will be affected?

      A. internal, but not external, genitals
      B. behavior, but not physical appearance
      C. hypothalamus, but not behavior
      D. genitals, behavior, and hypothalamus
      (D, p. 313, factual)

43.   What would cause a male mammal to develop an anatomy that looks
      like a female's?

      A. a deficit of testosterone during puberty
      B. a deficit of testosterone during an early stage of development
      C. exposure to a high level of estradiol during puberty
      D. exposure to a high level of estradiol during an early stage of
      development
      (B, p. 313, factual)

44.   If a mammal is exposed to fairly high levels of testosterone
      during an early stage of development, what type of anatomy will
      it develop?

      A. male
      B. female
      C. male on one side, female on the other
      D. either male or female, depending on the chromosomes
      (A, p. 313, conceptual)

45.   What would cause a mammal to develop the anatomy of a male,
      regardless of its chromosomes?

      A. exposure to high levels of testosterone during an early stage
         of development
      B. deprivation of estradiol during an early stage of development
      C. exposure to neither testosterone nor estradiol during an early
         stage of development
      D. an infusion of testosterone at puberty
      (A, p. 313, conceptual)

46.    A mammal will develop a female anatomy if, during an early stage
       of development, it is exposed to:

       A. high levels of testosterone.
       B. high levels of estradiol.
       C. little or no testosterone.
       D. little or no estradiol.
       (C, p. 313, conceptual)

47.    Nature's "default setting" is to make every mammal:

       A. male.
       B. female.
       C. intermediate between male and female.
       D. fully both male and female.
       (B, p. 313, factual)

48.    If you inject a male with estrogen, it will:

       A. still develop into a male.
       B. still develop into a male, but will act very much like a
          female.
       C. develop into something intermediate between female and male.
       D. develop into a female.
       (A, p. 313, factual)

49.    According to rodent studies, testosterone exerts a major part of
       its effect on:

       A. alpha-fetoprotein.
       B. the sex region Y gene.
       C. the thalamus.
       D. the hypothalamus.
       ("WWW" D, p. 313, factual)

50.    After testosterone enters a neuron, it is:

       A. inactivated.
       B. converted to androgen.
       C. converted to progesterone.
       D. converted to estradiol.
       (D, p. 313, factual)

51.    What process changes testosterone into estradiol?

       A. aromatization
       B. transmutation
       C. methylation
       D. alchemy
       (A, p. 313, factual)

52.   What chemical is aromatized into what other chemical in the brain
      cells?

      A. steroids into peptides
      B. peptides into steroids
      C. testosterone into estrogen
      D. estradiol into testosterone
      (C, p. 313, factual)

53.   In the brain, testosterone is aromatized into:

      A. steroids.
      B. peptides.
      C. estradiol.
      D. dopamine.
      (C, p. 313, factual)

54.   Before testosterone can masculinize the development of the
      hypothalamus of an infant mammal, it must first be converted
      into:

      A. estradiol.
      B. epinephrine.
      C. ACTH.
      D. dopamine.
      (A, p. 313, factual)

55.   Drugs which prevent testosterone from being aromatized to
      estradiol will:

      A. increase the organizing effects of testosterone on sexual
         development of the brain.
      B. block the organizing effects of testosterone on sexual
         development of the brain.
      C. increase heart rate and blood pressure.
      D. decrease heart rate and blood pressure.
      (B, p. 313, factual)

56.   Aromatase has been found in abundance in the:

      A. early sensitive period in brain areas that become larger in
         males than in females.
      B. brain areas that become larger in females than in males.
      C. genital organs of females.
      D. blood and CSF of intersexes.
      (A, p. 313, factual)

57.   Why does the estradiol normally found in the bloodstream of a
      female rat fetus neither masculinize nor feminize its
      development?

      A. It is chemically converted to testosterone.
      B. It is bound to alpha-fetoprotein.
      C. It dissolves in the fat supplies of the fetus.
      D. It would have no effect on cells even if it did enter them.
      (B, p. 313, factual)

58.   The estradiol normally found in the bloodstream of a female rat
      fetus neither masculinizes nor feminizes its development because
      it:

      A. is chemically converted to testosterone.
      B. is prevented from entering the developing cells.
      C. is chemically unstable at the body temperature of a fetus.
      D. would have no effect on cells even if it did enter them.
      (B, p. 313, factual)

59.   If a female rat fetus developed without any alpha-fetoprotein,
      her hypothalamus and genitals would:

      A. fail to develop beyond their early, immature state.
      B. develop like those of a normal female.
      C. develop in an exaggerated female manner.
      D. develop in a partly masculinized manner.
      (D, p. 313, conceptual)

60.   One function served by alpha-fetoprotein in the developing rat
      fetus is to:

      A. prevent estradiol from entering cells.
      B. help estradiol to cross the blood-brain barrier.
      C. help testosterone to cross the blood-brain barrier.
      D. prevent either testosterone or estradiol from being
         converted into aromatase.
      (A, p. 313, factual)

61.   Which of the following would tend to masculinize the development
      of a genetically female rat fetus?

      A. high levels of alpha-fetoprotein in the blood
      B. lower than normal level of estradiol
      C. lower than normal level of testosterone
      D. much higher than normal level of estradiol
      (D, p. 313, conceptual)

62.    During an early sensitive period of mammalian development, why is
       it that normal amounts of estradiol have little effect on
       development, while large amounts masculinize it?

       A. Large amounts are chemically converted to testosterone.
       B. Large amounts suppress the production of other hormones such
          as ACTH.
       C. Normal amounts are metabolized or bound to a protein in the
          blood.
       D. Normal amounts dissolve in the body's fat supplies.
       (C, pp. 313-314, factual)

63.    Which of the following possible variations would have the LEAST
       effect on early development of sexual differentiation in mammals?

       A. the amount of testosterone in the blood
       B. the amount of estradiol in the blood
       C. the amount of alpha-fetoprotein in the blood
       D. the amount of aromatase in the brain
       (B, p. 314, factual)

64.    An injection of a large amount of estradiol during an early
       sensitive period will:

       A. not affect a female.
       B. masculinize a female.
       C. feminize a male.
       D. delay sexual maturation for either males or females.
       (B, p. 314, factual)

65.    Spotted hyenas are different than most other species in the
       animal kingdom in that:

       A. the female hyenas look and act more like typical males.
       B. the male hyenas look more like typical females.
       C. male hyenas are predominantly homosexual.
       D. neither male nor female hyenas have testosterone.
       (A, p. 314, factual)

66.    Why do female spotted hyenas develop genital organs that appear
       similar to those of male spotted hyenas?

       A. A genetic defect on the X chromosome of a female causes her
          genitals to grow.
       B. A female hyena's clitoris grows if she eats a diet high in
          androstenedione, a precursor for testosterone.
       C. A female hyena fetus is exposed to higher levels of
          testosterone compared to other species.
       D. Female hyenas lack an enzyme that is necessary for the
          aromatizing estradiol.
       (C, p. 314, factual)

67.    The nerves and muscles that control the mammalian penis:

    A. are equally prominent in the area near the female's clitoris.
    B. are initially present in females, but die due to low testosterone levels.
    C. degenerate in females due to the presence of alpha-fetoprotein.
    D. degenerate in both males and females as a result of sexual activity.
    (B, p. 314, factual)

68.    The nerves and muscles that control the mammalian penis receive their neural input from:

    A. the thalamus.
    B. the hypothalamus.
    C. the cerebellum.
    D. motor nuclei in the spinal cord.
    (D, p. 314, factual)

69.    The neural input to the nerves and muscles that controls the mammalian penis:

    A. is actually more prominent in females than in males.
    B. exists in females as it does in males.
    C. is also present in females but comes from a different part of the brain.
    D. is smaller or absent in females.
    (D, p. 314, factual)

70.    Neurons in the spinal cord supporting the nerves and muscles to the mammalian penis:

    A. die early in development if not supported by testosterone.
    B. die out around the time of adolescence if enough testosterone is not available.
    C. require estrogen to survive and develop.
    D. require either estrogen or testosterone to survive.
    (A, p. 314, factual)

71.    What is the most likely effect on adult female monkeys who are exposed to testosterone during the sensitive period in early development?

    A. failure to demonstrate any sexual behavior
    B. more aggressive
    C. behavior similar to any other adult female monkeys
    D. lower levels of rough-and-tumble play
    (B, p. 314, factual)

72.  When a group of girls was exposed to higher than normal
     androgen levels during prenatal development, the girls:

     A. tended to choose more typically masculine toys to play with.
     B. tended to be more aggressive.
     C. tended to be more verbal.
     D. developed lower than normal intelligence.
     (A, p. 315, factual)

73.  As compared to males, females tend to have:

     A. lesser density of neurons in part of the occipital lobe.
     B. lesser density of neurons in part of the temporal lobe.
     C. greater density of neurons in part of the temporal lobe.
     D. smaller corpus callosums in proportion to total brain size.
     (C, p. 315, factual)

74.  As compared to males, females tend to have:

     A. lesser density of neurons in part of the occipital lobe.
     B. lesser density of neurons in part of the temporal lobe.
     C. smaller corpus callosums in proportion to total brain size.
     D. larger corpus callosums in proportion to total brain size.
     (D, p. 315, factual)

**Activating Effects of Sex Hormones**

75.  What effect does an injection of testosterone have on a castrated
     male rat?

     A. It has no effect.
     B. It elicits typical female sexual behavior.
     C. It restores male sexual behavior.
     D. It diminishes male sexual behavior.
     (C, p. 315, factual)

76.  The most effective way to stimulate sexual behavior in a female
     rodent is to inject her with:

     A. prolactin followed by estradiol.
     B. progesterone following by parathyroid hormone.
     C. alpha feto-protein followed by cholecystokinin.
     D. estradiol followed by progesterone.
     (D, p. 315, factual)

77.  One way that estrogen increases sexual responsiveness is by:

     A. synchronizing activity between the hypothalamus of the left
        and right hemispheres.
     B. suppressing the release of competing hormones such as
        testosterone.
     C. decreasing the rate of overall body activity.
     D. increasing the response of the pubic area to tactile stimuli.
     (D, p. 315, conceptual)

78.  What can change the response of sensory nerves to tactile
     stimulation in the pubic area?

     A. Nothing. The responses of peripheral nerves are fixed.
     B. Simultaneous stimulation of visual or auditory neurons
        increases the responses to tactile stimuli.
     C. Absence of other tactile stimulation increases the
        responsiveness in the pubic area.
     D. Estrogen increases the skin area that stimulates nerves in the
        pubic area.
     (D, p. 315, conceptual)

79.  Sex hormones most strongly affect which part of the hypothalamus?

     A. ventromedial nucleus.
     B. thalamus.
     C. optic nerve.
     D. sexually dimorphic nucleus.
     (D, p. 315, factual)

80.  Stimulation of the medial preoptic area:

     A. decreases female-typical sex behavior in females.
     B. increases male-typical sex behavior in females.
     C. increases female-typical sex behavior in males.
     D. increases male-typical sex behavior in males.
     (D, p. 315, factual)

81.  Stimulation of the medial preoptic area:

     A. increases female-typical sex behavior in females.
     B. increases male-typical sex behavior in females.
     C. increases female-typical sex behavior in males.
     D. decreases male-typical sex behavior in males.
     (A, p. 315, factual)

82.  Male sexual behavior depends heavily on neurons in the medial
     preoptic area of the hypothalamus releasing which substance?

     A. testosterone
     B. dopamine
     C. estrogen
     D. lutinizing hormone
     (B, p. 315, factual)

83.  In normal male rats, the medial preoptic area neurons strongly
     release which of the following during sexual activity?

     A. dopamine
     B. testosterone
     C. glutamate
     D. estradiol
     (A, p. 315, factual)

84.     In castrated male rats, the medial preoptic area:

A. does not have as much dopamine as other rats.
B. has as much dopamine as normal rats therefore they will attempt to copulate with a receptive female.
C. has as much dopamine as normal rats, but the presence of a receptive female does not evoke much release of it.
D. releases the same level of dopamine, but not testosterone, as a normal rat.
(C, p. 315, factual)

85.     In normal female rats, medial preoptic area activity is primed by:

A. dopamine.
B. testosterone.
C. a combination of testosterone and estrogen.
D. a combination of estradiol and oxytocin.
(D, pp. 315-316, factual)

86.     In the early stages of sexual arousal, which of the following types of neurotransmitter receptors are most likely to be stimulated in the hypothalamus?

A. glutamate type NMDA receptors and serotonin type 5HT-3A receptors
B. substance P receptors and glutamate type NMDA receptors
C. dopamine receptor types D1 and D5
D. dopamine type D2 receptors and serotonin type 5HT-3A receptors
(C, p. 316, factual)

87.     Dopamine stimulates mostly type D2 receptors when the concentration of released dopamine is:

A. almost undetectable.
B. moderate.
C. declining.
D. high.
(D, p. 316, factual)

88.     Dopamine stimulation of D2 receptors facilitates:

A. arousal.
B. orgasm.
C. erection of the penis.
D. sexually receptive postures in the female.
(B, p. 316, factual)

89.     What hormone more than triples in concentration in the blood of
        human males during orgasm, and has been tentatively linked to
        sexual pleasure?

        A. insulin
        B. aldosterone
        C. melatonin
        D. oxytocin
        (D, p. 317, factual)

90.     In adult men, the ability to ejaculate, ability to have an
        erection, and sexual activity are generally related to levels of
        which hormone?

        A. testosterone
        B. estradiol
        C. prolactin
        D. parathyroid hormone
        (A, p. 317, conceptual)

91.     A means of controlling sex offenders has involved reducing:

        A. testosterone levels.
        B. estrogen levels.
        C. prolactin.
        D. the alpha-fetoprotein level in their blood.
        (A, p. 317, factual)

92.     What are the effects of drugs that, in some cases, have reduced
        the frequency of sexual offenders?

        A. They reduce testosterone levels.
        B. They reduce estrogen levels.
        C. They induce high but equal levels of testosterone and
           estrogen.
        D. They mimic the effects of alpha-fetoprotein.
        (A, p. 317, factual)

93.     Cyproterone and medroxyprogesterone, drugs which reduce
        testosterone levels, have been used to treat:

        A. impotence.
        B. menopause.
        C. sex offenders.
        D. menarche.
        (C, p. 317, factual)

94.     Side effects of cyproterone and medroxyprogesterone include:

        A. Loss of appetite.
        B. menopause.
        C. menarche.
        D. breast growth.
        (D, p. 317, factual)

95.    Triptorelin blocks _____ thereby decreasing _____ production.

    A. gonadotropin; estrogen
    B. testosterone; gonadotropin
    C. gonadotropin; testosterone
    D. testosterone; progesterone
    (C, p. 317, factual)

96.    Triptorelin has been found to influence sex offenders by:

    A. decreasing testosterone levels but not their sexual fantasies.
    B. decreasing their deviant behavior, but not their testosterone levels.
    C. decreasing their deviant sexual fantasies and behaviors.
    D. increasing their interest in normal sexual outlets.
    (C, p. 317, factual)

97.    A woman's hypothalamus and pituitary interact with the _____ to produce the menstrual cycle.

    A. pineal
    B. ovaries
    C. thyroid
    D. adrenal glands
    (B, p. 317, factual)

98.    In women, which hormone stimulates the growth of a follicle in the ovary?

    A. FSH
    B. ACTH
    C. TSH
    D. prolactin
    (A, p. 317, factual)

99.    Follicle-stimulating hormone is released by the:

    A. pineal gland.
    B. anterior pituitary.
    C. thyroid.
    D. ovum.
    (B, p. 317, factual)

100.   Toward the middle of the menstrual cycle, the follicle produces increasing amounts of:

    A. TSH.
    B. ACTH.
    C. testosterone.
    D. estradiol.
    (D, p. 317, factual)

101.  In the middle of the menstrual cycle, an increased release of
      estradiol causes:

      A. a decrease in the release of FSH.
      B. a decrease in the release of LH.
      C. a sudden surge in the release of luteinizing hormone.
      D. an increase in the release of testosterone.
      (C, p. 318, factual)

102.  The hormones LH, FSH, and estradiol reach a peak:

      A. in the first month of pregnancy.
      B. at the start of the menstrual period.
      C. at the end of the menstrual period.
      D. around the time of ovulation.
      (D, p. 318, conceptual)

103.  During the menstrual cycle, estradiol and progesterone levels
      increase and decrease under the influence of hormones released by
      which gland?

      A. pineal
      B. adrenal
      C. thyroid
      D. pituitary
      (D, p. 318, conceptual)

104.  At the end of the menstrual cycle in women, the levels of LH,
      FSH _____; the levels of estradiol and progesterone _____.

      A. decrease; increase
      B. increase; decrease
      C. increase; increase
      D. decrease; decrease
      (D, p. 318, factual)

105.  The most widely used and most effective birth control pill is one
      that contains which hormone(s)?

      A. luteinizing hormone
      B. androgen, but not estrogen
      C. both estrogen and androgen
      D. both estrogen and progesterone
      (D, p. 318, factual)

106.  Birth control pills prevent pregnancy by:

      A. increasing the release of estrogen.
      B. increasing the release of FSH.
      C. interfering with the feedback cycle between the ovaries and
         the pituitary.
      D. inactivating both ovaries.
      (C, p. 318, factual)

107.  High levels of which of the following hormones, beginning shortly
      after the end of the menstrual period, would block the release of
      an ovum?

      A. FSH
      B. LH
      C. estrogen
      D. prolactin
      (C, p. 318, factual)

108.  What is the relationship between current hormone levels and
      sexual responsiveness in women?

      A. They are unrelated.
      B. Women are more likely to initiate sexual activity when
         estrogen levels are low.
      C. Women are more likely to initiate sexual activity when
         estrogen levels are high.
      D. Women are more likely to initiate sexual activity when
         estrogen levels are intermediate.
      (C, p. 318, factual)

109.  At what point in the menstrual cycle, if any, are women who are
      not on birth-control pills most likely to initiate sexual
      activity?

      A. at any point in the menstrual cycle
      B. just after the end of menstruation
      C. about midway between two menstrual periods
      D. just before the next menstrual period
      (C, p. 318, factual)

110.  In one study, women who were menstruating or approaching
      menstruation preferred male faces, on a continuum from very
      masculine to very feminine:

      A. which were very masculine in appearance.
      B. which were somewhat feminine.
      C. about halfway between feminized and masculinized.
      (B, p. 319, factual)

111.  In one study, women in the follicular phase, when the probability
      of becoming pregnant is greatest, preferred male faces, on a
      continuum from very masculine to very feminine:

      A. which were very masculine in appearance.
      B. which were somewhat feminine.
      C. about halfway between feminized and masculinized.
      (C, p. 319, factual)

112.  On which of the following does testosterone have an activating effect?

A. aggressive behavior
B. parental behavior
C. differentiation of the hypothalamus
D. differentiation of the cerebral cortex
(A, p. 319-320, conceptual)

113.  Increased levels of estrogen affect receptor sites in the brain by:

A. decreasing the number of dopamine receptors.
B. decreasing the sensitivity of receptors to serotonin.
C. increasing the number of certain types of dopamine and serotonin receptors.
D. increasing the number of certain types of acetylcholine receptors.
(C, p. 320, factual)

114.  A temporary growth of dendritic spines on dendrites in the hippocampus has been correlated with:

A. decreased estrogen production.
B. increased estrogen production.
C. decreased testosterone production.
D. increased GABA release.
(B, p. 320, factual)

115.  Increased estrogen production has been correlated with changes in parts of the brain associated with:

A. reinforcement.
B. unusual amounts of aggression.
C. depression.
D. irritability.
(A, p. 320, factual)

116.  When estrogen levels are low, many women report:

A. an increase in their sex drive.
B. a positive mood.
C. unpleasant mood changes.
D. improved verbal memory.
(C, p. 320, factual)

117.  What effect does a decreased level of estrogen have during the
      menstrual cycle?

      A. It may be related to depressed moods.
      B. It stimulates the release of the ovum.
      C. It is suspected to be connected with increased sexual
         activity.
      D. It is responsible for implantation failures of a fertilized
         egg.
      (A, p. 320, factual)

118.  At what point of the menstrual cycle is depression from hormonal
      fluctuations most likely to occur?

      A. just before ovulation
      B. when estrogen levels are at their highest
      C. when estrogen levels are at their lowest
      D. when FSH and LH levels are increasing
      (C, p. 320, factual

119.  Women who suffer from PMS have:

      A. abnormally low levels of estrogen.
      B. abnormally low levels of progesterone.
      C. normal levels of estrogen and progesterone.
      D. abnormally high levels of vasopressin.
      (C, p. 320, factual)

120.  Increased estrogen is correlated with:

      A. improved verbal memory.
      B. gross motor skills.
      C. improved spatial performance
      D. depression.
      (A, p. 320, factual)

121.  In one study women, tested for manual dexterity, performed best
      when:

      A. estrogen and progesterone levels were low.
      B. estrogen levels were low and progesterone levels were high.
      C. estrogen levels were high and progesterone levels were low.
      D. estrogen and progesterone levels were high.
      (D, p. 320, factual)

122.  The results of one study found that women, tested for verbal
      fluency, performed best when:

      A. estrogen and progesterone levels were low.
      B. estrogen levels were low and progesterone levels were high.
      C. estrogen levels were high and progesterone levels were low.
      D. estrogen and progesterone levels were high.
      ("WWW" D, p. 320, factual)

123.  A study, testing women for spatial tasks, found that they
      performed best when:

      A. estrogen and progesterone levels were low.
      B. estrogen levels were low and progesterone levels were high.
      C. estrogen levels were high and progesterone levels were low.
      D. estrogen and progesterone levels were high.
      (A, p. 320, factual)

124.  What is menopause?

      A. The time when a woman stops menstruating.
      B. The time when a woman starts menstruating.
      C. The period after ejaculation when a man cannot have another
         orgasm.
      D. The point in time when a man no longer produces active sperm.
      (A, p. 320, factual)

125.  Transsexuals who did well on tests of verbal memory:

      A. were taking estrogen treatments.
      B. were taking testosterone.
      C. had just decreased their estrogen levels.
      D. were an older population than those who performed poorly.
      (A, p. 321, factual)

126.  Older men who had been given extra testosterone to boost their
      levels back up to those typical of young men, exhibited improved
      performance on:

      A. verbal memory tasks.
      B. verbal fluency tasks.
      C. tasks of manual dexterity.
      D. spatial tasks.
      (D, p. 321, factual)

127.  Males outperform females on spatial tasks:

      A. but only when they are children.
      B. when the male's testosterone levels are low.
      C. when the female's estrogen levels are high.
      D. when the female's estrogen levels are low.
      (C, p. 321, factual)

**Puberty**

128.  What is the name of the first menstrual period a girl has?

      A. the periovulatory period
      B. menarche
      C. synergism
      D. diaschisis
      (B, p. 321, factual)

129.  How is the experience of menarche different for a young girl who keeps her weight low because of athletic training?

     A. She typically reaches menarche sooner than other girls.
     B. She typically reaches menarche later than other girls.
     C. Menarche will be timed normally but blood flow will be unusually heavy.
     D. There is no consistent difference.
     (B, p. 321, factual)

130.  What hormonal event marks the start of puberty?

     A. the first production of testosterone or estradiol
     B. increased release of alpha-fetoprotein
     C. hourly bursts of luteinizing hormone releasing hormone
     D. a cessation of the release of luteinizing hormone releasing hormone
     (C, p. 321, factual)

131.  Puberty begins when the hypothalamus releases hourly bursts of:

     A. luteinizing hormone releasing hormone.
     B. thyroid hormone releasing hormone.
     C. either estradiol or testosterone.
     D. adrenocorticotropic hormone.
     (A, p. 321, factual)

132.  If you wanted to determine whether a young girl had entered puberty, which of these questions should you ask?

     A. Does her bloodstream contain more estradiol than testosterone?
     B. Are the axons in her hypothalamus myelinated?
     C. Does her hypothalamus release bursts of a particular hormone?
     D. What is the level of alpha-fetoprotein in her bloodstream?
     (C, p. 321, conceptual)

133.  Luteinizing hormone releasing hormone causes the pituitary to release _____, which in turn causes the gonads to release _____.

     A. LH and FSH; estradiol or testosterone
     B. estradiol or testosterone; LH and FSH
     C. TSH and ACTH; cortisol and epinephrine
     D. cortisol and epinephrine; TSH and ACTH
     (A, p. 321, factual)

134.  During puberty, the hypothalamus is to _____ as the gonads are to_____.

     A. estradiol; testosterone
     B. luteinizing hormone releasing hormone; estradiol or testosterone
     C. females; males
     D. excitation; inhibition
     (B, p. 321, conceptual)

135.  Secondary sexual characteristics include:

      A. development of the gonads.
      B. development of the uterus in females.
      C. breast development in females.
      D. broadening of the hips in males.
      (C, p. 321, factual)

136.  Secondary sexual characteristics include:

      A. development of the gonads.
      B. development of the uterus in females.
      C. lowering of the voice in males.
      D. broadening of the shoulders in females.
      (C, p. 321, factual)

137.  Pregnant monkeys become more interested in baby monkeys as their:

      A. estrogen levels increase and progesterone levels decrease.
      B. estrogen levels decrease and progesterone levels increase.
      C. estrogen and progesterone levels decrease.
      D. estrogen and progesterone levels increase.
      (D, p. 321, factual)

138.  Many female mammals become very attentive after delivering
      their babies largely because of a sudden:

      A. drop in testosterone levels.
      B. surge of prolactin and oxytocin.
      C. decrease of prolactin and increase of oxytocin.
      D. increase of prolactin and decrease of oxytocin.
      (B, p. 321, factual)

139.  Which of the following can elicit parental behavior even in very
      young rats, long before they reach puberty?

      A. three hours of exposure to newborn rats
      B. direct electrical stimulation of the parietal cortex
      C. three hours of watching a mother rat care for her young
      D. injection with plasma from mother rats
      (D, p. 321, factual)

140.  Damage to what part of the brain will eliminate rats' maternal
      behavior?

      A. any part of the thalamus
      B. lateral hypothalamus
      C. medial preoptic area of the hypothalamus
      D. any part of the hypothalamus
      (C, p. 321, factual)

141. What is the contribution of hormonal changes to the parental behavior exhibited by rats and mice?

    A. It is necessary for such behavior.
    B. It is not necessary, but it speeds up the onset of such behavior.
    C. It is necessary for parental behavior by males, but not by females.
    D. It makes no difference in parental behavior.
    (B, p. 321, conceptual)

142. If a never pregnant female rat is left for 5-10 days with a litter of babies, she will:

    A. most likely kill them.
    B. initially ignore them, but eventually will become more attentive.
    C. initially be attentive, but eventually will ignore them.
    D. immediately respond to them as though she gave birth to them.
    (B, pp. 321-322, factual)

143. Hormones are most essential to which aspect of mammalian parental behavior?

    A. care for newborns during the first few days
    B. continuation of care after the first few days
    C. the parental care sometimes shown by males
    D. all aspects equally
    (A, p. 322, conceptual)

144. The first few days of rat parental care are to _____ as later days are to _____.

    A. experience; hormones
    B. hormones; experience
    C. females; males
    D. males; females
    (B, p. 322, conceptual)

145. What effect do the pheromones of newborn rats have on maternal behavior?

    A. They inhibit maternal behavior.
    B. They stimulate maternal behaviors directly.
    C. They stimulate the release of hormones that affect maternal behaviors.
    D. They stimulate paternal behaviors, but not maternal behaviors.
    (A, p. 322, factual)

146. If a rat is left for 5-10 days with a litter of babies (not its own), which ones, if any, will begin to take care of the young?

    A. only females that have previously given birth
    B. any female, but no males
    C. both females and males
    D. none
    (C, p. 322, conceptual)

147. In rats, parental care during the first few days depends mostly on which of the following?

    A. how many pups are in the litter
    B. experience
    C. hormones
    D. vision
    ("WWW" C, p. 321, factual)

148. In rats, parental care after the first few days depends mostly on which of the following?

    A. estrogen
    B. progesterone
    C. oxytocin
    D. experience
    (D, p. 322, conceptual)

149. Mammals need two mechanisms for maternal behavior to:

    A. compensate for the lack of hormones released during the first few days after birth.
    B. compensate for the lack of familiarity that mother has with the young.
    C. ensure that the hormones will be released when needed.
    D. ensure that only the mother provides care for the young.
    (B, p. 322, factual)

150. In mammalian species where the father helps rear the young, he will experience:

    A. no change in his hormonal levels.
    B. hormonal changes similar to those of the babies.
    C. hormonal changes similar to those of the mother.
    D. a drop in his prolactin levels.
    (C, p. 322, factual)

151. In a species of dwarf hamster, as the female approaches the end of pregnancy, the male's:

    A. testosterone level decreases.
    B. testosterone level increases.
    C. prolactin levels decrease.
    D. prolactin levels increase.
    (B, p. 322, factual)

152.  In a species of dwarf hamster, as soon as the mother delivers
      her babies, the male's:

      A. testosterone level increases.
      B. prolactin levels increase.
      C. prolactin levels decrease.
      D. behavior changes and he directs aggressive behavior toward the
         young.
      (B, p. 322, factual)

## Module 11.2: Variations in Sexual Development and Orientation

153.  What does a coral goby fish do if its mate dies after eggs have
      been laid?

      A. A male will abandon the eggs and find a new mate.
      B. A female will care for her young and then die.
      C. Either sex will care for the eggs and, if necessary, change
         sex to form a new mating pair.
      D. Either sex will abandon the eggs to find a new mate.
      (C, p. 324, factual)

### Determinants of Gender Identity

154.  Gender identity can be defined as:

      A. the pattern of sex chromosomes one has.
      B. the sex one identifies with and calls oneself.
      C. sexual awareness present in almost all mammalian species.
      D. the set of activities presumed to be common for one sex or
         another in a society.
      (B, p. 324, factual)

155.  Sex differences are to _____ as gender differences are to _____.

      A. anatomy; behaviors
      B. adults; children
      C. excitation; inhibition
      D. scientists; the public
      (A, p. 324, conceptual)

156.  Some XY males have poorly developed genitals as a result of:

      A. a mutation in the SRY gene.
      B. low body temperature during prenatal development
      C. too much testosterone.
      D. too much estrogen.
      (A, p. 324, factual)

157. What would cause a genetic female to develop a partly masculinized anatomy?

    A. excessive levels of alpha-fetoprotein in her blood
    B. exposure of her mother to stressful experiences late in pregnancy
    C. exposure to less than the usual amount of estrogen during an early sensitive period
    D. exposure to more than the usual amount of testosterone during an early sensitive period
    (D, p. 324, factual)

158. A genetic male who has low levels of testosterone or low responsiveness to it:

    A. will develop normally.
    B. is predisposed to become a sex offender.
    C. may develop intermediate between a female and a male.
    D. will have a nonfunctional SRY gene.
    (C, p. 324, factual)

159. What happens to a female human fetus exposed to excess testosterone during the sensitive period for genital development?

    A. She is unaffected, since she has no receptors for testosterone.
    B. She will often develop without any sexual organs.
    C. She will often develop with genitals that appear intermediate between male and female genitals.
    D. She will often develop a complete, functioning, set of male reproductive organs.
    (C, p. 324, factual)

160. A hermaphrodite is an individual:

    A. who dresses and lives as the opposite sex.
    B. whose genitals do not match the usual development for their genetic sex.
    C. with no sex drive.
    D. with too much testosterone.
    (B, pp. 324-325, factual)

161. Which of the following would probably develop as an intersex or pseudohermaphrodite?

    A. a genetic female exposed to more testosterone than normal during early development
    B. a genetic male exposed to more estradiol than normal during early development
    C. a genetic female deprived of her normal amount of estradiol during early development
    D. a genetic male exposed to a larger than normal amount of testosterone during early development
    (A, pp. 324-325, factual)

162.    What is an individual called whose genitals do not match the
        normal development for their genetic sex?

        A. an eunuch
        B. a hermaphrodite
        C. a homosexual
        D. a transvestite
        (B, p. 325, factual)

163.    What is a "true hermaphrodite"?

        A. Someone who has both XX and XY chromosome patterns.
        B. Someone who has one testis and one ovary.
        C. Someone who is female, but has sexual interest only in other
           females.
        D. Someone who dresses up as the opposite gender.
        (B, p. 325, factual)

164.    When a newborn baby is found to be a pseudohermaphrodite or
        intersex, how have most authorities over the past few decades
        recommended raising the child?

        A. Raise the child according to whether the chromosomes are male
           or female.
        B. Wait until later and let the child decide whether to be called
           male or female.
        C. When in doubt, call the child male.
        D. When in doubt, call the child female.
        (D, p. 325, factual)

165.    Studies of intersexes suggest that gender identity development:

        A. is primarily determined by prenatal hormone levels.
        B. is primarily determined by genes.
        C. is primarily determined by how the child was raised.
        D. follows a path that does not allow researchers to draw any
           firm conclusions at this time.
        ("WWW" D, p. 326, factual)

166.    Which of the following would cause a genetic male to develop a
        mostly feminine anatomy?

        A. exposure to more than the usual amount of estrogen during an
           early sensitive period
        B. exposure to more than the usual amount of testosterone during
           an early sensitive period
        C. a condition that prevents androgens from binding to genes in a
           cell's nucleus
        D. excessive levels of alpha-fetoprotein in his blood
        (C, p. 326, factual)

167.  Someone with androgen insensitivity is genetically:

   A. female, but looks intermediate between male and female.
   B. female, but fails to show any changes at puberty.
   C. male, looks like a normal male, but behaves more like a
      female.
   D. male, but develops looking more like a female.
   (D, p. 326, conceptual)

168.  Someone with testicular feminization:

   A. does not produce enough testosterone.
   B. produces too much estrogen.
   C. has cells which are insensitive to androgens.
   D. looks like a male but is infertile.
   (C, p. 326, factual)

169.  In what way are people with androgen insensitivity most like a
      normal male?

   A. in appearance
   B. genetically
   C. in gender identity
   D. in rearing
   (B, p. 326, conceptual)

170.  Which of the following is generally true about both
      pseudohermaphrodites and individuals with androgen insensitivity?

   A. Breasts automatically develop at puberty.
   B. They have no pubic hair.
   C. They are raised as females.
   D. They are shorter than average.
   (C, p. 326, conceptual)

171.  In the Dominican Republic, certain genetic males who were
      regarded in early childhood as girls have developed into boys at
      puberty.  What happened to their gender identity?

   A. Most adopted a clear male gender identity.
   B. Most retained a clear female gender identity.
   C. About half developed a clear male identity; the other half
      developed a clear female identity.
   D. Most developed a confused gender identity.
   (A, p. 327, factual)

172.  Certain genetic males in the Dominican Republic were born with
      low levels of the enzyme that converts testosterone into DHT.
      This resulted in:

   A. breast development.
   B. lack of pubic hair.
   C. minimal penis growth early in life.
   D. extreme shortness until the age of 30 or so.
   (C, p. 327, factual)

173.  What conclusion can be drawn from the unusual gender identity
      cases from the Dominican Republic?

      A. The environment has no affect on gender identity.
      B. If given the necessary hormones at puberty, any girl can
         become a boy.
      C. Early child-rearing experiences are not the sole determinant
         of gender identity.
      D. Chromosomes are the determining factor in gender identity.
      (C, p. 327, factual)

174.  The result of the sex reassignment in the case of the infant
      whose penis was accidentally removed was that:

      A. he developed a normal female gender identity.
      B. he developed a neutral gender identity with no sexual
         interest.
      C. he only experienced difficulties during adulthood.
      D. he decided to adopt a male gender identity during adolescence.
      (D, p. 327, factual)

**Possible Biological Bases of Sexual Orientation**

175.  The frequency of homosexuality in men is highest if:

      A. a sister is homosexual.
      B. an adopted brother is homosexual.
      C. a dizygotic twin brother is homosexual.
      D. a monozygotic twin brother is homosexual.
      (D, p. 328, factual)

176.  When examining the data on sexual orientation of twins and other
      siblings, what seems to be the most reasonable conclusion?

      A. Genetic factors completely determine sexual orientation.
      B. Genetic factors play no role in sexual orientation.
      C. Sexual orientation is determined by genetics as well as other
         factors.
      D. Genetic factors determine sexual orientation in men, but do
         not seem to play a role for women.
      (C, p. 328, conceptual)

177.  Research suggests that if one adult male identical twin is a
      homosexual, how likely is it that his twin brother will also be
      homosexual?

      A. approximately 1% of the time
      B. approximately 20% of the time
      C. approximately 50% of the time
      D. 100% of the time
      (C, p. 328, factual)

178.  Which hypothesis is LEAST plausible as a biological explanation for why some men have a homosexual orientation and others have a heterosexual orientation?

A. genetics
B. effects of prenatal hormones or stress
C. different structures within the hypothalamus
D. different levels of sex hormones in adulthood
(D, p. 328, factual)

179.  Most homosexual men, as compared to heterosexual men, have:

A. lower levels of testosterone.
B. testosterone levels within the same range.
C. higher levels of testosterone.
D. higher levels of estrogen.
("WWW" B, p. 328, factual)

180.  Of the various hypotheses based on hormone levels, which is the most plausible explanation for male homosexuality?

A. adult testosterone levels are low
B. adult estrogen levels are high
C. prenatal testosterone levels were low during some sensitive period
D. prenatal estrogen levels were high during some sensitive period
(C, p. 328-329, factual)

181.  Males of many different species have been exposed to much decreased levels of testosterone early in life resulting in:

A. a higher level of estradiol in the adult male.
B. a higher level of testosterone output in adult life.
C. sexual behavior directed towards other males.
D. an increase in sexual behavior.
(C, p. 328-329, factual)

182.  Which of the following has been shown to cause male rats to respond sexually to male rats more than female rats?

A. a higher level of estradiol than testosterone in the adult male rat
B. highly stressful experiences by their mothers late in pregnancy
C. exposure of their mothers to alcohol early in pregnancy
D. being reared with only females during early infancy
(B, p. 329, factual)

183.  Female rats exposed to much increased levels of testosterone
      early in life:

      A. showed an increase in sexual response toward infants.
      B. showed no sexual activity as adults.
      C. showed an increase in sexual activity with male partners.
      D. showed an increased probability of attempting to mount sexual
         partners in the way that males typically do.
      (D, p. 329, factual)

184.  If a female rat is exposed to highly stressful experiences late
      in pregnancy, what happens to the sexual development of her
      offspring?

      A. The genetic males become responsive to male partners.
      B. The genetic females become responsive to female partners.
      C. Both male and female offspring become unresponsive to all
         sexual partners.
      D. Both male and female offspring become highly aggressive in
         their sexual behaviors.
      (A, p. 329, factual)

185.  Exposure of a female rat to highly stressful experiences late in
      pregnancy has what effect on the development of her male
      offspring?

      A. They develop a female anatomy, although their behavior is the
         same as other males.
      B. They respond sexually to male partners, although their anatomy
         is the same as other males.
      C. Their sexual anatomy and behavior are typically male, but
         their nonsexual behaviors resemble females.
      D. They resemble females in all regards, including anatomy,
         sexual and nonsexual behaviors.
      (B, p. 329, conceptual)

186.  Experiments on rats suggest that male homosexuality might be
      related to which of the following?

      A. a low testosterone influence early in development
      B. a low level of testosterone during adulthood
      C. a high level of estradiol during adulthood
      D. dominant mothers and detached fathers
      (A, p. 329, factual)

187.  What has been found in studies that relate male homosexuality in
      humans to prenatal stressors?

      A. Prenatal stress is consistently related to homosexuality in
         men.
      B. There has been no evidence linking prenatal stress to
         homosexuality in men.
      C. Stress during delivery is weakly related to homosexuality in
         men.
      D. The findings are inconclusive.
      (D, p. 329, factual)

188.  The drug diethylstilbestrol (DES), used to prevent miscarriage or
      alleviate other problems, was found to have:

      A. masculinizing organizational effects on female offspring.
      B. masculinizing activating effects on the pregnant women.
      C. feminizing organizational effects on male offspring.
      D. feminizing activating effects on the male offspring.
      (A, p. 329, conceptual)

189.  The findings of the "DES studies" suggest that prenatal hormones:

      A. are the factor that determines sexual orientation in males.
      B. are the factor that determines sexual orientation in females.
      C. can influence homosexual responsiveness.
      D. do not influence sexual responsiveness.
      (C, p. 329, factual)

190.  A study looking at the differences between homosexual/bisexual
      and heterosexual women found:

      A. that the homosexual women had very masculinized brains.
      B. a partial masculinization of the brain in some homosexual and
         bisexual women.
      C. that there were no differences in the brain between the two
         groups.
      D. that the homosexual women had the highest level of estradiol
         and the heterosexual women had the lowest level of estradiol.
      ("WWW" B, pp. 329-330, factual)

191.  What measurable differences are apparently related to homosexual
      versus heterosexual orientation in adult men?

      A. their testosterone levels
      B. their estrogen levels
      C. the size of certain parts of their hypothalamus
      D. the pattern of dendritic branching in their cerebral cortex
      (C, p. 330, factual)

192.   The anterior commissure, on the average, is:

A. smaller in heterosexual women than heterosexual men.
B. larger in heterosexual women than heterosexual men.
C. smaller in homosexual men than heterosexual men.
D. the largest in heterosexual men as compared to homosexual men
   and heterosexual and homosexual women.
(B, p. 330, factual)

193.   In male rats with abnormalities of the suprachiasmatic nucleus,
preference for male vs. female sexual partners depends on:

A. diet.
B. room temperature.
C. age of the partner.
D. time of day.
(D, p. 330, factual)

194.   The interstitial nucleus 3 of the anterior hypothalamus is known
to be:

A. more than twice as large in heterosexual women as in men.
B. more than three times as large in heterosexual women as in
   men.
C. more than twice as large in heterosexual men as in women.
D. more than twice as large in homosexual men as in heterosexual
   men.
(C, p. 330, factual)

195.   When Simon LeVay examined interstitial nucleus 3 in 41 people who
had died, he found that in the homosexual males in his sample,
this nucleus was:

A. larger, but only in those who had died of AIDS.
B. comparable in size to the heterosexual males who had died of
   AIDS.
C. comparable in size to the whole group of heterosexual males.
D. comparable in size to the heterosexual females.
(D, p. 330, conceptual)

196.   When Simon LeVay examined interstitial nucleus 3 in 41 people who
had died, what did he find concerning this area?

A. It was the same size in male heterosexuals, female
   heterosexuals, and male homosexuals.
B. It was larger in female heterosexuals than either male
   heterosexuals or male homosexuals.
C. It was larger in male homosexuals than either male
   heterosexuals or female heterosexuals.
D. It was larger in male heterosexuals than either female
   heterosexuals or male homosexuals.
(D, p. 330, conceptual)

197.  Data gathered by studies such as the LeVay study suggest that:

  A. the hypothalamus determines sexual orientation.
  B. the suprachiasmatic nucleus determines sexual orientation.
  C. the hypothalamus may alter the probability of developing one
       sexual orientation or another.
  D. there is only a small probability that the brain has anything
       to do with sexual orientation.
  (C, p. 331, factual)

198.  LeVay's studies indicate a correlation between a man's sexual
      orientation (homosexuality vs. heterosexuality) and:

  A. the amount of testosterone in the blood.
  B. the amount of estradiol in the blood.
  C. the size of one nucleus of the hypothalamus.
  D. the size of one nucleus of the medulla.
  (C, p. 331, conceptual)

**Module 12.1 What is Emotion, Anyway?   And What Good is it?**

1.    One way to separate emotions from feelings is to define emotions
      as:

      A. private experiences.
      B. internal experiences.
      C. observable behaviors.
      D. the unconscious.
      (C, p. 336, factual)

2.    An operational definition:

      A. relates it to a theory of behavior.
      B. specifies the parameters one could use to measure something.
      C. is the one accepted by the largest number of people.
      D. defines the population a researcher is studying.
      (B, p. 336, factual)

3.    Based on observations of people who experience "absence
      seizures," it seems apparent that in order to experience emotion
      we need:

      A. a normal brain.
      B. a solid, stable memory.
      C. a certain level of consciousness and arousal.
      D. an interruption of habitual actions.
      (C, p. 336, factual)

4.    When a patient with extreme memory problems interacted with two
      people and was later asked to look at pictures of them (which he
      didn't recognize) and choose one for a friend, which one did he
      choose?

      A. the one who was smiling in the photo
      B. the one who was more attractive
      C. the one who had been nicer to him
      D. the one who looked younger
      (C, p. 336-337, factual)

5.    The hypothalamus, hippocampus, amygdala, olfactory bulb, septum
      and related structures constitute which system?

      A. the pyramidal system
      B. the sympathetic nervous system
      C. the parasympathetic nervous system
      D. the limbic system
      (D, p. 337, factual)

6.   The limbic system consists of structures that are believed to be
     important for which kind of responses?

     A. reflexes
     B. fine motor control
     C. spatial orientation
     D. emotional
     (D, p. 337, factual)

**Are Emotions Useful?**

7.   People with a striking loss of emotions usually suffer from
     damage to the:

     A. occipital lobe.
     B. temporal lobe.
     C. lateral hypothalamus.
     D. prefrontal cortex.
     ("WWW" D, p. 337, factual)

8.   Case studies suggest that individuals with prefrontal cortex
     damage are not able to:

     A. reason.
     B. rationalize behaviors.
     C. express emotions.
     D. recognize faces.
     (C, p. 337, factual)

9.   Investigators have found that individuals who suffer prefrontal
     cortex damage:

     A. often make bad decisions.
     B. become more logical than usual in their reasoning.
     C. become excessively inhibited in their dealings with others.
     D. perform poorly on IQ tests.
     (A, p. 337, factual)

10.  The reason individuals who suffer prefrontal cortex damage
     often make bad decisions is because they:

     A. do not care about the consequences.
     B. can't anticipate the unpleasantness of likely outcomes.
     C. have poor decision making skills.
     D. can't figure out what will happen if they make one decision
        over another.
     (B, pp. 337-338, factual)

**Emotions and Readiness for Action**

11.  The autonomic nervous system is divided into two parts; the _____
     nervous system (which prepares the body for emergency action),
     and the _____ nervous system (which increases digestion).

     A. sympathetic; parasympathetic
     B. parasympathetic; sympathetic
     C. somatic; craniosacral
     D. craniosacral; somatic
     (A, p. 338, factual)

12.  The branch of the autonomic nervous system that is responsible
     for preparing the body for intense, vigorous, emergency activity
     is the:

     A. somatic nervous system.
     B. craniosacral nervous system.
     C. sympathetic nervous system.
     D. parasympathetic nervous system.
     (C, p. 338, factual)

13.  The branch of the autonomic nervous system that is responsible
     for preparing the body for fight or flight behaviors is called
     the:

     A. parasympathetic nervous system.
     B. sympathetic nervous system.
     C. somatic nervous system.
     D. craniosacral nervous system.
     (B, p. 338, factual)

14.  The sympathetic nervous system is to _____ as the parasympathetic
     nervous system is to _____.

     A. fight; flight
     B. emergencies; relaxation
     C. assertiveness; aggressiveness
     D. striated muscles; smooth muscles
     (B, p. 338, conceptual)

15.  Which of the following would greatly activate the parasympathetic
     nervous system?

     A. a sudden loud noise
     B. removal of a stimulus that caused someone to be frightened
     C. a controllable or escapable electric shock
     D. a competitive task
     (B, p. 338, factual)

16.  Which of the following would greatly activate the sympathetic nervous system?

    A. a sudden loud noise
    C. removal of a stimulus that caused someone to be frightened
    C. relaxing after a big meal
    D. falling asleep
    ("WWW" A, p. 338, conceptual)

17.  Just after removal of a stimulus that excites the sympathetic nervous system:

    A. the sympathetic nervous system continues for some time and then gradually decreases.
    B. activity of the sympathetic and parasympathetic nervous systems return immediately to the resting condition.
    C. the animal actively seeks new stimuli to maintain sympathetic nervous system arousal.
    D. parasympathetic activity increases.
    (D, p. 338, factual)

18.  A scientist would be most likely to use which of the following when attempting to obtain an objective measure of emotion?

    A. a self report
    B. ratings by independent observers
    C. measures of sympathetic nervous system responses
    D. measures of parasympathetic nervous system responses
    (C, p. 338, conceptual)

19.  According to the James-Lange theory, we experience emotion:

    A. first, then come our actions.
    B. and act upon that emotion, simultaneously.
    C. after we experience autonomic arousal.
    D. and must label it before we can act on it.
    (C, p. 338, conceptual)

20.  Which evidence is most detrimental to the James-Lange theory?

    A. Quadriplegics experience emotions.
    B. Sometimes people have trouble reporting what they are feeling.
    C. Changes in arousal are reported as changes in emotions.
    D. Some people feel stronger emotions than others do.
    (A, p. 338, conceptual)

21.  Why is arousal of the sympathetic nervous system not totally satisfactory in measuring emotions?

    A. It cannot be measured reliably.
    B. It cannot differentiate emotions of different intensities.
    C. It is only marginally related to emotions.
    D. It does not indicate which emotion is being experienced.
    (D, p. 338, factual)

22.   Walter Cannon argued that the sympathetic nervous system responds
      too _____ to be the cause of emotional states.

      A. slowly
      B. quickly
      C. infrequently
      D. frequently
      (A, p. 338, factual)

23.   The James-Lange theory is to _____ as the Cannon-Bard theory is
      to _____.

      A. autonomic arousal then emotion; simultaneous autonomic arousal
         and emotion
      B. simultaneous autonomic arousal and emotion; emotion then
         autonomic arousal
      C. emotion then autonomic arousal; autonomic arousal then emotion
      D. emotion then autonomic arousal; simultaneous autonomic arousal
         and emotion
      (A, pp. 338-339, conceptual)

24.   According to the Cannon-Bard theory:

      A. an event evokes the emotional experience first and the
         physical arousal second.
      B. an event causes action first, and the emotional experience
         follows.
      C. an event causes physical arousal and emotional experience,
         simultaneously.
      D. we must label an emotion before we can act on it.
      (C, p. 339, conceptual)

25.   When people were forced to smile, by clenching a pen between
      their teeth, how did they rate a cartoon they were reading?

      A. funnier than if they were not forced to smile
      B. just as funny as when they were holding a pen between their
         lips
      C. not as funny as when they were holding a pen between their
         lips
      (A, p. 339, conceptual)

26.   People with "locked-in syndrome," lack the ability to produce any
      body changes, therefore, most report feeling:

      A. panic.
      B. anger.
      C. depression.
      D. tranquillity.
      (D, p. 339, factual)

**Module 12.2: Stress and Health**

**Stress and the Autonomic Nervous System**

27.  A nonspecific response of the body to any demand made upon it is
     a definition of:

     A. emotion.
     B. feeling.
     C. stress.
     D. psychosomatic illness.
     (C, p. 342, factual)

28.  If the onset of an illness in influenced by someone's
     personality, emotions, or experiences, we call the illness:

     A. iatrogenic
     B. psychosomatic.
     C. imaginary.
     D. a stressor.
     (B, p. 342, factual)

29.  Rats with specific damage to what area of the brain don't develop
     ulcers?

     A. cerebellum.
     B. prefrontal cortex.
     C. corpus callosum.
     D. superior colliculus.
     (B, p. 342, factual)

30.  Ulcers can be caused in rats:

     A. simply by shocking them.
     B. when they lack a sense of control over a stressful situation.
     C. simply by arranging them in yoked pairs.
     D. by rearing them in social isolation.
     ("WWW" B, p. 342, factual)

31.  In experiments with monkeys, a monkey that could press a lever to
     avoid shocks ordinarily developed:

     A. no ulcers.
     B. fewer ulcers than a monkey that could not press a lever to
        avoid shocks.
     C. the same number of ulcers as a monkey that could not press a
        lever to avoid shocks.
     D. more ulcers than a monkey that could not press a lever to
        avoid shocks.
     (D, p. 342, factual)

32.    In experiments with monkeys, a monkey that could press a lever to
       avoid shocks developed ulcers:

       A. during the shock-avoidance training.
       B. as a result of the shocks it received.
       C. during the rest periods between barpresses.
       D. after the experiment was over.
       (C, p. 342, factual)

33.    In experiments with monkeys, a monkey that could press a lever to
       avoid shocks developed ulcers:

       A. due to a sympathetic rebound effect.
       B. due to greater than normal stomach secretions and
          contractions.
       C. during the shock-avoidance sessions.
       D. due to a bacterium that invaded its system.
       (B, p. 342, factual)

34.    What is the status of the hypothesis that a bacterium causes
       ulcers?

       A. It has become widely accepted.
       B. It is in doubt because the bacterium is found in nonhumans but
          not in humans.
       C. It is in doubt because the bacterium is found as much in other
          organs as in the digestive system.
       D. It is in doubt because the bacterium is found in almost as
          many people without ulcers as people with ulcers.
       (D, p. 342-343, factual)

35.    Frequently expressing hostility has been found to be related to
       which of these disorders?

       A. absence seizures
       B. locked-in syndrome
       C. Huntington's disease
       D. heart disease
       (D, p. 343, factual)

36.    What variable has recently been found to be highly predictive of
       having a healthy heart?

       A. having a strong social support system
       B. a diet with much meat
       C. playing video games
       D. using tranquilizers
       (A, p. 343, factual)

37.    What variable has recently been found to be highly predictive of
       having a heart condition or heart attack?

       A. lacking a social support system
       B. exercising more than 3 times a week
       C. working indoors
       D. taking mineral supplements
       (A, p. 343, conceptual)

38.    Voodoo death refers to:

       A. a case wherein a sick person dies from a specific disease, but
          believes that a curse has made him sick.
       B. a case wherein a healthy person dies apparently because he
          believes that a curse has been put upon him.
       C. death from a poison administered by someone claiming to place
          a curse.
       D. death that is, in fact, caused by a supernatural curse.
       (B, p. 343, factual)

39.    Serendipity refers to:

       A. illness related to a curse.
       B. death from a curse.
       C. delving into the supernatural to cure illnesses.
       D. stumbling upon something interesting while looking for
          something else.
       (D, p. 343, factual)

40.    A dewhiskered rat, thrown into a tank of turbulent water,
       resembles a human victim of "voodoo death".  What is believed to
       be the cause of death in both instances?

       A. physical exhaustion
       B. lack of adequate sleep
       C. a shut-down of the limbic system
       D. excessive parasympathetic nervous system activity
       (D, p. 343-344, conceptual)

41.    In Richter's experiment, a rat's whiskers were cut off, then it
       was forced to swim in a tank of turbulent water.  It died
       quickly.  What was the probable DIRECT cause of death?

       A. Overactivity of the parasympathetic nervous system
       B. Overactivity of the sympathetic nervous system
       C. Inability to swim without its whiskers
       D. Rapid fatigue followed by drowning
       (A, p. 344, conceptual)

42. In a series of experiments on the swimming abilities of rats, Curt Richter dropped rats into water and timed how long they swam before they died.  Under what circumstances were they more likely to survive?

  A. if he used wild rats instead of domesticated rats
  B. if he cut off their whiskers
  C. if he used turbulent water instead of calm water
  D. if he rescued the rats from the water several times prior to the actual test trial
  (D, p. 344, factual)

43. Scientists believe that certain cases of sudden death, as in voodoo death, result from what?

  A. overactivity of the sympathetic nervous system
  B. underactivity of the sympathetic nervous system
  C. overactivity of the parasympathetic nervous system
  D. underactivity of the parasympathetic nervous system
  ("WWW" C, p. 344, conceptual)

**Stress and the Hypothalamus-Pituitary-Adrenal Cortex Axis**

44. Stress activates two systems. One is the:

  A. HPA axis which reacts more quickly than the other.
  B. HPA axis, which becomes increasingly important with prolonged stressors.
  C. autonomic nervous system which secretes the hormone ACTH.
  D. autonomic nervous system which secretes the hormone cortisol.
  (B, p. 344, factual)

45. An autoimmune disease occurs when:

  A. the immune system shuts down completely.
  B. the immune system attacks the body's normal cells.
  C. an invading virus or bacteria no longer activates the immune system.
  D. the respiratory system shuts down due to exposure to exhaust fumes.
  (B, p. 344, factual)

46. Leukocytes are produced in the:

  A. thymus gland.
  B. spleen.
  C. bone marrow.
  D. peripheral lymph nodes.
  (C, p. 345, factual)

47.    What are produced in the bone marrow and are the most important
       elements of the immune system?

       A. red blood cells
       B. leukocytes
       C. cytokines
       D. antigens
       (B, p. 345, factual)

48.    How do leukocytes identify intruder cells?

       A. by shape
       B. by chromosomal pattern
       C. by rate of cell division
       D. by surface proteins
       (D, p. 345, conceptual)

49.    An alien cell, marked by alien antigens, is attacked by which
       kind of cells?

       A. epithelial cells
       B. stem cells
       C. leukocytes
       D. astrocytes
       (C, p. 345, factual)

50.    A leukocyte attacks when it finds a cell with alien:

       A. antigens.
       B. contours.
       C. chromosomes.
       D. neurotransmitters.
       (A, p. 345, factual)

51.    Which type of leukocyte surrounds the bacterium or other intruder
       and digests it?

       A. an antigen
       B. a macrophage
       C. a B cell
       D. a T cell
       (B, p. 345, factual)

52.    Which type of leukocyte attaches to an intruder and produces a
       specific antibody to attack the intruder's antigen?

       A. a macrophage
       B. a B cell
       C. a T cell
       D. an A cell
       (B, p. 345, factual)

53.    Which type of leukocyte matures in the bone marrow?

       A. an antigen
       B. a macrophage
       C. a B cell
       D. a T cell
       (C, p. 345, factual)

54.    Proteins that circulate in the blood, specifically attaching to
       one kind of antigen are:

       A. macrophages.
       B. B cells.
       C. T cells.
       D. Antibodies.
       (D, p. 345, factual)

55.    What type of leukocyte matures in the thymus gland?

       A. an antigen
       B. a macrophage
       C. a B cell
       D. a T cell
       (D, p. 345, factual)

56.    Which leukocyte has two types or forms?

       A. macrophage
       B. B cell
       C. T cell
       D. antigen
       (C, p. 345, factual)

57.    Cytotoxic T cells:

       A. stimulate other T cells to multiply more rapidly.
       B. stimulate other B cells to multiply more rapidly.
       C. directly attack intruder cells.
       D. only travel in the cytoplasm.
       (C, p. 345, factual)

58.    Which type of leukocyte matures in the bone marrow and produces
       antibodies to attack specific targets?

       A. B cells
       B. Y cells
       C. T cells
       D. natural killer cells
       (A, p. 345, factual)

59.   Which leukocyte differentiates into memory cells?

      A. B cell
      B. T cell
      C. macrophage
      D. cytotoxic T cell
      (A, p. 345, factual)

60.   Blood cells that attach to types of tumor cells and cells
      infected with viruses are known as:

      A. B cells
      B. T cells
      C. cytotoxic T cells
      D. natural killer cells
      ("WWW" D, p. 345, factual)

61.   Which type of leukocyte destroys tumor cells and cells infected
      with viruses?

      A. T cells
      B. B cells
      C. Schwann cells
      D. natural killer cells
      (D, p. 345, factual)

62.   What is one of the main differences between natural killer cells
      and T cells?  Natural killer cells

      A. attack normal tissue.
      B. attack several kinds of intruders.
      C. are cancer cells.
      D. are more specific in their targets.
      (B, p. 345-346, factual)

63.   Which of the following are NOT leukocytes?

      A. B cells
      B. Schwann cells
      C. T cells
      D. natural killer cells
      (B, p. 346, factual)

64.   Chemicals released by the immune system that attack infections
      and communicate with the brain to elicit anti-illness behaviors
      are:

      A. macrophages.
      B. cytotoxic cells.
      C. cytokines.
      D. natural killer cells.
      (C, p. 346, factual)

65.   The immune system's way of telling the brain that the body is ill
      are:

      A. macrophages.
      B. cytotoxic cells.
      C. cytokines.
      D. natural killer cells.
      (C, p. 346, factual)

66.   Cytokines in the periphery stimulate receptors on the____ nerve.

      A. optic
      B. olfactory
      C. cytokine
      D. vagus
      (D, p. 346, factual)

67.   Information from cytokines is relayed to the brain, specifically
      to the:

      A. hypothalamus and hippocampus.
      B. cerebellum and basal ganglia.
      C. pineal gland and reticular formation.
      D. locus coeruleus and inferior colliculus
      (A, p. 346, factual)

68.   Why do humans suffer from fever when ill?

      A. The body is so weakened from illness that it cannot maintain
         its normal temperature.
      B. It is an important defense since most viruses do not thrive at
         high temperatures.
      C. The viruses drive the body's temperature up.
      D. Increased temperature is a direct result of decreased body
         activity.
      (B, p. 346, factual)

69.   Why do humans suffer from sleepiness, decreased muscle activity,
      and decreased sex drive during illness?

      A. The body is so weakened from illness that it cannot do much of
         anything.
      B. The virus saps the organism's energy and uses it to attack the
         body.
      C. They are useful ways of conserving energy while the body is
         attacking the illness.
      D. Maintaining the normal activity level would strengthen the
         virus.
      (C, p. 346, factual)

70.    One explanation for why we experience decreased appetite while
       ill is that:

       A. finding food is hard work so it is better to live off one's
          stored reserves during that time.
       B. digestive reactions are slower at increased body temperatures.
       C. food tastes bad at increased temperatures.
       D. the organism needs its parasympathetic nervous system to fight
          off the illness, not digest.
       (A, p. 346, factual)

71.    Studies have found that rats subjected to inescapable shocks:

       A. develop a fever.
       B. decrease their sleep.
       C. increase their sex drive.
       D. increase their appetite.
       (A, p. 346, factual)

72.    Brief activation of which system strengthens the immune response?

       A. parasympathetic nervous system
       B. sympathetic nervous system
       C. blood-brain barrier
       D. excretory system
       (A, p. 346, factual)

73.    Occasional bursts of emotion:

       A. are harmful to an organism.
       B. are harmful if the emotion is anger.
       C. boost the activity of the immune system.
       D. directs energy away from the synthesis of proteins.
       ("WWW" C, p. 346, factual)

74.    What did researchers find in the people who stayed in the area
       after the Three Mile Island incident?

       A. strong social relationships
       B. lower levels of leukocytes
       C. leukocytes that would attack radioactive cells
       D. an outbreak of autoimmune diseases
       (B, p. 346, factual)

75.    What did researchers find in Antarctic research scientists who
       spent a 9-month period of social isolation in the cold and dark?

       A. T cell functioning increased by about 50%
       B. T cell functioning decreased by about half
       C. leukocytes stopped functioning
       D. an outbreak of autoimmune diseases
       (B, p. 346, factual)

76.    The immune system is weakened by:

       A. either short-term or long-term stress.
       B. short-term stress but not long-term stress.
       C. long-term stress but not short-term stress.
       D. neither short-term nor long-term stress.
       (C, p. 346, factual)

77.    Which is NOT a typical effect of chronic stress?

       A. secretions of the hormone cortisol
       B. elevated blood sugar levels
       C. strengthened immune system
       D. enhanced metabolism
       (C, p. 346, conceptual)

78.    Which of the following is known to strengthen the immune response
       in humans?

       A. prolonged stress
       B. injections of morphine
       C. having a sense of control
       D. accepting that they don't have control over most of their
          problems
       (C, p. 346, factual)

79.    What is one effect of chronic stress?

       A. the onset of autoimmune diseases
       B. a decrease in the number of certain leukocytes
       C. an increase in natural killer cells
       D. a drop in cortisol levels
       (B, p. 346, factual)

80.    Which of the following is NOT associated with chronic stress?

       A. elevated cortisol levels
       B. an increase in natural killer cells
       C. increased metabolism
       D. decreased immune functioning
       (B, p. 346, factual)

81.    Which is more characteristic of the body's response to chronic
       stress than the response to short-term stress?

       A. sympathetic nervous system involvement
       B. elevated heart rate
       C. a sudden burst of activity ("fight or flight" response)
       D. secretions of cortisol
       (D, p. 346, conceptual)

82.   In what way can high cortisol levels be harmful to an individual?

      A. it can increase the vulnerability of the hippocampus
      B. it can kill off natural killer cells
      C. it can increase metabolism
      D. it can elevate fevers
      (A, p. 346, factual)

83.   High cortisol levels increase the likelihood that hippocampal
      cells will be:

      A. responsive to new learning.
      B. capable of generating a circadian rhythm.
      C. synchronized to sensory stimulation.
      D. vulnerable to damage by toxins.
      (D, p. 346, factual)

84.   Aged people with the highest cortisol levels tend to be those
      with:

      A. the largest hippocampus.
      B. the greatest memory problems.
      C. the greatest amount of social support.
      D. the most cellulose in the diet.
      (B, pp. 346-347, factual)

85.   One surprising feature about people with posttraumatic stress
      Disorder (PTSD) is that, on the average, they have:

      A. lower than normal cortisol levels.
      B. a larger than normal hippocampus.
      C. a stronger, healthier immune system than most people.
      D. a weaker than normal startle response to a loud noise.
      (A, p. 347, factual)

**Module 12.3: Attack and Escape Behaviors**

86.   What is the purpose of many of the "play" behaviors seen when a
      cat catches a mouse?

      A. play and self-amusement
      B. self-defense
      C. sadistic
      D. to get the mouse to be more active and be more desirable prey
      (B, p. 349, conceptual)

87.    Some cats "play" with a mouse before killing it.  How can this
       kind of behavior best be explained?

       A. the cat's perverse pleasure in prolonging the mouse's pain
       B. an instinctive need for additional pursuit behaviors prior to
          eating
       C. a conflict between attack and escape behaviors
       D. regression to infantile patterns of activity in the
          hippocampus
       (C, p. 349, factual)

88.    A cat is most likely to withdraw from a mouse if the:

       A. mouse puts up an aggressive fight.
       B. cat has recently killed, but not eaten, several mice.
       C. mouse is very small.
       D. cat is not hungry.
       (A, p. 349, conceptual)

**Attack Behaviors**

89.    A loud fight between two cats in an alley is most likely to
       involve:

       A. a quiet biting attack.
       B. an effective attack.
       C. an affective attack.
       D. a courtship behavior.
       (C, p. 349, factual)

90.    If a hamster in its home territory attacks an intruder, what will
       the hamster do if a second intruder arrives shortly after the
       first intruder leaves?

       A. withdraw from the second intruder
       B. play with the second intruder
       C. attack the second intruder quickly and vigorously
       D. attack the second intruder but less vigorously than the first
       (C, p. 349, factual)

91.    If a hamster is primed for a fight, increased activity will most
       likely be found:

       A. in the corticomedial amygdala.
       B. all over the cortex.
       C. all over the temporal lobe.
       D. in the occipital lobe.
       (A, p. 349, factual)

92.   Studies of aggressive and criminal behaviors have found that:

      A. there doesn't appear to be a genetic link.
      B. there appears to be more aggression by twins than non-twins.
      C. monozygotic twins resemble each other more closely than
         dizygotic twins.
      D. dizygotic twins resemble each other more closely than
         monozygotic twins.
      ("WWW" C, p. 349, factual)

93.   An important prenatal factor associated with criminal activities
      found in two studies implicated the mother's:

      A. cigarette smoking.
      B. alcohol intake.
      C. age.
      D. diet.
      (A, pp. 349-350, factual)

94.   One study found that boys who were aggressive at age 3 tended to
      be:

      A. shorter than average.
      B. reared on a high-sugar diet.
      C. aggressive when tested at a later age.
      D. less aggressive when tested at a later age.
      (C, p. 350, factual)

95.   A study of conduct disorders and aggressive behavior in adopted
      children supported the generalization that:

      A. spankings and other physical punishments increase aggressive
         behavior than decrease it.
      B. criminals are born, not made.
      C. criminals are made, not born.
      D. behaviors depend on a combination of genes and environment,
         not on either one alone.
      (D, p. 350, factual)

96.   According to Lyons et al. (1995), under what circumstances do the
      criminal behaviors of monozygotic twins resemble each other more
      than dizygotic twins?

      A. when the monozygotic twins have been raised apart
      B. when the dizygotic twins have been raised together
      C. in terms of adult aggression
      D. in terms of juvenile aggression
      (C, pp. 350-351, factual)

97.   When do genetics seem to have more of an influence than
      environment on criminal and aggressive behaviors?

      A. in children
      B. in adults
      C. in males
      D. in females
      (B, p. 351, conceptual)

98.   Which group of humans tends to be the most violent?

      A. males 15-25 years old
      B. males 25-35 years old
      C. females 15-25 years old
      D. females 25-35 years old
      (A, p. 351, factual)

99.   Among men of a given age, what is the relationship between
      testosterone levels and violent behavior?

      A. Testosterone levels are the strongest predictor we have of who
         will commit violent acts.
      B. High testosterone is related to only a slightly increased
         probability of violent behavior.
      C. Hormone levels have zero correlation with violent behavior.
      D. Those with the highest testosterone levels are the least
         likely to commit violent acts.
      (B, p. 351, factual)

100.  Females demonstrate about the same level of aggression as males
      when:

      A. they are seriously provoked.
      B. their aggression is directed towards other women.
      C. their aggression is directed towards a man.
      D. they have time to plan.
      (A, p. 351, factual)

101.  Studies which have failed to find differences in aggression
      between males and females measured aggression:

      A. by observing behaviors.
      B. through self-reports.
      C. using physiological data.
      D. when studying young adults.
      (B, p. 351, factual)

102.  Stimulation of areas of the _____ will lead to aggressive
      behaviors.

      A. hypothalamus
      B. precentral gyrus
      C. hippocampus
      D. frontal lobe
      (A, p. 351, factual)

103.   Stimulation of the _____ will lead to aggressive behaviors.

       A. ventromedial nucleus of the hypothalamus
       B. locus coeruleus
       C. precentral gyrus
       D. hippocampus
       (A, p. 351, factual)

104.   Stimulation of the _____ will lead to vigorous affective attacks.

       A. hippocampus
       B. amygdala
       C. precentral gyrus
       D. frontal lobe
       (B, pp. 351-352, factual)

105.   Rabies, which leads to furious, violent behavior, is a disease
       caused by a virus that attacks much of the:

       A. hippocampus.
       B. frontal lobe.
       C. temporal lobe.
       D. precentral gyrus.
       (C, p. 352, factual)

106.   Which part of the cerebral cortex is most vulnerable to damage by
       the rabies virus?

       A. occipital lobe
       B. parietal lobe
       C. temporal lobe
       D. frontal lobe
       (C, p. 352, factual)

107.   Damage to or removal of the amygdala usually leads to:

       A. extreme aggression.
       B. tameness and placidity.
       C. an acceleration of the circadian rhythm.
       D. dominance in a hierarchy or pecking order.
       (B, p. 352, factual)

108.   Monkeys with damage to the amygdala have trouble interpreting:

       A. information concerning the location of objects.
       B. the relationship between visual and olfactory information.
       C. social stimuli from other monkeys.
       D. simple visual stimuli which have changed their meaning.
       (C, p. 352, conceptual)

109.  What would be the most likely result if an amygdala lesion is
      made in the most dominant monkey in a group?

      A. It would become even more aggressive.
      B. It would fail to show any emotions.
      C. It would avoid all socialization.
      D. It would quickly sink to the lowest status in the hierarchy.
      (D, p. 352, conceptual)

110.  Which of the following typically characterizes temporal lobe
      epilepsy?

      A. uncontrollable flailing of the arms and legs
      B. prolonged lack of expression of any emotions
      C. repetitive utterance of nonsense words and sounds
      D. hallucinations, lip smacking, and emotional behaviors
      (D, p. 352, factual)

111.  What do certain patients with temporal lobe epilepsy have in
      common with those who suffer from rabies?

      A. long periods of unconsciousness
      B. excessive sensitivity to bright lights
      C. unprovoked violent behavior
      D. severe decline in intellectual functioning
      (C, p. 352, conceptual)

112.  Which of the following has been shown to be effective in
      suppressing violent behavior in some of the people who are prone
      to outbursts of unprovoked violent attacks?

      A. alcohol
      B. benzodiazepine tranquilizers
      C. antiepileptic drugs
      D. testosterone
      (C, p. 352, factual)

113.  In certain cases, antiepileptic drugs have been found to be
      effective in treating people with which of the following
      problems?

      A. panic disorder
      B. obsessive-compulsive behavior
      C. seasonal affective disorder
      D. unprovoked violent outbursts
      (D, p. 352, factual)

114.  Increases in aggressive behavior are associated with a drop in:

      A. blood pressure.
      B. serotonin release.
      C. norepinephrine release.
      D. heart rate.
      ("WWW" B, p. 352, factual)

115. The term "serotonin turnover" refers to the amount of serotonin that is:

    A. released at synapses and resynthesized.
    B. currently present in the brain.
    C. radioactively labeled.
    D. converted into another transmitter.
    (A, p. 352-353, factual)

116. The concentration of 5-HIAA in the blood, cerebrospinal fluid, or urine provides an estimate of:

    A. serotonin stores.
    B. serotonin turnover.
    C. dopamine stores.
    D. dopamine turnover.
    (B, p. 352-353, factual)

117. A convenient way to estimate the level of serotonin turnover in the brain is to measure the level of _____ in the blood, cerebrospinal fluid, or urine.

    A. serotonin metabolites.
    B. serotonin itself.
    C. L-dopa.
    D. dopamine precursors.
    (A, p. 352-353, factual)

118. According to a number of animal studies, under which of the following conditions is the probability of violent behavior greatest?

    A. low acetylcholine turnover
    B. high acetylcholine turnover
    C. low serotonin turnover
    D. high serotonin turnover
    (C, p. 353, factual)

119. If mice show a decrease in serotonin turnover in response to social isolation, what other behavior can one expect?

    A. an increase in aggressive behavior
    B. a decrease in aggressive behavior
    C. an increase in sexual behavior
    D. a decrease in sexual behavior
    ("WWW" A, p. 353, factual)

120. Which mice showed a decrease in serotonin turnover in response to social isolation?

    A. males with high testosterone levels
    B. females in estrus
    C. males in general
    D. females in general
    (C, p. 353, factual)

121. Excessive attack behaviors were found in mice that:

    A. had more type 5-HT 1B receptors than normal.
    B. were deficient in 5-HT 1B receptors.
    C. had many more serotonin receptors than normal.
    D. had many more dopamine receptors than normal.
    (B, p. 353, factual)

122. Although it is not known why they are related, studies on animals show a strong relationship between:

    A. increased GABA turnover and decreased sexual responsiveness.
    B. decreased acetylcholine turnover and decreased social behaviors.
    C. increased dopamine turnover and increased anxiety.
    D. decreased serotonin turnover and increased aggressiveness.
    (D, p. 353, factual)

123. Suppose you want to predict whether a given mouse or rat, which has been isolated from its species for weeks, will act aggressively when it is placed with another of its species. Which of the following measures would aid you in making that prediction?

    A. level of 5-HIAA in the blood
    B. uptake of 2-DG in the basal ganglia
    C. latency of evoked potentials in the occipital lobe
    D. ratio of red blood cells to white blood cells
    (A, p. 353, application)

124. In mice and monkeys, the level of 5-HIAA in the blood is a predictor of which type of behavior?

    A. food-seeking
    B. sexual
    C. aggressive
    D. playful
    (C, p. 353, conceptual)

126. In a study of serotonin turnover in male monkeys, it was found that those with:

    A. low levels were most dominant.
    B. high levels had the most scars.
    C. high levels were the most aggressive.
    D. low levels were usually dead by age 6.
    (D, p. 353, factual)

127.  Many studies have found that violent criminals and arsonists
      released from prison had a greater probability of committing
      other violent crimes:

      A. after undergoing surgical removal of the amygdala.
      B. if they ate diets low in corn.
      C. if they had lower than normal serotonin turnover.
      D. if they had higher than normal 5-HIAA levels in the blood.
      (C, p. 353, factual)

128.  Blood and urine levels of which chemicals are related to a
      history of violent suicide attempts?

      A. high levels of 5-HIAA
      B. low levels of 5-HIAA
      C. high levels of L-dopa
      D. low levels of L-dopa
      (B, p. 353, conceptual)

129.  If you wanted to predict the probability that a given
      individual might attempt suicide based only on the level of some
      chemicals in the blood, you should measure:

      A. L-dopa levels.
      B. dopamine metabolites.
      C. serotonin metabolites.
      D. acetylcholine metabolites.
      (C, p. 353, conceptual)

130.  Which of the following has been associated with an increased
      probability of suicide attempts?

      A. high dopamine turnover
      B. high GABA turnover
      C. low serotonin turnover
      D. low substance-P turnover
      (C, p. 353, factual)

131.  A Belgian study investigating suicide rates found that the rates
      were highest:

      A. in the winter, when serotonin turnover was also high.
      B. in the winter, when serotonin turnover was lowest.
      C. in the spring, when serotonin turnover was also high.
      D. in the spring, when serotonin turnover was lowest.
      (D, p. 353, factual)

132.  A precursor for the synthesis of serotonin has been identified
      as:

      A. tryptophan.
      B. phenylalanine.
      C. monoamine.
      D. norepinephrine.
      (A, p. 354, factual)

133.  One study found that many young men showed an increase in
      aggressive behavior a few hours after eating a diet:

      A. high in tryptophan.
      B. high in both tryptophan and phenylalanine.
      C. low in tryptophan and high in phenylalanine.
      D. low in both tryptophan and phenylalanine.
      (C, p. 354, factual)

134.  Why do certain people suspect that a diet high in corn may lead
      to an increase in aggressive behavior?

      A. Corn is low in tryptophan and high in phenylalanine.
      B. Corn contains a chemical similar to testosterone.
      C. Corn is deficient in thiamine and other B vitamins.
      D. Corn is high in fats and contains no proteins or amino acids.
      (A, p. 354, factual)

135.  Which change in the diet may increase the probability of
      aggressive behavior?

      A. decreased consumption of corn
      B. increased consumption of tryptophan
      C. increased consumption of Nutrasweet
      D. decreased consumption of iodized salt
      (C, p. 354, conceptual)

136.  What dietary components may alter the probability of aggressive
      behavior?

      A. corn may decrease the probability
      B. tryptophan may decrease the probability
      C. Nutrasweet may decrease the probability
      D. thiamine may increase the probability
      (B, p. 354, conceptual)

137.  Phenylalanine might affect the probability of aggressive behavior
      by:

      A. converting to testosterone in the body.
      B. converting to L-dopa in the body.
      C. interfering with the production of serotonin.
      D. interfering with the production of GABA.
      (C, p. 354, conceptual)

138.  Suppose you want to DECREASE the aggressive behavior of an
      animal, and all you are allowed to use is a nutritional
      supplement. Which might be a good choice?

      A. increase tryptophan
      B. increase phenylalanine
      C. decrease thiamine
      D. decrease lecithin
      (A, p. 354, conceptual)

139.  Depression is linked to _____ serotonin and aggressive behavior
      is linked to _____ serotonin.

      A. low; low
      B. low; high
      C. high; low
      D. high; high
      ("WWW" A, p. 354, factual)

140.  If a treatment suddenly lowered your serotonin level:

      A. you would experience depression.
      B. you would become violent.
      C. you would become both depressed and violent.
      D. we could not predict how and when your behavior would change.
      (D, p. 354, factual)

141.  Which of the following characterizes people who are subject to
      panic attacks?

      A. an underresponsive sympathetic nervous system
      B. an overresponsive sympathetic nervous system
      C. misinterpretation of respiratory signals in the brain
      D. high levels of zinc in the blood
      (C, p. 354, factual)

142.  People who have panic attacks often react to certain signals from
      their bodies as if they were experiencing which of the following?

      A. anger
      B. hunger
      C. suffocation
      D. REM sleep
      (C, p. 354, factual)

143.  One of the surest ways to trigger a panic attack in someone who
      is susceptible to panic attacks is to:

      A. tell the person he or she really doesn't have anything to
         worry about.
      B. prevent REM sleep over a period of 3-4 nights.
      C. increase blood levels of lactate and carbon dioxide.
      D. damage cells in the amygdala or medial forebrain bundle.
      (C, pp. 354-355, factual)

144.  Many people with panic attacks make their own problems worse by:

      A. drinking milk before going to bed.
      B. hyperventilating.
      C. increasing their REM sleep by staying in bed in the morning.
      D. eating foods high in phenylalanine.
      (B, p. 355, factual)

145.  Most people with panic disorder can be treated with:

      A. psychotherapy and tranquilizers.
      B. altered sleep schedules and breathing exercises.
      C. tranquilizers and altered sleep schedules.
      D. deep breathing and ECT.
      (A, p. 355, factual)

**Escape Behaviors**

146.  What is the relationship between fear and anxiety?

      A. fear is acute while anxiety is longer lasting
      B. fear activates the parasympathetic nervous system, whereas
         anxiety activates the sympathetic nervous system.
      C. anxiety has an identifiable stimulus, fear does not
      D. fear activates the left hemisphere, whereas anxiety activates
         the right hemisphere.
      (A, p. 354, factual)

147.  Anxiety is physiologically most similar to:

      A. depression.
      B. fear.
      C. euphoria.
      D. grief.
      (B, p. 354, conceptual)

148.  A startle reflex occurs in response to:

      A. grief.
      B. depression.
      C. anxiety.
      D. an unexpected loud noise.
      (D, p. 355, factual)

149.  After a loud noise, information travels from the medulla to the:

      A. pons.
      B. neck muscles.
      C. cochlear nucleus.
      D. hypothalamus.
      (A, p. 355, factual)

150.  What is a common measure of fear or anxiety that is popular
      because it can be used with non-humans as well as humans?

      A. eyeblinking
      B. spontaneous muscle twitches
      C. the startle response
      D. hyperventilation
      (C, p. 355, factual)

151. Which of the following is true concerning the startle response to a loud noise?

    A. It decreases with age.
    B. It is common across species.
    C. It is unaffected by environmental factors.
    D. It is learned in early infancy.
    (B, p. 355, conceptual)

152. What is the startle response like in people suffering from posttraumatic stress disorder?

    A. It is generally absent.
    B. It is generally weaker than in other people.
    C. It is the same, since it is an innate response unaffected by learning.
    D. It is generally stronger than in other people.
    (D, p. 355, conceptual)

153. How is the startle response to a loud noise affected by a prior stimulus?  If the stimulus:

    A. has been paired with something fearful, the startle response is increased.
    B. has been paired with something pleasant, the startle response is increased.
    C. has been paired with something neutral, the startle response is increased.
    D. has been paired with soft noises, the startle response is increased.
    (A, p. 355, factual)

154. One key area of the brain associated with learned fears is the:

    A. medulla.
    B. amygdala.
    C. pons.
    D. brain stem.
    (B, p. 355, factual)

155. What area of the brain seems to be a key area for learned fears?

    A. the prefrontal cortex
    B. the lateral hypothalamus
    C. the ventromedial hypothalamus
    D. the amygdala
    (D, p. 355, factual)

156. Many cells in the amygdala get input from sensory modalities, especially the _____ nuclei.

    A. basolateral and central
    B. lateral and medial
    C. hypothalamic
    D. brain stem
    (A, p. 356, factual)

157. Output from the amygdala to the _____ controls autonomic fear responses.

    A. brain stem
    B. hypothalamus
    C. basolateral nuclei
    D. prefrontal cortex
    (B, p. 356, factual)

158. Output from the amygdala to the _____ modifies interpretation of potentially frightening stimuli.

    A. brain stem
    B. hypothalamus
    C. prefrontal cortex
    D. basolateral nuclei
    (C, p. 356, factual)

159. To what part of the brain does the amygdala send axons which ultimately controls the startle reflex?

    A. central gray in the midbrain
    B. caudate nucleus
    C. cingulate gyrus
    D. pineal gland
    (A, p. 356, factual)

160. A rat with damage to the amygdala:

    A. will not show a normal startle reflex.
    B. will not show an enhanced startle reflex if it gets a signal before a loud noise.
    C. will show an exaggerated startle reflex.
    D. will show a startle reflex to stimuli which would not elicit this reflex under normal circumstances.
    (B, p. 356, factual)

161. Studies show that damage to the amygdala:

    A. enhances the startle reflex.
    B. makes the animal more likely than usual to learn new fears.
    C. reduces or eliminates learned or enhanced fears.
    D. results in the lack of a startle reflex because the animal cannot hear the stimulus very well.
    (C, p. 356, factual)

162. Which of the following effects would result from damage to the amygdala?

    A. lack of a startle response
    B. a normal startle response, but absence of learned fears
    C. an enhanced startle response and an enhanced response to learned fears
    D. a fear response to any novel stimulus
    (B, p. 356, factual)

163. Animals with damage to the amygdala exhibit which of the following?

    A. They neither learn new fears nor retain previously learned fears.
    B. They fail to show a startle response to any stimulus.
    C. They become extremely aggressive and emotional.
    D. They are unable to store new memories of any kind.
    (A, p. 356, conceptual)

164. If amygdala damage is confined to one hemisphere, what is the effect on a rat?

    A. It is oblivious to all stimuli.
    B. It will attack anything in his environment.
    C. Its startle reflect is magnified.
    D. Its memories of unpleasant events are weakened.
    (D, p. 356, factual)

165. Researchers found that when they compared right-hemisphere versus left-hemisphere amygdala damage, fear reactions were:

    A. suppressed more with left-hemisphere damage.
    B. suppressed more with right-hemisphere damage.
    C. suppressed equally by damage to either hemisphere.
    D. not suppressed by damage to either hemisphere.
    (B, p. 356, factual)

166. Human amygdala activity was found to be greatest when looking at a picture of a:

    A. face with a fearful expression.
    B. face with a happy expression.
    C. puppy.
    D. young child.
    (A, p. 356, factual)

167. Human amygdala activity was found to be greatest when looking at a picture of:

    A. people showing emotional expressions.
    B. people with neutral expressions.
    C. a puppy or kitten.
    D. an infant.
    (A, p. 356, factual)

168.  Human amygdala activity was found to be greatest when looking at
      a picture:

      A. repeatedly.
      B. for the first time.
      C. of a male rather than a female.
      D. of a child rather than an adult.
      (B, p. 356, factual)

169.  What deficits are commonly seen in people with Urbach-Wiethe
      disease?

      A. They have trouble understanding speech.
      B. They have trouble recognizing faces.
      C. They feel a heightened sense of aggression.
      D. They feel little or no fear.
      (D, p. 356, factual)

170.  When asked to identify different emotional expressions, people
      with Urbach-Wiethe disease had the most difficulty identifying:

      A. surprise.
      B. anger.
      C. fear.
      D. joy.
      (C, p. 356-357, factual)

171.  When asked to draw pictures expressing different emotions, which
      picture caused difficulty for the woman with Urbach-Wiethe
      disease?

      A. happy
      B. disgusted
      C. angry
      D. afraid
      (D, p. 357, factual)

172.  Increased fear, anxiety, or panic is related to increased
      activity of _____ and decreased activity of _____ .

      A. CCK; GABA
      B. acetylcholine; glutamate
      C. dopamine; norepinephrine
      D. serotonin; NPY
      (A, p. 357, conceptual)

173.  Most tranquilizers reduce anxiety by:

      A. decreasing GABA.
      B. increasing GABA.
      C. blocking dopamine.
      D. increasing CCK.
      (B, p. 357, factual)

174. One could reduce anxiety by:

     A. decreasing GABA.
     B. increasing CCK.
     C. blocking CCK.
     D. blocking dopamine.
     (C, p. 357, factual)

175. Which once-popular class of tranquilizers is now much less popular because they are strongly habit forming and can easily result in a fatal overdose?

     A. benzodiazepines
     B. amphetamines
     C. barbiturates
     D. tricyclics
     (C, p. 357, factual)

176. Which class of drugs is most commonly used today as tranquilizers?

     A. tricyclics
     B. monoamine oxidase inhibitors
     C. barbiturates
     D. benzodiazepines
     (D, p. 357, factual)

177. Valium, Librium, and Xanax are examples of:

     A. amphetamines.
     B. benzodiazepines.
     C. monoamine oxidase inhibitors.
     D. tricyclics.
     (B, p. 357, factual)

178. Benzodiazepines relieve anxiety by _____ transmission at _____ synapses.

     A. facilitating; dopamine
     B. inhibiting; serotonin
     C. facilitating; GABA
     D. inhibiting; norepinephrine
     (C, pp. 357-358, factual)

179. Benzodiazepines relieve anxiety by facilitating transmission of:

     A. dopamine.
     B. serotonin.
     C. GABA.
     D. norepinephrine.
     (C, pp. 357-358, factual)

180.  How do benzodiazepine tranquilizers affect GABA synapses?

    A. They stimulate GABA receptors.
    B. They facilitate binding of GABA to its receptors.
    C. They inhibit GABA receptors.
    D. They decrease binding of GABA to its receptors.
    (B, pp. 357-358, factual)

181.  A drug that facilitates transmission at GABA-A synapses has what effect on behavior?

    A. increases anxiety
    B. decreases anxiety
    C. increases overall arousal
    D. decreases aggressiveness
    (B, p. 358, conceptual)

182.  Which of the following is true about benzodiazepines?

    A. They are more habit forming than barbiturates.
    B. They are not as safe as barbiturates.
    C. They are used to treat sleeping problems and epilepsy, as well
       as anxiety.
    D. They are rarely prescribed in current medical practice.
    (C, p. 358, factual)

183.  The GABA-A receptor complex controls the flow of which ion across the membrane?

    A. sodium
    B. potassium
    C. calcium
    D. chloride
    (D, p. 358, factual)

184.  A benzodiazepine molecule attaches to its receptor and affects the cell by:

    A. increasing receptor response to GABA.
    B. blocking the sodium gates in the membrane.
    C. increasing the flow of potassium.
    D. temporarily decreasing serotonin turnover.
    (A, p. 358, factual)

185.  A benzodiazepine molecule attaches to the receptors and:

    A. opens chloride channels.
    B. closes chloride channels.
    C. alters the shape of the receptor.
    D. stimulates release of a second messenger within the cell.
    (C, p. 358, factual)

186.  Endozepines are naturally occurring chemicals that attach to the same binding sites in the brain as:

A. lithium.
B. tricyclics.
C. benzodiazepines.
D. amphetamine.
(C, p. 358-359, factual)

187.  Endozepines attach to the same binding sites as ____ and affect the receptors in the _____ way.

A. lithium; same
B. tricyclics; same
C. benzodiazepines; opposite
D. amphetamine; opposite
(C, pp. 358-359, factual)

188.  Which of the following increases anxiety?

A. benzodiazepines
B. barbiturates
C. alcohol
D. endozepines
(D, p. 359, conceptual)

189.  Alcohol decreases anxiety by:

A. promoting chloride flow at the GABA-A receptor complex.
B. inhibiting chloride flow at the GABA-A receptor complex.
C. promoting sodium flow at serotonin synapses.
D. inhibiting sodium flow at serotonin synapses.
(A, p. 359, factual)

190.  A combination of benzodiazepines and alcohol should be avoided because:

A. each magnifies the effects of the other.
B. each cancels the effects of the other.
C. they react with each other chemically to form a new compound.
D. the combination produces excessive anxiety.
(A, p. 359, conceptual)

191.  Someone who had developed a tolerance to alcohol is likely to show a cross-tolerance to:

A. benzodiazepines.
B. amphetamines.
C. lithium.
D. antidepressants.
(A, p. 359, conceptual)

192.    An experimental drug, Ro15-4513, has been shown to block the
        behavioral effects of:

        A. tricyclics.
        B. amphetamines.
        C. alcohol.
        D. endozepines.
        (C, p. 359, factual)

193.    The experimental drug Ro15-4513:

        A. reduces anxiety.
        B. induces sleep.
        C. blocks the effects of alcohol.
        D. is used to treat phobias.
        (C, p. 359, factual)

**Module 13.1: Learning, Memory, Amnesia, and Brain Functioning**

1.      In the case of "C", the specific part of his brain that was
        damaged by encephalitis was the:

        A. parietal lobe.
        B. cerebellum.
        C. temporal lobe.
        D. frontal lobe.
        (C, p. 364, factual)

2.      What kind of memory impairments did "C" experience?

        A. forgot spatial locations of remembered objects
        B. forgot his own name
        C. forgot motor skills
        D. forgot his most recent experiences
        (D, p. 364, factual)

**Localized Representations of Memory**

3.      In Pavlov's experiments he presented a sound followed by meat.
        Gradually the sound came to elicit salivation.  What was the
        sound in this experiment?

        A. an unconditioned stimulus
        B. an unconditioned response
        C. a conditioned stimulus
        D. a conditioned response
        (C, p. 364, factual)

4.      In Pavlov's experiments he presented a sound followed by meat.
        Gradually the sound came to elicit salivation.  What was the meat
        in this experiment?

        A. an unconditioned stimulus
        B. an unconditioned response
        C. a conditioned stimulus
        D. a conditioned response
        (A, p. 364, factual)

5.      In Pavlov's experiments he presented a sound followed by meat.
        Gradually the sound came to elicit salivation.  What was the
        salivation to the meat in this experiment?

        A. an unconditioned stimulus
        B. an unconditioned response
        C. a conditioned stimulus
        D. a conditioned response
        (B, p. 364, factual)

6.    In Pavlov's experiments he presented a sound followed by meat.
      Gradually the sound came to elicit salivation.  What was the
      salivation to the sound in this experiment?

      A. an unconditioned stimulus
      B. an unconditioned response
      C. a conditioned stimulus
      D. a conditioned response
      (D, p. 364, factual)

7.    A puff of air is blown into a rabbit's eye, causing it to blink.
      The researcher then pairs a tone with the puff of air. In this
      experiment the air puff is the:

      A. unconditioned stimulus.
      B. unconditioned response.
      C. conditioned stimulus.
      D. conditioned response.
      (A, p. 366, conceptual)

8.    A puff of air is blown into a rabbit's eye, causing it to blink.
      The researcher then pairs a tone with the puff of air. In this
      experiment the blink to the air puff is the:

      A. unconditioned stimulus.
      B. unconditioned response.
      C. conditioned stimulus.
      D. conditioned response.
      (B, p. 366, conceptual)

9.    A puff of air is blown into a rabbit's eye, causing it to blink.
      The researcher then pairs a tone with the puff of air. In this
      experiment the tone is the:

      A. unconditioned stimulus.
      B. unconditioned response.
      C. conditioned stimulus.
      D. conditioned response.
      (C, p. 366, conceptual)

10.   A puff of air is blown into a rabbit's eye, causing it to blink.
      The researcher then pairs a tone with the puff of air. In this
      experiment the blink to the tone is the:

      A. unconditioned stimulus.
      B. unconditioned response.
      C. conditioned stimulus.
      D. conditioned response.
      (D, p. 366, conceptual)

11.    What should be the usual relationship between the conditioned
       stimulus and the unconditioned stimulus in classical
       conditioning?

       A. The conditioned stimulus should be presented first.
       B. The unconditioned stimulus should be presented first.
       C. They should be presented simultaneously.
       D. It depends on what each stimulus is.
       (A, p. 364, conceptual)

12.    In operant conditioning terms a reinforcement is best defined as:

       A. any food that the organism likes.
       B. a stimulus that produces a reflexive response.
       C. an event that decreases the future probability of a response.
       D. an event that increases the future probability of a response.
       (D, p. 364, factual)

13.    In operant conditioning terms a punishment is best defined as:

       A. a stimulus that produces a reflexive response.
       B. an event that decreases the future probability of a response.
       C. an event that increases the future probability of a response.
       D. an event that prevents a response.
       (B, p. 364, factual)

14.    Which of the following is hardest to classify as classical vs.
       operant conditioning?

       A. pressing a lever to get food
       B. pressing a lever to escape shock
       C. salivating after a sound previously paired with food
       D. song learning by male birds
       (D, p. 364, factual)

15.    Pavlov believed that classical conditioning reflected a
       strengthened connection between two brain areas representing:

       A. reinforcement and punishment.
       B. a response and a consequence.
       C. UCS activity and UCR activity.
       D. CS activity and UCS activity.
       (D, p. 364, factual)

16.    The hypothesis that Lashley was testing in his search for the
       engram was:

       A. Pavlov's view of classical conditioning.
       B. Skinner's view of operant conditioning.
       C. Garcia's view of taste aversion learning.
       D. Bandura's view of social learning.
       (A, p. 364, factual)

17.    Lashley's term "engram" referred to:

       A. a drug that facilitates learning.
       B. the physical representation of learning.
       C. a procedure that improved memory.
       D. an automatic response to a sensory stimulus.
       (B, p. 364, factual)

18.    An "engram" is a physiological representation of:

       A. emotion.
       B. memory.
       C. sensation.
       D. innate drives.
       ("WWW" B, p. 364, conceptual)

19.    What did Lashley call the physical basis of learning that he set
       out to find?

       A. an amyloid
       B. an engram
       C. a plaque
       D. a synapse
       (B, p. 364, factual)

20.    Lashley trained rats on a variety of mazes, then made deep cuts
       in their cortexes.  He found that the cuts produced:

       A. a temporary impairment.
       B. a permanent impairment.
       C. day-to-day fluctuations in performance.
       D. little apparent effect.
       (D, pp. 364-365, factual)

21.    Lashley found that a deep cut in a rat's cerebral cortex
       completely eliminated the effects of learning under what
       circumstances, if any?

       A. if the cut was made after the learning
       B. if the learned task was simple
       C. if the learned task was complex
       D. under none of the circumstances he studied
       (D, p. 365, factual)

22.    Lashley's experiments in search of the engram involved damaging
       cells in the:

       A. cerebral cortex.
       B. cerebellum.
       C. hippocampus.
       D. hypothalamus.
       (A, p. 365, factual)

23.     Lashley found that when he removed parts of the brain:

        A. only the removal of frontal lobe tissue disrupted performance.
        B. only the removal of parietal lobe tissue disrupted performance.
        C. the amount of tissue removed was more important than its location.
        D. he found no loss of memories at all.
        ("WWW" C, p. 365, factual)

24.     "All parts of the cortex contribute equally to complex behaviors such as learning" defines:

        A. operant conditioning.
        B. classical conditioning.
        C. equipotentiality.
        D. mass action.
        (C, p. 366, factual)

25.     The cortex works as a whole, and the more cortex the better, defines:

        A. operant conditioning.
        B. classical conditioning.
        C. equipotentiality.
        D. mass action.
        (D, p. 366, factual)

26.     Recent researchers have felt that Lashley's conclusions about the results of his search for the engram reflected some INAPPROPRIATE assumptions.  One of those assumptions was that:

        A. memory involves a physical change in the nervous system.
        B. the best place to search for the engram is the cerebral cortex.
        C. more than one kind of memory exists.
        D. different memories involve different sets of neurons.
        (B, p. 366, factual)

27.     Lashley's conclusions from his engram research were based on certain unnecessary assumptions, which later psychologists have discarded.  One of those assumptions was that the:

        A. brain treats all kinds of memory the same way.
        B. left hemisphere of the brain is simply the mirror image of the right hemisphere.
        C. physiological mechanisms of learning in rats are similar to those in humans.
        D. hippocampus is more important for storage than it is for retrieval.
        (A, p. 366, factual)

28.   In studies that paired a tone with an airpuff to the cornea of
      rabbits, learning was found to depend on one nucleus of the:

      A. cerebellum.
      B. hypothalamus.
      C. thalamus.
      D. hippocampus.
      (A, p. 366, factual)

29.   In studies of eyelid conditioning in rabbits, Thompson and his
      colleagues have demonstrated that learning for this conditioned
      response takes place in the:

      A. red nucleus of the midbrain.
      B. temporal lobe of the cerebral cortex.
      C. lateral interpositus nucleus of the cerebellum.
      D. ventromedial nucleus of the hypothalamus.
      (C, p. 366, factual)

30.   Suppose that while studying classical conditioning of the eyelid
      response in rabbits, investigators suppressed the activity of the
      lateral interpositus nucleus in the cerebellum.  What results
      would be expected?

      A. That procedure alone would not interfere with learning.
      B. Suppressing the lateral interpositus nucleus would prevent
         learning, while it is suppressed.
      C. Suppressing the lateral interpositus nucleus would temporarily
         prevent the response, but would not interrupt learning.
      D. The rabbit would never again be able to learn the response.
      (B, pp. 366-367, conceptual)

31.   A mid-brain motor area, involved in conditioning, that receives
      input from the cerebellum is the:

      A. lateral interpositus nucleus.
      B. red nucleus.
      C. ventromedial nucleus of the hypothalamus.
      D. medulla.
      (B, p. 367, factual)

32.   Research indicates that the red nucleus is necessary for:

      A. the learning of a conditioned response.
      B. the performance of a conditioned response.
      C. the learning AND performance of a conditioned response.
      D. suppression of the conditioned response.
      (B, p. 367, factual)

33.     Preventing learning is to _____ as suppressing a response is to
        _____.

        A. classical conditioning; operant conditioning
        B. operant conditioning; classical conditioning
        C. the red nucleus; the lateral interpositus nucleus
        D. the lateral interpositus nucleus; the red nucleus
        (D, p. 367, conceptual)

34.     Research has demonstrated that synapses in the lateral
        interpositus nucleus _____ their responsiveness to incoming
        stimuli during _____.

        A. increase; learning
        B. decrease; learning
        C. increase; forgetting
        D. decrease; forgetting
        (A, pp. 367-368, factual)

35.     The cerebellum's role in memories may be limited to what kind of
        learning or memory?

        A. language learning
        B. imprinting
        C. classical conditioning
        D. operant conditioning
        (C, p. 368, factual)

**Types of Memory**

36.     Donald Hebb (1949) distinguished between two types of memory and
        he called them:

        A. implicit and explicit.
        B. declarative and procedural.
        C. short-term and long-term.
        D. repressed and unrepressed.
        (C, p. 368, factual)

37.     Short-term memory may be characterized as:

        A. having a limited capacity.
        B. having an unlimited capacity.
        C. elaborative in nature.
        D. rehearsal free.
        (A, p. 368, factual)

38.      In the context of memory, the term consolidation refers to:

        A. the formation of a long-term memory.
        B. the formation of a short-term memory.
        C. disruption of the formation of long-term memory.
        D. disruption of the formation of short-term memory.
        ("WWW" A, p. 368, conceptual)

39. In Hebb's original theory, consolidation depended primarily on:

    A. which area of the cortex is activated.
    B. the emotional content of the information.
    C. the semantic nature of the information being remembered.
    D. the length of time the memory stays in short-term memory.
    (D, p. 368, factual)

40. One line of evidence that argues AGAINST Hebb's original consolidation theory is the fact that:

    A. short-term memories can form rapidly.
    B. some long-term memories last a lifetime.
    C. electroconvulsive shock to the brain interferes with consolidation.
    D. some memories take much longer than others to consolidate.
    (D, p. 368, factual)

41. What is true about the amount of time that it takes for memories to consolidate?

    A. It is consistent across species and tasks.
    B. It varies across species, but is consistent across tasks.
    C. It varies across tasks.
    D. It can be predicted from a mathematical formula.
    (C, pp. 368-369, conceptual)

42. Flashbulb memories refer to:

    A. memories of one's own idea or insights.
    B. memories which have been rehearsed over some period of time.
    C. memories that fade rapidly.
    D. meaningful and emotional memories formed quickly.
    (D, p. 369, factual)

43. Exciting experiences are remembered because such experiences arouse the sympathetic nervous system, increasing secretions of _____ into the bloodstream.

    A. GABA
    B. acetylcholine
    C. endorphin
    D. epinephrine
    (D, p. 369, factual)

44. Research on humans and animals has demonstrated that the storage and consolidation of recent experiences can be enhanced with direct injections of:

    A. epinephrine.
    B. GABA.
    C. endorphin.
    D. acetylcholine.
    (A, p. 369, factual)

45.    Exciting experiences are remembered well, because such
       experiences arouse the sympathetic nervous system, increasing
       secretions of which substance into the bloodstream?

       A. GABA
       B. acetylcholine
       C. endorphin
       D. epinephrine
       (D, p. 369, factual)

46.    How can memory consolidation be enhanced?

       A. by removal of the hippocampus
       B. by temporarily inhibiting the hypothalamus
       C. by increasing the level of epinephrine
       D. by decreasing glucose levels in the blood
       (C, p. 369, factual)

47.    Research on humans and animals has demonstrated that the storage
       and consolidation of recent experiences can be enhanced with
       direct injections of:

       A. cortisol.
       B. GABA.
       C. endorphin.
       D. acetylcholine.
       (A, p. 369, factual)

48.    Excitement enhances memory by _____ hormones that directly or
       indirectly activate the _____.

       A. stimulating; cerebellum
       B. stimulating; amygdala
       C. suppressing; cerebellum
       D. suppressing; amygdala
       (B, p. 369, factual)

49.    Hebb believed that short-term memory:

       A. should not be distinguished from long-term memory.
       B. was a temporary holding station on the way to long-term
          memory.
       C. was more important than long-term memory.
       D. was low-level memory.
       (B, p. 369, factual)

50.    What concept has largely replaced "short-term" memory?

       A. the central executive
       B. delayed-response memory
       C. working memory
       D. low-level memory
       (C, p. 369, factual)

51.  The general function of working memory is to:

     A. hold information until it has time to get to long-term
        storage.
     B. store memories of life events permanently.
     C. attend to and operate on current information.
     D. store information related to repetitious motor movements.
     (C, p. 369, conceptual)

52.  According to Baddeley and Hitch, what stores auditory
     information, including words?

     A. a phonological loop
     B. a visuospatial sketchpad
     C. the central executive
     D. long term memory
     (A, p. 369, factual)

53.  According to Baddeley and Hitch, what stores visual information?

     A. a phonological loop
     B. a visuospatial sketchpad
     C. the central executive
     D. long term memory
     (B, p. 369, factual)

54.  According to Baddeley and Hitch, which directs attention toward
     one stimulus or another and determines which items will be stored
     in working memory?

     A. a phonological loop
     B. a visuospatial sketchpad
     C. the central executive
     D. long term memory
     (C, p. 369, factual)

55.  Which of the following is NOT considered a component of working
     memory?

     A. a semantic interpreter
     B. a central executive
     C. a visuospatial sketchpad
     D. a phonological loop
     (A, p. 369, factual)

56.  The distinction was made between the phonological loop and the
     visuospatial sketchpad because:

     A. verbal memory seems to be independent of visual memory.
     B. certain items can't be stored in working memory.
     C. verbal memory is distinctly more complex than any other type
        of memory.
     D. directing attention toward visual memory requires one more
        process than does verbal memory.
     (A, p. 369, factual)

57.  Which brain area is active in monkeys during a delay when they
     have to remember the location of a light and look there only
     after a several-second delay?

     A. cerebellum
     B. the prefrontal cortex
     C. the occipital lobes
     D. ventromedial hypothalamus
     (B, pp. 369-370, factual)

58.  People with prefrontal cortex damage:

     A. cannot store auditory information.
     B. cannot store visual information.
     C. are impaired on delayed response tasks.
     D. do not use their short-term memory.
     (C, p. 370, factual)

59.  Which component of working memory is the most difficult to
     identify and test?

     A. the semantic interpreter
     B. the central executive
     C. the visuospatial sketchpad
     D. the phonological loop
     (B, p. 370, factual)

60.  People with damage in the prefrontal cortex have the most
     difficulty:

     A. with visual memory.
     B. with auditory memory.
     C. performing a verbal task.
     D. shifting attention between one task and another.
     (D, p. 370, factual)

**The Hippocampus and Amnesia**

61.  Following damage to the hippocampus and neighboring areas, the
     patient H.M. experienced:

     A. loss of events from long before the operation.
     B. a drop in IQ score.
     C. difficulty forming new memories and recalling them later.
     D. an inability to learn new motor skills.
     (C, p. 370, conceptual)

62.  The patient H.M. suffered severe memory disorders following a
     surgical operation that removed the:

     A. corpus callosum.
     B. hippocampus.
     C. lateral interpositus nucleus and hypothalamus.
     D. prefrontal cortex and dorsomedial thalamus.
     (B, p. 370, factual)

63.    Anterograde amnesia is to _____ as retrograde amnesia is to
       _____.

       A. storing new memories; memories of the past
       B. memories just prior to the damage; memories from childhood
       C. short-term memory; long-term memory
       D. emotional memories; nonemotional memories
       (A, p. 370, conceptual)

64.    Retrograde amnesia is to _____ as anterograde amnesia is to
       _____.

       A. temporary loss of memory; permanent loss of memory
       B. loss of short-term memory; loss of long-term memory
       C. inability to form new memories; loss of memory for old events
       D. loss of memory for old events; inability to form new memories
       (D, p. 370, conceptual)

65.    The patient H.M., who had major surgery for severe epilepsy in
       1953, suffered a severe difficulty in remembering events:

       A. of that year.
       B. during or after 1953.
       C. long before 1953.
       D. of his childhood.
       (B, p. 370, conceptual)

66.    What actually improved after H.M.'s surgery?

       A. his sense of humor
       B. his musical ability
       C. his IQ score
       D. his short-term memory
       (C, p. 370, factual)

67.    H.M. was able to learn and remember:

       A. people's names.
       B. how to find his way to a new residence.
       C. skills like mazes and puzzles.
       D. events in recent history.
       (C, p. 371, factual)

68.    A peculiarity of the memory of the neurological patient H.M. was
       that he was able to:

       A. retain new skills but not remember having learned them.
       B. form new long-term memories but not short-term memories.
       C. find his way to a new residence.
       D. remember people's names but not which name went with which
          person.
       (A, p. 371, conceptual)

69.     The memory for the development of motor skills is termed:

        A. implicit memory.
        B. explicit memory.
        C. procedural memory.
        D. declarative memory.
        ("WWW" C, p. 372, factual)

70.     The ability to state a memory in words is termed:

        A. procedural memory.
        B. declarative memory.
        C. implicit memory.
        D. short term memory.
        (B, p. 372, factual)

71.     How would one most accurately describe H.M.'s memory problems?

        A. inability to form short-term memories
        B. inability to establish new implicit memories
        C. inability to establish new declarative memories
        D. inability to establish new procedural memories
        (C, p. 372, conceptual)

72.     A question one might ask in order to test explicit memory would
        be:

        A. "How are you today?"
        B. "What did you do last night?"
        C. "Which one of these individuals would you ask for a favor?"
        D. "Would you please try playing this piano?"
        (B, p. 372, factual)

73.     Which of the following accurately describes H.M.'s memory
        problems?

        A. impaired short-term memory, but not long-term memory
        B. impaired procedural memory, but not declarative memory
        C. impaired explicit memory, but not implicit memory
        D. impaired personal memories, but not impersonal memories
        (C, p. 372, factual)

74.     Procedural memory is to _____ as declarative memory is to _____.

        A. jogging; walking
        B. reading; writing
        C. carrying on a conversation; listening to the radio
        D. juggling; explaining the sequence of moves in juggling
        (D, p. 372, conceptual)

75.  The delayed matching-to-sample task and the delayed nonmatching-
     to-sample tasks are considered to be examples of:

     A. declarative memory.
     B. procedural memory.
     C. the Morris search task.
     D. Korsakoff's syndrome.
     (A, p. 372, factual)

76.  Damage to the _____ impairs performance on the delayed matching-
     to-sample and delayed nonmatching-to-sample tasks.

     A. hypothalamus
     B. thalamus
     C. hippocampus
     D. parietal cortex
     (C, p. 372, factual)

77.  If a researcher makes minor changes to the procedure of the
     delayed matching-to-sample and delayed nonmatching-to-sample
     tasks, monkeys with hippocampal damage:

     A. perform well, regardless of the procedure.
     B. perform poorly, regardless of the procedure.
     C. perform differently, depending on the procedure.
     D. improve temporarily, regardless of procedure, and then return
        to their normal level of performance.
     ("WWW" C, p. 372, factual)

78.  Although there are different versions of the delayed matching-
     and non-matching-to-sample tasks, results suggest that the
     hippocampus is:

     A. necessary for all versions.
     B. necessary for some versions of the task but not others.
     C. not necessary for any of the versions.
     (B, p. 372, factual)

79.  A study with London taxi drivers found that answering _____
     activated their hippocampus more than answering _____.

     A. nonspatial questions; spatial questions
     B. spatial questions; nonspatial questions
     C. long questions; short questions
     D. short questions; long questions
     (B, pp. 373, factual)

80.  The radial maze task is a way to measure an animal's memory of:

     A. shape.
     B. color.
     C. time.
     D. space.
     (D, p. 373, conceptual)

81.   A rat is placed in a radial maze in which it has already been
      trained for many trials.  As compared to rats without damage to
      their hippocampus, rats with damage are more likely to:

      A. enter an alley at random.
      B. fail to eat the food they find.
      C. enter one of the correct alleys repeatedly.
      D. enter an alley that is never correct.
      (C, p. 373, factual)

82.   Which of the following experiments would be a reasonable test of
      whether an animal has suffered damage to its hippocampus?

      A. Does it reenter a single arm before entering all the other
         appropriate arms in a radial maze?
      B. Does it sometimes enter an arm in a radial maze that is never
         correct?
      C. Can it learn to climb along a thin wire without losing its
         balance?
      D. Can it learn to turn one direction when it hears a loud tone
         and a different direction when it hears a soft tone?
      (A, p. 373, conceptual)

83.   What area of the brain is particularly important for coding
      spatial information?

      A. hippocampus
      B. hypothalamus
      C. pons
      D. reticular formation
      (A, p. 373, conceptual)

84.   Which is true about the role of the hippocampus in memory?

      A. Most memories are stored in the hippocampus.
      B. Damage to the hippocampus impairs the storage of new
         procedural memories.
      C. Damage to the hippocampus impairs the storage of new
         declarative memories.
      D. Damage to the hippocampus impairs the retrieval of old
         memories.
      (C, p. 373, conceptual)

85.   A rat must swim through murky water to find a rest platform that
      is just under the surface in the:

      A. radial maze.
      B. Morris search task.
      C. configural learning task.
      D. delayed matching-to-sample task.
      (B, p. 373, factual)

86. A rat with hippocampal damage has difficulty with the Morris search task because it:

    A. loses its motivation to find the platform.
    B. cannot remember how to swim.
    C. has difficulty remembering where the platform is from trial to trial.
    D. develops a water phobia.
    (C, p. 373, factual)

87. There is compelling evidence for the role of the hippocampus in _____ memory.

    A. short term
    B. implicit
    C. spatial
    D. auditory
    (C, p. 373, factual)

88. A number of species of jays differ in their spatial memory. The species with the largest hippocampus performs best on tasks of:

    A. spatial memory.
    B. color memory.
    C. auditory memory.
    D. implicit memory.
    (A, p. 373, factual)

89. Researchers have found that different species of birds differ in terms of how much they depend on food they have stored to get through the winter. What factor is related to depending on and finding stored food?

    A. overall brain size
    B. relative size of the cortex
    C. relative size of the amygdala
    D. relative size of the hippocampus
    (D, p. 373, factual)

90. "The meaning of a stimulus depends on what other stimuli are paired with it," is the definition of:

    A. procedural memory.
    B. declarative memory.
    C. configural learning.
    D. classical conditioning.
    (C, p. 374, factual)

91.   Hippocampal damage usually impairs configural learning because:

A. such learning is trained and tested without any repetitions.
B. such learning is usually complicated and difficult.
C. the hippocampus is important for precisely measuring time
   spans.
D. the hippocampus is important in determining shape.
(B, p. 374-375, factual)

92.   Most researchers agree that the hippocampus is important for:

A. performance of motor skills.
B. precisely timing responses.
C. retrieving old memories.
D. consolidating memories.
(D, p. 375, factual)

**Other Types of Brain Damage and Amnesia**

93.   What type of deficiency causes Korsakoff's syndrome?

A. thiamine
B. protein
C. sodium
D. calcium
(A, p. 375, factual)

94.   Who is most likely to develop Korsakoff's syndrome?

A. those exposed to chronic stress
B. chronic alcoholics
C. certain ethnic groups
D. vegetarians
(B, p. 375, factual)

95.   An effective, early treatment for Korsakoff's syndrome is:

A. choline.
B. glucose.
C. benzodiazepines.
D. thiamine.
(D, p. 375, factual)

96.   What might prevent many cases of Korsakoff's syndrome?

A. alcoholic beverages fortified with thiamine
B. prohibition of the use of herbicides
C. warning labels on cigarettes
D. prohibition of the use of aluminum in cooking pots and pans
(A, p. 375, conceptual)

97.   Most Korsakoff's victims have a loss or shrinkage of neurons
      throughout the brain, especially in the:

      A. cingulate gyrus.
      B. occipital lobe.
      C. dorsomedial thalamus.
      D. cerebellum.
      ("WWW" C, p. 375, factual)

98.   A disorder most often associated with damage to the dorsomedial
      thalamus and mamillary bodies is:

      A. Alzheimer's disease.
      B. Korsakoff's syndrome.
      C. phenylketonuria.
      D. Down syndrome.
      (B, p. 375, factual)

99.   Damage to the _____ produces symptoms similar to Korsakoff's
      syndrome.

      A. prefrontal cortex
      B. basal ganglia
      C. occipital cortex
      D. precentral gyrus
      (A, p. 375, factual)

100.  What memory impairments are found in patients with Korsakoff's
      syndrome?

      A. only anterograde amnesia
      B. only retrograde amnesia
      C. anterograde and retrograde amnesia
      D. neither anterograde nor retrograde amnesia
      (C, p. 375, factual)

101.  Behaviors commonly seen in patients with Korsakoff's syndrome
      include:

      A. aggression and violence.
      B. apathy and confusion.
      C. sadness and depression.
      D. mistrust and suspicion.
      (B, p. 375, factual)

102.  People with Korsakoff's syndrome show:

      A. better implicit than explicit memory.
      B. better explicit than implicit memory.
      C. better declarative than procedural memory.
      D. memory for the order of events, but not memory for colors of
         common objects.
      (A, p. 375, factual)

103.  When prompted with cues, Korsakoff's victims can often produce
      words from lists they saw but claim to have never seen.  This
      exemplifies what kind of memory?

      A. reference
      B. procedural
      C. implicit
      D. explicit
      (C, p. 376, factual)

104.  When Korsakoff's syndrome patients read over a list of words,
      what evidence of memory, if any, do they demonstrate?

      A. None at all.
      B. They remember the first word and the last word only.
      C. They remember reading a list, although they cannot remember
         any of the words.
      D. They say many of the correct words if they are given the first
         three letters.
      (D, p. 376, conceptual)

105.  What memory task would a typical patient with Korsakoff's
      syndrome be able to do without difficulty?

      A. recall the temporal order of events
      B. remember someone he or she met in the past week
      C. an implicit memory task
      D. an explicit memory task
      (C, p. 376, conceptual)

106.  Confusing a made-up answer as a memory of an actual experience is
      referred to as:

      A. procedural memory.
      B. declarative memory.
      C. configuration.
      D. confabulation
      (D, p. 376, factual)

107.  What is confabulation?

      A. confusing a made-up answer as a memory of an actual experience
      B. having the two sides of the body working antagonistically
      C. confusing procedural memory for declarative memory
      D. remembering names, but being unable to put them with a face
      (A, p, 376, conceptual)

108.  Korsakoff's patients best remember a list of short sentences by:

A. reading and rereading them.
B. testing themselves on each sentence before going on to the
   next.
C. creating an elaborate story integrating the content of the
   sentences.
D. relating each sentence to a past personal experience.
(A, p. 376, factual)

109.  Restlessness, depression, hallucinations and loss of appetite all
accompany:

A. Korsakoff's syndrome.
B. Alzheimer's disease.
C. confabulation.
D. Aplysia.
(B, p. 376, factual)

110.  What percent of people between 65 – 74 years of age are affected
by Alzheimer's disease?

A. 5%
B. 25%
C. 50%
D. 85%
(A, p. 376, factual)

111.  What percent of those over 85 are affected by Alzheimer's
disease?

A. 5%
B. 10%
C. 50%
D. 85%
(C, p. 376, factual)

112.  As with Korsakoff's patients, Alzheimer's patients have
impairments in _____ memory, but are relatively unimpaired in
_____ memory.

A. short-term; long-term
B. implicit; explicit
C. procedural; declarative
D. declarative; procedural
(D, p. 377, factual)

113.  Alzheimer's patients are relatively unimpaired in:

A. declarative memory.
B. procedural memory.
C. short-term memory.
D. implicit and explicit memory.
(B, p. 377, factual)

114. Someone with a mild to moderate case of Alzheimer's disease would be most likely to remember which of the following?

    A. how to drive a car
    B. what make of car he or she drives
    C. where he or she parked the car
    D. the time he or she most recently drove a car
    (A, p. 377, conceptual)

115. Korsakoff's patients, and Alzheimer's patients are most successful at learning and remembering:

    A. facts.
    B. skills.
    C. names of people.
    D. words.
    (B, p. 377, factual)

116. Korsakoff's patients, and Alzheimer's patients have better memory for:

    A. recent events than events of the remote past.
    B. what is happening at a given moment than general principles.
    C. skills than facts.
    D. verbal information than visual information.
    (C, p. 377, conceptual)

117. If people with Down syndrome live long enough, they almost invariably develop:

    A. Korsakoff's syndrome.
    B. Parkinson's disease.
    C. Huntington's disease.
    D. Alzheimer's disease.
    (D, p. 377, factual)

118. Who is most likely to develop Alzheimer's disease?

    A. a chronic alcoholic
    B. a person with Down syndrome
    C. a person exposed to herbicides
    D. a person with epilepsy
    (B, p. 377, conceptual)

119. Researchers begin to look for clues to the genetics of Alzheimer's by investigating the chromosome related to:

    A. Korsakoff's disease.
    B. Down syndrome.
    C. epilepsy.
    D. alcoholism.
    (B, p. 377, factual)

120. In some cases of Alzheimer's disease that run in families, the
     cause of the disease appears to involve which gene(s)?

     A. a gene on the X chromosome
     B. a gene on the Y chromosome
     C. a series of genes on chromosome 4
     D. genes on several different chromosomes
     (D, p. 377, conceptual)

121. The genes related to Alzheimer's lead to the accumulation, in the
     brain, of:

     A. glucose.
     B. amyloid deposits.
     C. Ab40.
     D. serotonin.
     (B, p. 377, factual)

122. What is believed to be the likely cause of the brain damage
     typical of Alzheimer's disease?

     A. a relative deficit of thiamine
     B. a relative increase in Ab42 proteins
     C. a relative increase in Ab40 proteins
     D. a relative excess of acetylcholine
     (B, p. 377, conceptual)

123. Alzheimer's is associated with brain damage as a result of:

     A. loss of the fibers connecting the substantia nigra to the
        basal ganglia.
     B. loss of cell bodies in the dorsomedial thalamus.
     C. tangles and plaques in the cerebral cortex and hippocampus.
     D. an epileptic focus in the temporal lobe of the cortex.
     (C, p. 377, factual)

124. Plaques and tangles in the cerebral cortex are characteristic of
     people with:

     A. retrograde amnesia.
     B. anterograde amnesia.
     C. Korsakoff's syndrome.
     D. Alzheimer's disease.
     (D, p. 377, factual)

125. What is believed to be the likely cause of tangles and plaques?

     A. a relative deficit of thiamine
     B. increased pressure from cerebrospinal fluid
     C. amyloid deposits in the brain
     D. a relative deficit of acetylcholine
     (C, p. 377, factual)

126.   Amyloid beta protein 42 impairs the functions of:

       A. neurons but not glia.
       B. glia but not neurons.
       C. neurons and glia.
       D. the tau protein.
       (C, p. 377, factual)

127.   Most researchers now believe that the accumulation of amyloid and
       tau protein:

       A. is a result of the Alzheimer's disease.
       B. are partly the cause of Alzheimer's disease.
       C. are byproducts of acetylcholine.
       D. are byproducts of dying glial cells.
       (B, p. 377, factual)

128.   Structures formed from degenerating neuronal cell bodies are
       called:

       A. tau proteins.
       B. amyloid beta proteins.
       C. tangles.
       D. confabulations.
       (C, p. 377, factual)

129.   Structures formed from degenerating axons and dendrites are
       referred to as:

       A. tau proteins.
       B. amyloid beta proteins.
       C. confabulations.
       D. plaques.
       (D, p. 377, factual)

130.   People with Alzheimer's disease have tangles and plaques, which
       form from degenerating:

       A. chromosomes.
       B. neurons.
       C. glia.
       D. blood vessels.
       (B, p. 377, factual)

131.   One of the most heavily damaged areas in the brains of
       Alzheimer's patients is the:

       A. hippocampus.
       B. hypothalamus.
       C. thalamus.
       D. entorhinal cortex.
       (D, p. 377, factual)

132. One area, whose cells arouse the rest of the cortex, suffers consistent damage during Alzheimer's disease.  This area is the:

    A. hippocampus.
    B. hypothalamus.
    C. thalamus.
    D. basal forebrain.
    (D, p. 377, factual)

133. In rats, damage to the basal forebrain produces deficits best summarized as:

    A. impaired attention.
    B. manic symptoms.
    C. overstimulation of acetylcholine receptors.
    D. overstimulation of serotonin receptors.
    (A, p. 377, factual)

134. Researchers have found that Alzheimer's patients' memories can be enhanced by:

    A. elevating blood glucose levels.
    B. decreasing insulin secretion.
    C. inhibiting acetylcholine receptors.
    D. Increasing Ab42 production.
    (A, p. 377, factual)

135. A possible treatment for Alzheimer's is the administration of drugs that:

    A. stimulate acetylcholine receptors.
    B. inhibit the basal forebrain.
    C. inhibit acetylcholine release.
    D. increase Ab42 production.
    (A, p. 378, factual)

136. Research with an inbred strain of mouse found that injections of small amounts of Ab42 into young mice caused:

    A. a degeneration of tangles.
    B. a degeneration of plaques.
    C. increased immune system attacks of Ab42.
    D. an inhibition of acetylcholine release.
    (C, p. 378, factual)

137. The study of amnesic patients leads us to the conclusion that people have _____ kind of memory, and that memory depends on _____ of the brain.

    A. one; one specific location
    B. one; different parts
    C. more than one; one specific location
    D. more than one; different parts
    (D, p. 378, conceptual)

### Infant Amnesia

138.  One explanation of why people forget most of what happened in the
      first four or five years of life is that:

      A. the hippocampus is not yet mature.
      B. the corpus callosum is not yet mature.
      B. the hypothalamus has not yet made connections to the pituitary
         gland.
      D. they are unable to store procedural memories during that time.
      (A, p. 378, factual)

139.  According to one hypothesis, early declarative memories are weak
      because the:

      A. hippocampus is slow to mature.
      B. corpus callosum is slow to mature.
      C. hypothalamus is slow to mature.
      D. thalamus is slow to mature.
      (A, p. 378, factual)

140.  The memory performances of children in the first four or five
      years of life mildly resemble that of adults who have suffered
      damage to what area?

      A. parietal lobe
      B. lateral interpositus nucleus
      C. corpus callosum
      D. hippocampus
      ("WWW" D, pp. 378-379, conceptual)

## Module 13.2: Storing Information in the Nervous System

### Learning and the Hebbian Synapse

141.  A "Hebbian" synapse is one in which:

      A. activity at that synapse strengthens the response of the
         postsynaptic neuron to all of its synapses.
      B. repeated use of the synapse over a limited period of time
         leads to habituation.
      C. calcium flows into the cell while magnesium flows out of the
         cell.
      D. activity of the synapse, paired with an action potential in
         the postsynaptic cell, strengthens that synapse.
      (D, p. 381, conceptual)

142.  It is believed that Hebbian synapses may be critical for:

      A. associative learning.
      B. reflexes.
      C. loudness perception.
      D. color vision.
      (A, p. 381, factual)

143.  What kind of a synapse increases in effectiveness because of
      simultaneous activity in the presynaptic and postsynaptic
      neurons?

      A. a nicotinic synapse
      B. a muscarinic synapse
      C. a Hebbian synapse
      D. a Pavlovian synapse
      (C, p. 381, factual)

**Single-Cell Mechanisms of Invertebrate Behavior Change**

144.  What is a major advantage of Aplysia for studies on the
      physiology of learning?

      A. Their memories are more permanent than those of
         vertebrates.
      B. There are no differences between one neuron and another.
      C. There is great similarity of nervous system anatomy from one
         individual to another.
      D. They have only one type of learning.
      (C, pp. 381-382, factual)

145.  Why is the Aplysia such a popular animal for single-cell studies
      of learning?

      A. Individual cells identified in one animal can be recognized in
         another.
      B. Aplysi have greater learning abilities than other
         invertebrates.
      C. Aplysia have short-term learning but not long-term learning.
      D. Aplysia have only two neurotransmitters, one excitatory and
         one inhibitory.
      (A, pp. 381-382, factual)

146.  The studies of learning in Aplysia are most useful for
      determining:

      A. how single cells change as learning takes place.
      B. the differences between implicit memory and explicit memory.
      C. the relative contributions of cortical versus subcortical
         areas to learning.
      D. the differences between anterograde amnesia and retrograde
         amnesia.
      (A, pp. 382-383, conceptual)

147.  A commonly studied behavior in Aplysia is:

      A. the withdrawal response.
      B. spatial memory in a radial maze.
      C. explicit memory tasks.
      D. implicit memory tasks.
      (A, p. 383, factual)

148.    When Penfield stimulated the temporal cortex of alert and awake
        brain surgery patients he found that they:

        A. went into spastic convulsions.
        B. remembered specific events from earlier in their lives in
           great detail.
        C. lost all memory for events during and shortly preceding the
           stimulation.
        D. had a dream-like experience.
        (D, p. 382, factual)

149.    One line of research that initially appeared promising, but has
        since faded, was to study learning in decapitated:

        A. fish
        B. rats
        C. monkeys
        D. cockroaches
        (D, p. 383, factual)

150.    Why did some experimenters in the 1960's and 1970's grind up the
        brains of some rats and inject extracts into other rats?

        A. It was believed that the extra neurotransmitter would speed up
           learning.
        B. It was believed that memories could be transferred in this
           way.
        C. They were interested in brain transplants, and wanted to see
           if the material would be rejected.
        D. Studies of human cannibals had found extraordinary
           memory abilities.
        (B, p. 382-383, factual)

151.    What is the current status of research on transfer of training
        through brain extracts?

        A. It is generally accepted that this works under a variety of
           conditions.
        B. Transfer succeeds only in planaria: it has never worked with
           any other species.
        C. It has been revealed that claims of such a phenomenon were
           based on fraud.
        D. Research ended without a conclusion because the phenomenon was
           difficult to replicate.
        (D, p. 383, factual)

152.    If a stimulus is presented repeatedly, followed by no other
        stimulus, the animal will gradually stop responding.  This is
        known as:

        A. sensitization.
        B. habituation.
        C. classical conditioning.
        D. imprinting.
        (B, p. 383, factual)

153.   Which of the following is an example of habituation?

   A. After a tone occurs many times, a person stops responding to
      it.
   B. After repeated shocks, a person responds more strongly to the
      shock.
   C. After repeated shocks, a person stops responding to other
      stimuli.
   D. After a tone is repeatedly paired with a shock, a person
      responds more strongly to the tone.
   (A, p. 383, conceptual)

154.   If a jet of water is repeatedly squirted at the gills of an
       Aplysia, _____ occurs.

   A. sensitization
   B. habituation
   C. operant conditioning
   D. classical conditioning
   (B, pp. 383-384, factual)

155.   If you stimulate the gills of an Aplysia by squirting them with a
       brief jet of seawater, at first it will:

   A. ignore the water.
   B. withdraw its gills.
   C. take in the water through the gills.
   D. squirt the water in the direction of the source.
   (B, p. 383-384, factual)

156.   Habituation of the gill withdrawal response in Aplysia depends
       on:

   A. muscle fatigue.
   B. a decreased response by the sensory nerve to the stimulus.
   C. a change in the synapse between the sensory neuron and the
      motor neuron.
   D. an increase in the inhibitory impulses from sources other than
      the sensory nerve.
   (C, p. 383-384, factual)

157.   During habituation of the gill-withdrawal reflex in Aplysia, the
       change in the nervous system takes place at the:

   A. axon hillock of the sensory receptor.
   B. axon of the motor neuron.
   C. synapse between the sensory neuron and the motor neuron.
   D. inhibitory neurons that connect to the motor neuron.
   (C, p. 384, factual)

158.    Which of the following is an example of sensitization?

   A. Following a series of electrical shocks, a person overresponds
      to noises.
   B. Following a series of loud noises, a person is no longer
      aroused by additional noises.
   C. After repeated pairings of a noise with shock, a person is
      aroused less than usual by any mild stimulus.
   D. After repeated pairings of a noise with shock, a person is
      aroused less than usual only by the noise.
   (A, pp. 384-385, conceptual)

159.    After a series of electrical shocks, a person becomes
        overresponsive to lights and noises.  This exemplifies:

   A. habituation.
   B. sensitization.
   C. operant conditioning.
   D. classical conditioning.
   (B, pp. 384-385, factual)

160.    Habituation and sensitization differ depending upon whether:

   A. the effect is retroactive or proactive.
   B. the response grows weaker or stronger.
   C. the animal's behavior changes or fails to change.
   D. it occurs in all species or just mammals.
   (B, pp. 384-385, conceptual)

161.    Strong stimulation anywhere on the skin of an Aplysia excites
        axons that release:

   A. substance P.
   B. serotonin.
   C. neuropeptide Y.
   D. dopamine.
   (B, p. 384-385, factual)

162.    Strong stimulation anywhere on the skin of an Aplysia excites
        axons that attach to receptors and:

   A. open potassium channels in the membrane.
   B. close potassium channels in the membrane.
   C. opens sodium channels in the membrane.
   D. close sodium channels in the membrane.
   (B, p. 384, factual)

163. Following a certain kind of experience in Aplysia, a facilitating interneuron causes changes that block the potassium channels at the end of the axon of the sensory neuron, leading to:

    A. sensitization.
    B. habituation.
    C. both sensitization and habituation.
    D. death of the individual sensory neuron.
    (A, p. 385, conceptual)

164. In Aplysia, sensitization has been found to depend on a series of events that:

    A. block sodium channels in the motor neuron.
    B. decrease calcium concentration in the area surrounding the sensory neuron.
    C. open chloride channels in the motor neuron.
    D. block potassium channels in the sensory neuron.
    (D, p. 385, factual)

165. Research on Aplysia shows us that at least one physiological basis for learning involves which of the following?

    A. changes in RNA molecules
    B. presynaptic changes
    C. increased dendrite branching
    D. changes in glia
    (B, p. 385, conceptual)

**Long-Term Potentiation in Mammals**

166. How does one produce long-term potentiation of cells in the mammalian nervous system?

    A. a burst of many stimuli within a few seconds
    B. many stimuli spaced at exactly equal intervals over a period of minutes
    C. minutes of uninterrupted inhibitory stimulation
    D. a simultaneous pairing of an excitatory stimulus and an inhibitory stimulus
    (A, p. 385, factual)

167. If there is a burst of many stimulations to the mammalian nervous system during a one to four second period, it will result in:

    A. long-term potentiation of the cell's response to stimuli.
    B. long-term inhibition of the cell's response to stimuli.
    C. potentiation of the cell's response to stimuli for a few seconds.
    D. inhibition of the cell's response to stimuli for a few seconds.
    (A, p. 385, factual)

168.  What is true about a neuron that is "potentiated?"

A. It is highly responsive to new input similar to the stimuli
   that potentiated it.
B. It is unresponsive to any stimulus other than the specific
   stimulus that potentiated it.
C. It has increased numbers of collaterals branching from its
   axon.
D. It has an elevated spontaneous rate of firing.
(A, p. 385, factual)

169.  It is hoped that long-term potentiation (LTP) will help to
explain:

A. Alzheimer's disease.
B. Korsakoff's syndrome.
C. learning and memory.
D. inherited intelligence.
(C, p. 385, factual)

170.  If some of the synapses onto a cell have been highly active and
others have not, only the active ones become strengthened.  This
is known as the property of:

A. specificity.
B. cooperativity.
C. associativity.
D. NMDA.
("WWW" A, p. 385, factual)

171.  Nearly simultaneous stimulation by two or more axons produces
LTP, whereas stimulation by just one produces it weakly, if at
all.  This is known as the property of:

A. specificity.
B. cooperativity.
C. associativity.
D. LTD.
(B, p. 385, factual)

172.  Pairing a weak input with a strong input enhances later responses
to the weak input.  This is known as the property of:

A. specificity.
B. cooperativity
C. associativity.
D. LTD.
(C, p. 385, factual)

173. A long-term depression (LTD) in a neuron is:

    A. a burst of intense stimulation.
    B. a prolonged decrease in response to a synaptic input that has
       been repeatedly paired with some other input.
    C. the pairing of a weak input with a strong input.
    D. the result of cells having been highly active.
    (B, p. 385-386, factual)

174. At many hippocampal synapses, long-term potentiation depends on
    the activation of NMDA receptors, which are responsive to:

    A. GABA.
    B. glutamate.
    C. dopamine.
    D. norepinephrine.
    (B, p. 386, factual)

175. At many hippocampal synapses, long-term potentiation depends on
    the activation of which type of receptor?

    A. nicotinic.
    B. muscarinic.
    C. NMDA.
    D. GABA.
    (C, p. 386, factual)

176. In addition to the neurotransmitter glutamate, in order to
    activate the NMDA receptors, the neuron requires:

    A. serotonin.
    B. dopamine.
    C. increased release of magnesium ions from the presynaptic
       neuron.
    D. removal of magnesium ions from sodium and calcium channels.
    (D, p. 386, factual)

177. Under most conditions, NMDA receptors do NOT respond to their
    neurotransmitter because:

    A. magnesium ions block the passage of calcium through the
       receptor's channel.
    B. too many sodium ions enter through the AMPA channels.
    C. any recent depolarization of the membrane inactivates the NMDA
       receptors.
    D. the channel can open only when the potassium concentration
       inside the neuron exceeds a certain high level.
    (A, p. 386, factual)

178. The NMDA receptor responds to its transmitters when:

     A. magnesium is present in the membrane.
     B. enough sodium ions exit through AMPA channels.
     C. the membrane is already at least partly depolarized.
     D. the dendrite is depolarized enough to produce an action
        potential.
     ("WWW" C, p. 386, factual)

179. Which is known to be critical for long-term potentiation?

     A. high levels of magnesium
     B. only one axon being active at a time
     C. the absence of NMDA receptors
     D. a massive inflow of calcium
     (D, p. 386, factual)

180. Blocking NMDA synapses has what effect, if any, on LTP?

     A. There is no effect on LTP.
     B. It enhances the establishment of LTP.
     C. It interferes with the maintenance of LTP.
     D. It prevents the establishment of LTP.
     (D, p. 386, factual)

181. When glutamate massively stimulates AMPA receptors, the resulting
     depolarization:

     A. keeps glutamate from stimulating nearby NMDA receptors.
     B. keeps calcium from entering the cell.
     C. enables glutamate to stimulate nearby NMDA receptors.
     D. inhibits the dendrite's responsiveness to glutamate.
     (C, p. 387, factual)

182. When glutamate massively stimulates AMPA receptors, the
     NMDA receptors:

     A. increase their responsiveness to glutamate.
     B. decrease their responsiveness to glutamate.
     C. inhibit further AMPA responsiveness.
     D. increase their responsiveness to GABA.
     (A, p. 387, factual)

183. Once LTP has been established:

     A. it remains dependent on NMDA synapses.
     B. it fades quickly.
     C. AMPA receptors convert into NMDA receptors.
     D. the AMPA receptors stay potentiated for hours, or longer.
     ("WWW" D, p. 387, factual)

184. Drugs that block NMDA synapses:

    A. interfere with the maintenance of LTP.
    B. prevent the establishment of LTP.
    C. facilitate the maintenance of LTP.
    D. facilitate the establishment of LTP.
    (B, p. 387, factual)

185. The critical period of development in the visual system
     apparently is related to how easy it is to stimulate which type
     of receptor?

    A. nicotinic
    B. AMPA
    C. NMDA
    D. dopamine
    (C, p. 388, factual)

186. What type of activity affects the length of the critical period
     in the development of the visual system?

    A. thyroid gland secretions
    B. sensitivity of NMDA receptors
    C. increased activity in a small nucleus in the cerebellum
    D. hormone bursts from the anterior pituitary
    (B, p. 388, factual)

187. As animals undergo training, LTP occurs in the hippocampus and
     one also can detect LTP:

    A. nowhere else in the brain.
    B. simultaneously in parts of the cortex.
    C. in parts of the cortex within approximately two hours.
    D. in the spinal cord within approximately two hours.
    (C, p. 388, factual)

188. Mice with genes that cause abnormalities of the NMDA receptor:

    A. do not live to maturity.
    B. have difficulty learning.
    C. have "leaky" calcium channels.
    D. have impaired coordination of movement.
    (B, p. 388, factual)

189. In aged mammals, drugs can enhance memory by:

    A. blocking calcium channels.
    B. increasing calcium levels.
    C. blocking COMT channels.
    D. increasing COMT levels.
    (A, p. 388, factual)

190.  A reason that memory declines in aged animals is that:

   A. endorphin levels drop.
   B. the levels of the hormones ACTH and vasopressin are higher in
      old age.
   C. calcium channels allow too much calcium into the cells when at
      rest.
   D. acetylcholine levels in the brain rise.
   (C, p. 388, conceptual)

191.  Drugs that partially_____ calcium channels can _____ learning and
   memory in old age.

   A. excite; enhance
   B. excite; interfere with
   C. block; enhance
   D. block; interfere with
   (C, p. 388, factual)

**Module 14.1: Lateralization of Function**

1.    The left hemisphere is connected to skin receptors mainly on the
      _____ half of the body, and controls muscles mainly on the _____
      side of the body.

      A. left; right
      B. left; left
      C. right; left
      D. right; right
      (D, p. 394, factual)

2.    The brain has _____ control of the facial muscles.

      A. ipsilateral
      B. contralateral
      C. bilateral
      D. no
      (C, p. 394, conceptual)

3.    Information passes from one hemisphere of the brain to the other
      through the:

      A. medulla.
      B. corpus callosum.
      C. cerebellum.
      D. brain stem.
      (B, p. 394, factual)

4.    Most of the information passing from one hemisphere to the other
      does so by passing through which structure?

      A. cerebellum
      B. inferior colliculus
      C. corpus callosum
      D. massa intermedia
      (C, p. 394, conceptual)

5.    In most humans, control of language is centered in the:

      A. left hemisphere.
      B. right hemisphere.
      C. corpus callosum.
      D. cerebellum.
      (A, p. 394, factual)

6.    What is the name given to the specialization of function between
      the two hemispheres?

      A. hemispherectomy
      B. lateralization
      C. polarization
      D. symmetry
      (B, p. 394, factual)

7.     Lateralization refers to the:

       A. formation of the sulci and gyri in the cortex.
       B. functional asymmetries of the brain.
       C. slow rate of maturation in forebrain structures.
       D. physical changes that occur in neurons as learning takes
          place.
       (B, p. 394, conceptual)

8.     Lateralization refers to the:

       A. formation of ventricles in the forebrain.
       B. division of labor between the two hemispheres.
       C. rate of maturation in forebrain structures.
       D. physical changes that occur in neurons as learning takes
          place.
       ("WWW" B, p. 394, conceptual)

9.     You see the effects of lateralization more readily than normal
       after damage to:

       A. the suprachiasmatic nucleus.
       B. the corpus callosum.
       C. one or the other eye.
       D. the pineal gland.
       (B, p. 394, conceptual)

**Visual and Auditory Connections to the Hemispheres**

10.    The left hemisphere of the human brain sees the:

       A. left visual field.
       B. right visual field.
       C. left visual field of the left eye and right visual field of
          the right eye.
       D. right visual field of the left eye and left visual field of
          the right eye.
       (B, p. 395, factual)

11.    Given the way the right hemisphere of the human brain is
       connected to the retinas of the eyes, what does it see?

       A. the left visual field
       B. the right visual field
       C. only a strip along the center of the visual field
       D. all the light that strikes the left eye
       (A, p. 395, factual)

12.   The left hemisphere of the human brain receives visual input from the:

      A. retina of the left eye.
      B. retina of the right eye.
      C. left half of each retina.
      D. right half of each retina.
      ("WWW" C, p. 395, factual)

13.   The right hemisphere of the human brain receives visual input from the:

      A. retina of the left eye.
      B. retina of the right eye.
      C. left half of each retina.
      D. right half of each retina.
      (D, p. 395, factual)

14.   Information from the left visual field stimulates neurons in the:

      A. retina of the left eye.
      B. retina of the right eye.
      C. left half of both retinas.
      D. right half of both retinas.
      (D, p. 395, factual)

15.   Information from the retina of the right eye is received by:

      A. the left hemisphere.
      B. the right hemisphere.
      C. both hemispheres.
      D. neither hemisphere.
      (C, p. 395, factual)

16.   Someone who suffered damage to the visual cortex of the left hemisphere would probably have impaired vision in the:

      A. left eye.
      B. right eye.
      C. left visual field.
      D. right visual field.
      (D, p. 395, application)

17.   A small vertical strip down the center of each retina connects to:

      A. the right hemisphere.
      B. the left hemisphere.
      C. both hemispheres.
      D. neither hemisphere.
      (C, p. 395, conceptual)

18.    The axons from the two eyes:

       A. cross at the first cranial nerve.
       B. cross at the optic chiasm.
       C. cross at the anterior commissure.
       D. do not cross in humans.
       (B, p. 395, factual)

19.    What you see in your right visual field goes to:

       A. the right hemisphere.
       B. the left hemisphere.
       C. both the right and left hemispheres.
       D. the right half of each retina.
       (B, p. 396, factual)

20.    Visual stimuli in the right visual field stimulate:

       A. the right half of each retina.
       B. the left half of each retina.
       C. the right hemisphere.
       D. both hemispheres.
       (B, p. 396, factual)

21.    A condition in which brain neurons have repeated episodes of
       excessive, synchronized activity is called:

       A. dyslexia.
       B. epilepsy.
       C. hippocampal commissure.
       D. Broca's aphasia.
       (B, p. 396, factual)

22.    The causes of epilepsy:

       A. include genetics, trauma, and infections.
       B. are limited to infections of the brain.
       C. are limited to genetic abnormalities.
       D. are currently unknown.
       (A, p. 396, factual)

23.    Genes that cause epilepsy do so by altering:

       A. voltage-gated ion channels.
       B. neurotransmitter chemicals.
       C. the arrangement of blood vessels in the brain.
       D. the shapes of astroglia cells.
       (A, p. 396, factual)

24.   A seizure which spreads quickly across neurons over a large
      portion of both hemispheres of the brain is a:

      A. partial seizure.
      B. petit mal seizure.
      C. generalized seizure.
      D. psychomotor seizure.
      (C, p. 396, factual)

25.   Another name for an absence seizure in which the victim stares
      unresponsive to the environment for a brief period of time is a:

      A. grand mal seizure
      B. petit mal seizure
      C. psychomotor seizure
      D. partial seizure
      (B, p. 397, factual)

26.   Generalized seizures that spread over both hemispheres of the
      brain and result in sudden, repetitive jerking movements and a
      loss of consciousness are referred to as:

      A. grand mal seizures.
      B. petit mal seizures.
      C. complex seizures
      D. psychomotor seizures.
      (A, p. 396, factual)

27.   A seizure that begins with a focus somewhere in the brain and
      then spreads to nearby areas is called a:

      A. grand mal seizure.
      B. generalized seizure.
      C. partial seizure.
      D. petit mal seizure.
      (C, p. 397, factual)

28.   Which symptoms are NOT typically seen in someone who experiences
      temporal lobe seizures?

      A. convulsions and loss of consciousness
      B. lip smacking or chewing
      C. dreamlike hallucinations
      D. repetitive thoughts
      (A, p. 397, factual)

29.   More than 90% of epileptic patients:

      A. have been successfully treated with drugs.
      B. have been successfully treated with surgery.
      C. do not respond to any of the current forms of treatment.
      D. have at least three generalized seizures per month.
      (A, p. 397, factual)

### Cutting the Corpus Callosum

30.    Damage to the corpus callosum prevents:

       A. hyperpolarization of neurons there.
       B. release of pituitary hormones.
       C. exchange of information between the two hemispheres.
       D. exchange of information between pre- and postsynaptic
          membranes.
       (C, p. 396, factual)

31.    Several patients have had their corpus callosum cut surgically as
       a treatment for severe cases of:

       A. schizophrenia.
       B. obsessive-compulsive disorder.
       C. epilepsy.
       D. dyslexia.
       (C, p. 396, factual)

32.    It was discovered that severing the corpus callosum to treat
       severe epilepsy:

       A. relieved the epileptic symptoms in fewer than 10% of cases.
       B. also produced severe intellectual and emotional impairments.
       C. was helpful to older, but not younger, patients.
       D. was more effective than was anticipated.
       (D, p. 396, conceptual)

33.    Damage to the corpus callosum in lab animals interfered with:

       A. normal sensation.
       B. control of movement.
       C. reaching for something in the right visual field with the left
          paw.
       D. memory for complex discrimination tasks learned prior to the
          surgery.
       (C, p. 396, factual)

34.    Damage to the corpus callosum in lab animals resulted in abnormal
       behavior:

       A. when sensory stimuli were limited to one side of the body.
       B. for movement control.
       C. for memory of tasks requiring conditioning.
       D. for visual stimuli only.
       (A, p. 396, factual)

35.    A split-brain patient is someone who has had the:

       A. corpus callosum severed.
       B. cerebellum severed.
       C. frontal lobe separated from the rest of the cortex.
       D. cerebral cortex separated from the rest of the brain.
       (A, p. 396, factual)

36.     Split brain patients suffer:

        A. little or no impairment of overall intellectual performance.
        B. a lack of motor control.
        C. sensation deficits.
        D. memory deficits.
        (A, p. 397, factual)

37.     Roger Sperry conducted important research in what field of study?

        A. epilepsy
        B. the physiological effects of addictive drugs
        C. split-brain patients
        D. language training for chimpanzees
        (C, p. 397, factual)

38.     A split-brain patient sees something in her left visual field,
        and must reach behind a screen and select the object out of a
        group of objects.  She will select the object correctly with:

        A. the left hand.
        B. the right hand.
        C. either hand.
        D. neither hand.
        (A, p. 397, factual)

39.     A typical split-brain patient who stares straight ahead CANNOT
        name something seen:

        A. in the right visual field.
        B. in the left visual field.
        C. with the right eye.
        D. with the left eye.
        (B, p. 397, factual)

40.     In order for a split-brain patient to name something, he must see
        it:

        A. with the left eye.
        B. with the right eye.
        C. in the left visual field.
        D. in the right visual field.
        ("WWW" D, p. 397, conceptual)

41.     A split-brain patient who sees something in his left visual field
        can point to it with the:

        A. left hand but cannot name it.
        B. right hand but cannot name it.
        C. left hand and can name it.
        D. right hand and can name it.
        (A, p. 397, factual)

42.    A split-brain patient who sees something in her right visual
       field can point to it with the:

       A. left hand but cannot name it.
       B. right hand but cannot name it.
       C. left hand and can name it.
       D. right hand and can name it.
       (D, p. 397, conceptual)

43.    A split-brain patient who sees something in one visual field and
       later can point to it with the left hand must:

       A. have seen it in the right visual field.
       B. have seen it in the left visual field.
       C. be able to say what it was.
       D. be able to point to it with the right hand, also.
       (B, p. 397, conceptual)

44.    A patient who only can name objects after seeing them in the
       right visual field but can point out objects she saw in the left
       visual field has probably suffered damage to:

       A. Wernicke's area.
       B. Broca's area.
       C. the visual cortex in the right hemisphere.
       D. the corpus callosum.
       (D, p. 397, conceptual)

45.    Which self-contradiction occurs in people who have had their
       corpus callosum cut?

       A. saying they are not hungry while eating
       B. saying they do not know the answer while pointing it out with
          the left hand
       C. writing with one hand but not being able to write with the
          other
       D. suddenly changing from a manic state to depression
       (B, p. 397, conceptual)

46.    A physician injects sodium amytal into the carotid artery on one
       side of the head during the:

       A. Wada test.
       B. dichotic listening task.
       C. hippocampal commissure test.
       D. split brain operation.
       (A, p. 398, factual)

47.   After sodium amytal is injected into the right hemisphere, a
      person with left-hemisphere dominance for speech will:

      A. continue to speak.
      B. speak more slowly.
      C. speak grammatically but without correct names of objects.
      D. stop speaking.
      (A, p. 398, factual)

48.   While wearing headphones a person listens to different words
      presented to the two ears at the same time during the:

      A. Wada test.
      B. dichotic listening task.
      C. hippocampal commissure test.
      D. split brain operation
      (B, p. 398, factual)

49.   If a person identifies mostly words heard in the right ear during
      the dichotic listening task, she would be language dominant in:

      A. the right hemisphere.
      B. the left hemisphere.
      C. both hemispheres.
      D. the left hemisphere for listening and the right hemisphere for
         language.
      (B, p. 398, factual)

50.   Several months after split-brain surgery the number of incidents
      of conflicts between the two hemispheres:

      A. diminishes.
      B. is unchanged from shortly after the surgery.
      C. increases dramatically.
      D. increases and then experiences a sharp drop.
      (A, p. 399, factual)

51.   Several months after split-brain surgery the number of incidents
      of conflicts between the two hemispheres diminishes because:

      A. portions of the corpus callosum grow back.
      B. the right hemisphere begins to control all body muscles.
      C. the hemispheres learn ways of cooperating with each other.
      D. the cerebellum assumes the former functions of the corpus
         callosum.
      (C, p. 399, factual)

52. Conflicts between the two hemispheres eventually diminish because:

    A. brain swelling decreases.
    B. the callosum partly reconnects.
    C. the left hemisphere suppresses the right hemisphere's interference.
    D. the right hemisphere simply takes control for some situations.
    (C, p. 399, factual)

53. A split-brain person watches as a picture is flashed in the left visual field. When asked, "Was it a round object?" he replies, "Yes. I mean no," when "no" is the correct answer. The patient gets the correct answer from:

    A. information passed from the right hemisphere through a few regenerated axons.
    B. changes in facial expression controlled by the right hemisphere.
    C. axons that connect the speech areas directly to the right visual cortex.
    D. changes in blood flow to the left hemisphere.
    (B, p. 399, conceptual)

54. If a split-brain patient sees the word sky in his left visual field and the word scraper in his right visual field, which picture will he draw with the left hand?

    A. the sky only.
    B. the scraper only.
    C. a sky and a scraper, separately.
    D. a skyscraper.
    (C, p. 399, factual)

55. A split-brain patient sometimes drew interesting pictures with his left hand after two words were presented, one to each hemisphere. Following his pattern, after seeing the words "water" and "pitcher," he likely would draw:

    A. a glass of clear liquid.
    B. clear liquid surrounding a glass.
    C. a "picture" of a waterfall.
    D. somebody throwing water.
    (D, p. 399, conceptual)

56. In the typical split-brain person, the left hand is to _____ as the right hand is to _____.

    A. picking up objects; pointing at objects
    B. pointing at objects; picking up objects
    C. writing the word "car"; drawing a car
    D. drawing a car; writing the word "car"
    (D, p. 399, conceptual)

57.  Researchers believe that the right hemisphere is:

     A. the mirror image of the left hemisphere, with the same
        functions.
     B. subordinate to the left hemisphere for all functions.
     C. in control of speech.
     D. specialized in functions that differ from the left.
     ("WWW" D, p. 399, factual)

58.  Control of the emotional content of speech depends on:

     A. the right hemisphere.
     B. the left hemisphere.
     C. both hemispheres equally.
     (A, p. 399, factual)

59.  People who speak with little inflection or expression usually
     have suffered damage to the:

     A. ventromedial spinal pathway.
     B. left hemisphere.
     C. right hemisphere.
     D. corpus callosum.
     (C, p. 399, factual)

60.  The right hemisphere probably contributes more than the left
     hemisphere to the _____ of speech.

     A. semantic content
     B. emotional content
     C. grammatical structure
     D. volume
     (B, p. 399, factual)

61.  Damage to the left hemisphere is more likely than right
     hemisphere damage to impair which ability?

     A. understanding the meaning of language
     B. understanding that someone is joking when they speak
     C. producing facial expressions of emotion
     D. understanding other people's facial expressions
     (A, p. 399, conceptual)

62.  After damage to the right hemisphere, many people suffer what
     kind of loss?

     A. control of the muscles on the right side of the body
     B. hunger and thirst
     C. ability to remember the names of objects
     D. facial expressions
     (D, p. 400, factual)

63.  Following damage to the _____, a patient has a decrease in facial
     expressions of emotion and decreased understanding of the
     emotional content of other people's speech.

     A. corpus callosum
     B. left hemisphere of the cerebral cortex
     C. right hemisphere of the cerebral cortex
     D. occipital lobe on both sides
     (A, p. 400, conceptual)

64.  Emotions such as fear and anger mostly activate:

     A. the right hemisphere.
     B. the left hemisphere.
     C. both hemispheres.
     D. the right hemisphere in females and the left hemisphere in
        males.
     (A, p. 401, factual)

65.  The emotion happiness mostly activates:

     A. the right hemisphere.
     B. the left hemisphere.
     C. both hemispheres.
     D. the left hemisphere in females and the right hemisphere in
        males.
     (B, p. 401, factual)

66.  If you were advising the make-up artist for a movie involving a
     character with a facial disfigurement, where would you suggest
     the disfigurement be located for the maximum emotional impact on
     the audience?

     A. the upper part of the face
     B. the lower part of the face
     C. the right side of the face (viewer's left)
     D. the left side of the face (viewer's right)
     (C, p. 400 conceptual)

67.  If you are given directions composed of detailed information,
     they will be processed mainly by:

     A. the right hemisphere.
     B. the left hemisphere.
     C. the right hemisphere in young children but the left hemisphere
        in adults.
     D. the left hemisphere in young children but the right hemisphere
        in adults.
     (B, p. 400, factual)

68.  The right hemisphere is more important than the left hemisphere
     for:

     A. remembering the names of objects.
     B. assembling puzzles.
     C. moving the right hand.
     D. understanding language.
     (B, p. 400, conceptual)

69.  What kind of person can assemble puzzles and draw pictures more
     successfully with the left hand than with the right hand?

     A. most normal people
     B. right-handers only
     C. people who have suffered damage to the right hemisphere of the
        cerebral cortex
     D. people who have suffered damage to the corpus callosum
     (D, p. 400, conceptual)

70.  Right-hemisphere damage would cause impairment to individuals
     trying to:

     A. imagine visual and spatial information.
     B. respond to weak visual stimuli, just above the threshold of
        detection.
     C. name the objects seen.
     D. coordinate movements of the right hand with objects seen in
        the right visual field.
     (A, p. 400, factual)

71.  People with right-hemisphere damage have particular trouble with
     tasks that require:

     A. understanding sentences with a complex grammatical structure.
     B. visual imagery.
     C. control of the right hand.
     D. memory of recent events.
     (B, p. 400, factual)

72.  The right hemisphere is better at spatial processing, in part,
     due to the fact that the:

     A. parvocellular path is stronger in the right hemisphere.
     B. parvocellular path is stronger in the left hemisphere.
     C. magnocellular path is stronger in the right hemisphere.
     D. magnocellular path is stronger in the left hemisphere.
     (C, p. 400, factual)

73.   A person who doesn't understand your jokes may have suffered
      damage to:

      A. the right hemisphere.
      B. the left hemisphere.
      C. the cerebellum.
      D. the pineal gland.
      (A, p. 401, factual)

74.   When an English speaking person listens to a language with a
      singing quality, activity occurs:

      A. mainly in the right hemisphere.
      B. mainly in the left hemisphere.
      C. in both hemispheres about equally.
      D. in the right hemisphere if you are a child.
      (C, p. 401, factual)

75.   Thai and other tonal languages have a musical quality.  Listening
      to Thai activates _____ in native Thai speakers and _____ in
      English speakers.

      A. both hemispheres about equally; both hemispheres about
         equally.
      B. mainly the left hemisphere; both hemispheres about equally.
      C. mainly the left hemisphere; mainly the left hemisphere.
      D. both hemispheres about equally; mainly the left hemisphere.
      (B, p. 401, factual)

76.   A person is asked to tap her index finger as fast as possible for
      one minute.  What difference, if any, would it make if she were
      talking during the task?

      A. Talking would decrease tapping in the right hand more than in
         the left hand.
      B. Talking would decrease tapping in the left hand more than in
         the right hand.
      C. Talking would decrease tapping in both hands equally.
      D. Talking typically would not affect the tapping rate of either
         hand.
      (A, p. 401, conceptual)

**Development of Lateralization and Handedness**

77.   At what age is it first noticeable that a person's brain activity
      changes in reaction to changes in sound?

      A. immediately after birth
      B. not until one month old
      C. not until one year old
      D. not until three years old
      (A, p. 401, factual)

78.    For a majority of humans, one part of the _____ cortex is larger
       on the _____ side of the brain than on the opposite side.

       A. temporal; right
       B. temporal; left
       C. occipital; right
       D. occipital; left
       (B, p. 401, factual)

79.    The planum temporale can be found in the:

       A. frontal lobe.
       B. parietal lobe.
       C. temporal lobe.
       D. occipital lobe.
       (C, p. 402, factual)

80.    The planum temporale is large in the:

       A. right hemisphere for most people.
       B. left hemisphere for most people.
       C. right hemisphere but only for newborns.
       D. left hemisphere but only for newborns.
       (B, p. 402, factual)

81.    Which of the following is true about the planum temporale?

       A. It is larger in the left hemisphere for most people.
       B. It is symmetrical in adult humans but asymmetrical in infants.
       C. It is symmetrical in humans, but is asymmetrical in nonhuman
          primates.
       D. It is abnormally large in the brains of many dyslexic
          individuals.
       (A, p. 402, factual)

82.    MRI scans have found that healthy children with  _____ performed
       _____ on language tests.

       A. the smallest ratio of left to right planum temporale; best
       B. an equal ratio of left to right planum temporale; best
       C. the largest ratio of left to right planum temporale; best
       D. the largest ratio of left to right planum temporale; worse
       (C, p. 402, factual)

83.    At what point in human development do physical differences
       between the left and right hemispheres of the brain first become
       apparent?

       A. in early infancy, before the start of speech
       B. around age 1-2 years, when children begin to speak
       C. around age 4-5, when speech is approaching maturity
       D. around age 11-14, the time of puberty
       (A, p. 402, conceptual)

84.    MRI scans have found that healthy children with an almost equal
       ratio of left to right planum temporale performed better than
       those with a larger planum temporale on:

       A. practically all tasks.
       B. nonverbal tasks.
       C. speech fluency.
       D. language understanding.
       (B, p. 402, factual)

85.    What determines which axons in the corpus callosum survive to
       maturity?

       A. The ones that develop first survive.
       B. The ones that develop first die.
       C. The ones that develop connections between cells with similar
          functions survive.
       D. The ones that develop connections between cells with similar
          functions die.
       (C, p. 402, factual)

86.    How does experience affect the development of the corpus
       callosum?

       A. It determines how many axons will grow in the corpus callosum.
       B. It determines which axons in the corpus callosum will survive.
       C. It determines the speed of conduction in the corpus callosum.
       D. It determines where axons in the corpus callosum will go on
          the opposite sides of the brain.
       (B, p. 402, conceptual)

87.    A 9-week-old child does not reach with the right hand toward an
       object in the left visual field:

       A. until connections are mature enough between the right eye and
          the brain.
       B. because the child cannot maintain balance when the center of
          gravity moves to one side.
       C. until the visual cortex is mature.
       D. because the corpus callosum is not yet mature.
       (D, p. 402, conceptual)

88.    Children are asked to feel two fabrics and to determine whether
       they are the same or different.  This is more difficult for _____
       children who have to feel the fabrics with _____.

       A. younger; the same hand
       B. younger; different hands
       C. older; the same hand
       D. older; different hands
       (B, p. 402, factual)

89.   A similarity between a young child and a split-brain
      patient is that both:

      A. show frequent spontaneous changes in personality.
      B. have trouble describing what they see through the left eye.
      C. have a greater than normal number of back-and-forth eye
         movements.
      D. have trouble comparing what they feel with the two hands at
         one time.
      (D, p. 402, conceptual)

90.   UNLIKE adults who have had their corpus callosum cut, children
      born without a corpus callosum are generally able to:

      A. move their hands with better than normal speed and
         coordination.
      B. learn foreign languages more rapidly than intact people can.
      C. verbally describe what they feel with the left hand.
      D. verbally describe what they feel with the right hand.
      (C, p. 403, conceptual)

91.   Who would probably be able to name an object after feeling it
      with either hand?

      A. all people who have had their corpus callosum cut in
         adulthood
      B. right-handed people who have had their corpus callosum cut in
         adulthood
      C. people born without a corpus callosum.
      D. people who have had their somatosensory regions of the cortex
         removed.
      (C, p. 403, factual)

92.   People born without a corpus callosum can perform some tasks as
      do people with a corpus callosum.  They can perform these tasks:

      A. because the corpus callosum eventually does grow, to a degree.
      B. because the brain's other commissures become larger than
         usual.
      C. because the right hemisphere develops the abilities normally
         reserved for the left and the left develops the abilities
         normally reserved for the right.
      D. because the two hemispheres communicate through the exchange
         of hormones.
      ("WWW" B, p. 403, factual)

93.   Which hemisphere is dominant for language in left-handed people?

      A. The left hemisphere is dominant in about 99%.
      B. The right hemisphere is dominant in about 99%.
      C. The left hemisphere is usually dominant, but most left-handers
         have some control by both hemispheres.
      D. The right hemisphere is usually dominant, but most left-
         handers have some control by both hemispheres.
      (C, p. 403, factual)

94.    On the average, left-handed people, compared to right-handed
       people, have:

       A. a thinner corpus callosum.
       B. a thicker corpus callosum.
       C. poorer vision in the left visual field.
       D. poorer vision in the right visual field.
       (B, p. 403, factual)

95.    Most tasks evoke:

       A. greater activity in the left hemisphere than the right.
       B. greater activity in the right hemisphere than the left.
       C. activity in one hemisphere over the other only for the very
          simplest tasks.
       D. activity in one hemisphere over the other only for the most
          complex tasks.
       (C, p. 403, factual)

96.    What kind of task is most likely to require activity by just one
       hemisphere, instead of both?

       A. visual task
       B. auditory task
       C. very simple task
       D. very complicated task
       (C, p. 403, factual)

**Module 14.2: Evolution and Physiology of Language**

**Nonhuman Precursors of Language**

97.    Early studies taught chimpanzees to use symbols to communicate
       with a computer and each other.  Which of the following does NOT
       characterize their use of symbols?

       A. They consistently used the same symbol patterns.
       B. They frequently made requests.
       C. They learned to type messages to other chimps.
       D. They frequently used new and original combinations.
       (D, p. 405, factual)

98.    Chimpanzees using symbols:

       A. often used them to describe things.
       B. seemed to understand others' requests as well as make
          requests.
       C. almost always used the symbols to request and rarely to
          describe.
       D. often used them in new, original combinations.
       (C, p. 405, factual)

99.  The nonhuman species that has made the most spectacular progress
     toward learning to communicate by an approximation of human
     language is the:

     A. common chimpanzee.
     B. pygmy chimpanzee.
     C. gorilla.
     D. dolphin.
     (B, p. 405, factual)

100. The training of Kanzi differed from the earlier language studies
     using other chimpanzees in that Kanzi:

     A. observed his mother being trained while he was an infant.
     B. was given food reinforcements for associating arbitrary
        symbols with meanings.
     C. was given only verbal praise.
     D. was raised from birth in a human family, in total isolation
        from other animals.
     (A, p. 406, factual)

101. What distinguished Kanzi and Mulika from other chimpanzees used
     in earlier studies was that Kanzi and Mulika:

     A. only used symbols to make requests.
     B. were able to say English words, with a vocabulary equal to a
        2-year-old child.
     C. were not able to make creative requests as were other chimps.
     D. occasionally used symbols to relate events of the past.
     (D, p. 406, factual)

102. What is NOT a possible explanation for Kanzi and Mulika's
     language abilities?

     A. Their species may be more adapted to learning language.
     B. Learning through imitation is more effective than learning
        with rewards.
     C. They began learning at an earlier age.
     D. They were raised as "children" and given attention only for
        communicating.
     (D, p. 406, factual)

103. Studies of nonhuman language abilities call attention to the:

     A. ability of many species to learn language.
     B. close relationship between language and classical
        conditioning.
     C. difficulty of defining language.
     D. close relationship between language and brain size.
     (C, pp. 406-407, factual)

104.  What can we learn about human language abilities from the studies
      of nonhuman language abilities?

      A.  Language is totally limited to humans.
      B.  The only important language advantage of humans is in our
          vocal apparatus.
      C.  We may gain some insights into how best to teach language to
          those who do not learn it easily.
      D.  Language is indistinguishable from the forms of communication
          that other species use.
      (C, p. 407, conceptual)

105.  It appears that human language evolved from a precursor that was
      probably:

      A.  present only in human ancestors.
      B.  a byproduct of total brain size.
      C.  present in the ancient ancestor from which humans and Bonobos
          evolved.
      D.  a single gene mutation.
      (C, p. 408, factual)

**How Did Humans Evolve Language?**

106.  Based on brain-to-body weight, it appears that:

      A.  language is a by-product of this ratio.
      B.  humans have the highest ratio of all species.
      C.  this ratio is a constant across vertebrates.
      D.  intelligence and language are not simple outcomes of this
          ratio.
      (D, p. 408, factual)

107.  People in one family have a gene that seriously impairs language
      without decreasing overall intelligence.  This observation argues
      AGAINST the theory that:

      A.  language learning is based on a "language acquisition device."
      B.  intelligence consists of a series of more or less separate
          "modules."
      C.  language evolved from a precursor ability present in other
          primates.
      D.  Language evolved as a byproduct of selection for overall
          intelligence.
      (D, pp. 408-409, conceptual)

108.  Children with Williams syndrome are characterized by:

      A.  good language abilities despite low overall intelligence.
      B.  loss of language abilities at approximately four years of age.
      C.  problems creating grammatical sentences.
      D.  repetition of what they hear others say, with little
          indication of understanding.
      (A, p. 409, factual)

109. A paradoxical characteristic of children with Williams syndrome is that they:

A. seem retarded during childhood but develop into normal or even bright adults.
B. can write, but cannot read what they just finished writing.
C. show a better memory after a delay than they show immediately after an event has occurred.
D. have very large vocabularies, but cannot learn simple skills.
(D, p. 409, factual)

110. Which of the following is a rare condition in which people are retarded in many ways, but yet are remarkably skilled in their use of language?

A. Williams syndrome
B. dyslexia
C. Wernicke's aphasia
D. anomia
(A, p. 409, factual)

111. Characteristic of the brains of people with Williams syndrome is:

A. a larger than normal right hemisphere, but smaller than normal left hemisphere.
B. a larger than normal left hemisphere, but smaller than normal right hemisphere.
C. less than normal overall mass in the cerebral cortex.
D. a greatly diminished limbic system.
(C, p. 409, factual)

112. What is the apparent relationship between language abilities and other intellectual abilities?

A. Impairments in either results in impairments in the other.
B. It is possible to have good language and poor intelligence, but not the reverse.
C. It is possible to have good intelligence and poor language, but not the reverse.
D. Either can be impaired independently of the other.
(D, p. 410, factual)

113. Most researchers agree that humans have specially evolved something to allow them to learn language. That something is:

A. an extremely high level of intelligence.
B. a larger brain than any other species.
C. the largest brain-to-body ratio of all species.
D. still unknown.
(D, pp. 410-411, factual)

114. One way to test the hypothesis that people are biologically adapted to learn best during a critical period is to:

    A. compare the vocabularies of children and adults.
    B. determine whether people learn a second language better than a first language.
    C. determine whether people learn a second language if they start young.
    D. compare the grammar use of children and adults.
    (C, p. 411, factual)

115. Profoundly deaf children without a chance to learn sign language at an early age:

    A. cannot learn it if they do not during childhood.
    B. can easily learn it after adolescence.
    C. cannot learn it unless they attempt to learn a spoken language first.
    D. never catch up to those who begin when young.
    (D, p. 411, factual)

116. Research with deaf children suggests that it is essential to:

    A. learn any language when you are young if you don't want to be forever disadvantaged.
    B. learn language through reinforcements for correct usage.
    C. be able to hear language if you are to learn sign language.
    D. learn spoken language before sign language.
    ("WWW" A, p. 411, factual)

**Effects of Brain Damage on Language**

117. The first to publish a detailed description linking a specific part of the brain to a loss of speech was:

    A. Roger Sperry.
    B. Jerre Levy.
    C. David and Ann Premack.
    D. Paul Broca.
    (D, p. 412, factual)

118. Broca's area is located in the:

    A. left parietal lobe.
    B. left frontal lobe.
    C. right temporal lobe.
    D. right occipital lobe.
    (B, p. 412, factual)

119. A loss of language ability, in general, is referred to as:

    A. apraxia
    B. dyslexia
    C. aphasia
    D. anomia
    (C, p. 412, factual)

120. The discovery that language depends on a specific part of the brain:

    A. found great resistance, at first.
    B. was eventually discredited.
    C. was deduced by researchers in phrenology.
    D. was a twentieth century discovery.
    ("WWW" A, p. 412, factual)

121. Someone with Broca's aphasia has the greatest difficulty:

    A. understanding spoken language.
    B. understanding written language.
    C. remembering the names of objects.
    D. speaking.
    (D, p. 412, factual)

122. Nonfluent aphasia, in which the victim is unable to speak fluently, is due to brain damage that includes:

    A. Broca's area
    B. the postcentral gyrus of the parietal lobe
    C. Wernicke's area
    D. the corpus callosum
    (A, p. 412, factual)

123. People with Broca's aphasia speak meaningfully but:

    A. do so without feeling.
    B. do so in a monotone.
    C. omit pronouns, tense and number endings.
    D. omit nouns and verbs.
    (C, p. 412, factual)

124. People with Broca's aphasia cannot read aloud "To be or not to be" because they:

    A. cannot control the muscles of their throat.
    B. have difficulty with words that have no clear meaning out of context.
    C. cannot pronounce those sounds.
    D. cannot read.
    (B, p. 412, factual)

125. Someone with Broca's aphasia is least likely to use:

    A. prepositions and conjunctions.
    B. adjectives and adverbs.
    C. nouns.
    D. verbs.
    (A, p. 412, factual)

126. Deaf people with Broca's aphasia:

    A. do not have any difficulty producing sign language.
    B. do not have the same problem with gesturing that hearing
       people do.
    C. have little use of their arms and hands.
    D. have trouble producing sign language.
    (D, 412, factual)

127. A stroke patient speaks in short, inarticulate but meaningful
     phrases such as "Weather hot" and "Dog bite man." This person is
     probably suffering from:

    A. Broca's aphasia.
    B. Wernicke's aphasia.
    C. Williams syndrome.
    D. apraxia.
    (A, p. 412, conceptual)

128. Broca's aphasia patients have difficult understanding language in
     that they cannot:

    A. remember the meaning of nouns, especially unusual nouns.
    B. understand a sentence if its meaning depends on verbs.
    C. understand a sentence if its meaning depends on word order or
       grammatical devices.
    D. hear many of the words spoken.
    (C, p. 412, factual)

129. A person who has a great deal of trouble understanding a sentence
     if its meaning depends on word order is a:

    A. split-brain patient.
    B. patient with damage to Wernicke's area.
    C. patient with damage to Broca's area.
    D. patient suffering from apraxia.
    (C, p. 412, factual)

130. A person with Broca's aphasia:

    A. has lost total knowledge of grammar.
    B. has lost total knowledge of use of verbs.
    C. recognizes that something is wrong with grammatically
       incorrect sentences.
    D. insists that his or her utterances are grammatically correct
       and that other people are wrong.
    (C, p. 413, factual)

131.  The process of relating skull anatomy to behavioral capacities is
      known as:

      A. phrenology.
      B. Wernicke's aphasia.
      C. Broca's aphasia.
      D. Williams syndrome.
      (A, p. 413, factual)

132.  Someone suffering from Wernicke's aphasia has difficulty:

      A. articulating speech.
      B. reading aloud.
      C. understanding speech.
      D. using prepositions and conjunctions.
      (C, p. 414, factual)

133.  Wernicke discovered that damage to the _____ produced language
      impairment.

      A. right temporal cortex.
      B. left temporal cortex.
      C. right frontal cortex.
      D. left frontal cortex.
      (B, p. 414 factual)

134.  Fluent aphasia, in which the victim has difficulty comprehending
      language but is still able to speak smoothly, is due to damage
      to:

      A. Broca's area.
      B. Wernicke's area.
      C. the prefrontal cortex.
      D. the corpus callosum.
      (B, p. 414, factual)

135.  Anomia involves difficulty:

      A. using prepositions and conjunctions.
      B. understanding written, as opposed to spoken, language.
      C. remembering the names of objects.
      D. speaking rapidly and fluently.
      (C, p. 414, factual)

136.  As compared to a person with Broca's aphasia, a person with
      Wernicke's aphasia can:

      A. remember the names of objects.
      B. understand written language.
      C. understand spoken language.
      D. speak fluently and rapidly.
      (D, p. 414, factual)

137.  Wernicke's aphasia is to _____ as Broca's aphasia is to _____.

    A. parietal lobe; temporal lobe
    B. nouns; verbs
    C. spoken language; sign language
    D. understanding; speaking
    (D, p. 414, conceptual)

138.  Reading a sentence aloud causes activity in:

    A. Broca's area only.
    B. Wernicke's area only.
    C. the cortex surrounding Broca's and Wernicke's areas.
    D. many areas surrounding Broca's and Wernicke's as well as both
       of those areas.
    ("WWW" D, p. 414, factual)

139.  One study found that different parts of the temporal lobe become
      activated by speech, depending on whether the person was naming:

    A. large objects or small objects.
    B. animals or tools.
    C. familiar animals or uncommon animals.
    D. heavy objects or light objects.
    (B, p. 416, factual)

140.  The results of a study suggest that when people think of and name
      a function they activate the:

    A. hypothalamus.
    B. hippocampus.
    C. the areas that they would use to perform that function.
    D. the occipital lobe.
    (C, p. 416, factual)

141.  Studies suggest that naming activates:

    A. different brain areas depending on the number of syllables.
    B. different areas depending on the objects.
    C. one area only and that is Broca's area.
    D. one area only and that is Wernicke's area.
    (B, p. 416, factual)

142.  The frontal cortex is most likely involved in reading if the
      person:

    A. must state a use for the object they are reading about.
    B. must decide whether two words rhyme.
    C. must read nonsense syllables.
    D. has suffered damage to the motor area that would enable them
       to perform that function related to the object they are
       reading about.
    (A, p. 416, factual)

**Dyslexia**

143.  A specific impairment of reading in a person with adequate vision
      and adequate skills in other academic areas is referred to as:

      A. Broca's aphasia.
      B. Wernicke's aphasia.
      C. Williams' syndrome.
      D. dyslexia.
      ("WWW" D, p. 416, factual)

144.  More typical of dyslexic people than of nondyslexics is a:

      A. larger than normal fovea.
      B. smaller than normal fovea.
      C. relatively unresponsive magnocellular paths in the visual
         system.
      D. relatively unresponsive parvocellular paths in the visual
         system.
      (C, p. 416, factual)

145.  The impairments dyslexic individuals show in detecting overall
      patterns and with rapidly changing stimuli seem to be related to:

      A. a relatively unresponsive magnocellular pathway in the visual
         system.
      B. a relatively overresponsive parvocellular pathway in the
         visual system.
      C. a larger than normal planum temporale in the left hemisphere.
      D. an abnormality in the photopigments found in the rods and
         cones of the retina.
      (A, p. 417, factual)

146.  More typical of dyslexic people than of other people is:

      A. a planum temporale that is larger in the left hemisphere than
         the right hemisphere.
      B. a bilaterally symmetrical cerebral cortex.
      C. damage to the posterior portion of the corpus callosum.
      D. an overresponsive magnocellular pathway in the visual system.
      (B, p. 417, factual)

147.  Dyslexia is apparently not just a problem of reading but also an
      abnormality of:

      A. attention.
      B. color vision.
      C. distribution of rods and cones on the retina.
      D. velocity of action potentials.
      (A, p. 417, factual)

148.  According to the results of recent research, one task people with
      dyslexia can generally do better on than normal readers is:

      A. solving geometrical problems.
      B. reading words in the periphery of their vision.
      C. reading words that are spelled incorrectly.
      D. forming near-photographic mental images of what they have
         seen.
      (B, p. 417, conceptual)

149.  According to recent research, people with dyslexia:

      A. have trouble discriminating one letter from another.
      B. suffer from interference among letters on the line they are
         reading.
      C. have trouble controlling their eye movements.
      D. are slower than other people are in remembering the meanings
         of words.
      ("WWW" B, p. 417, conceptual)

150.  One effective technique that seems to help increase the reading
      skills of dyslexics is one involving the use of:

      A. a special cutout sheet of paper to expose only one word at a
         time.
      B. a sheet of paper to expose only one line at a time.
      C. flash cards.
      D. sounding out each word.
      (A, p. 418, factual)

151.  One drawback some dyslexics report when they improve their
      reading skills by focusing on one word at a time is that:

      A. it was helpful for reading print but not cursive writing.
      B. they no longer receive special attention from those around
         them.
      C. they read the words, but lose comprehension.
      D. they lose their ability to do several tasks at once.
      (D, p. 418, factual)

**Module 15.1: Alcoholism**

1.     A maladaptive pattern of substance use leading to clinically significant impairment or distress, is DSM-IV's definition of:

     A. depression.
     B. substance abuse.
     C. dependent personality.
     D. mood disorders.
     (B, p. 424, factual)

**Genetics**

2.     Type I (or A) alcoholism is characterized by:

     A. a strong genetic basis.
     B. rapid, early onset.
     C. an equal incidence in men and women.
     D. a high association with criminality.
     (C, p. 424, factual)

3.     As compared to Type I alcoholism, Type II (or B) is characterized:

     A. by a stronger genetic basis.
     B. by a more gradual development.
     C. by an equal occurrence in men and women.
     D. as less severe.
     (A, p. 424, factual)

4.     What is highly characteristic of Type II alcoholism?

     A. low dopamine turnover
     B. low acetylcholine turnover
     C. low serotonin turnover
     D. low GABA turnover
     ("WWW" C, p. 425, factual)

5.     In experiments with rats and alcohol, it was found that alcohol:

     A. decreased impulsive behavior.
     B. increased impulsive behavior.
     C. was related to very aggressive behavior.
     D. resulted in the choice of a large, delayed reward over a small immediate reward.
     (B, p. 425, factual)

6.     The highest concordance rate for alcohol abuse is found among:

     A. children and their adoptive parents.
     B. siblings.
     C. dizygotic twins.
     D. monozygotic twins.
     (D, p. 425, factual)

7.    In what ways do genetics contribute to alcoholism?

      A. There are multiple genes that increase the risk of alcoholism.
      B. A recessive gene has been found to cause alcoholism.
      C. There has been no evidence of a genetic connection.
      D. The genes responsible are only passed from father to son.
      (A, p. 425, factual)

**Alcohol Metabolism and Antabuse**

8.    A toxic substance occurring during the normal metabolism of
      alcohol is:

      A. dehydrogenase.
      B. acetaldehyde.
      C. ethyl alcohol.
      D. acetic acid
      (B, p. 425, factual)

9.    Acetaldehyde is converted into:

      A. dehydrogenase.
      B. acetaldehyde dehydrogenase.
      C. ethyl alcohol.
      D. acetic acid.
      (D, p. 425, factual)

10.   One reason that may explain why alcohol abuse is less common
      among people of Asian ancestry is that:

      A. they have lower than average body weight.
      B. they have low levels of enzymes that metabolize alcohol.
      C. there are cultural biases toward abstinence.
      D. they have overly sensitive acetylcholine receptors.
      (B, p. 425, factual)

11.   Alcohol abuse is less common among people in China and Japan
      because about half of the people have a gene that:

      A. speeds up acetaldehyde metabolism.
      B. slows acetaldehyde metabolism.
      C. causes their acetylcholine receptors to be overly sensitive.
      D. increases their levels of enzymes that metabolize alcohol.
      (B, p. 425, factual)

12.   Physiologically, the drug Antabuse decreases the consumption of
      alcohol by:

      A. blocking the enzyme that breaks it down into acetic acid.
      B. modifying the taste buds.
      C. increasing the rate of activity in the left frontal cortex.
      D. inducing a temporary "high" that competes with the effects of
         alcohol.
      (A, p. 425, conceptual)

13.    Why does a person who drinks alcohol after taking the drug
       Antabuse get sick?

       A. It blocks the conversion of acetaldehyde to acetic acid.
       B. It prevents thiamine from crossing the blood-brain barrier.
       C. It produces effects on the synapses similar to those produced
          by alcohol itself.
       D. It increases the rate at which alcohol enters the central
          nervous system.
       ("WWW" A, p. 425, conceptual)

14.    Antabuse (disulfiram) was discovered by accident when someone
       noticed that:

       A. shoe salespeople drank less alcohol than other sales people.
       B. beer develops a bad aftertaste when kept in iron containers.
       C. rubber factory workers developed a distaste for alcohol.
       D. the sight and smell of alcohol made dental students ill.
       (C, p. 425, factual)

15.    What is the idea behind giving Antabuse to alcoholics?

       A. It may cause them to associate alcohol with illness.
       B. It provides a less debilitating, less addictive high.
       C. It helps them to sober up after getting drunk.
       D. It prevents them from experiencing the intoxicating effects.
       (A, pp. 425-426, factual)

16.    Psychologically, how does the drug Antabuse decrease the
       consumption of alcohol?

       A. It makes alcohol taste very bad.
       B. It increases the rate of activity in the right frontal cortex.
       C. It reduces anxiety so there is no need to drink alcohol.
       D. It serves to reaffirm the decision to abstain.
       (D, pp. 425-426, factual)

**Risk Factors for Alcohol Abuse**

17.    Studies have identified two characteristics that are predictive
       of males becoming alcoholics and they are:

       A. getting to drink some alcohol in childhood and being a
          "nontaster."
       B. getting to drink some alcohol in childhood and having
          excessive activity in the prefrontal cortex.
       C. having an alcoholic father and underestimating intoxication.
       D. having an alcoholic father and accurately estimating
          intoxication.
       (C, p. 426, factual

**Module 15.2: Mood Disorders**

**Major Depressive Disorder**

18.  The differences between ordinary and major depression depend on:

A. when they occur in one's lifetime.
B. intensity and duration.
C. geographic location and gender.
D. society and diet.
("WWW" B, p. 428, factual)

19.  Which of the following is NOT a characteristic of depression?

A. impulsiveness
B. sleep disorders
C. inactivity
D. suicidal tendencies
(A, p. 428, factual)

20.  According to a 1994 survey of more than 8,000 U.S. adults, approximately what percent of people suffer from some form of psychiatrically significant depression at some time in their lives?

A. 1%
B. 5%
C. 20%
D. 50%
(C, p. 428, factual)

21.  Which is true when considering the role of genetics in depression?

A. Depression in females runs in families, depression in males does not.
B. Depression in males runs in families, depression in females does not.
C. Adopted children who become depressed are more likely to have depressed biological relatives than depressed adoptive relatives.
D. Adopted children who become depressed are more likely to have depressed adoptive relatives than depressed biological relatives.
(C, p. 428, factual)

22.  If an adopted child experiences episodes of depression, it is most likely that those suffering similar episodes are:

A. adoptive parents.
B. adoptive siblings.
C. biological relatives.
D. female biological relatives, only.
(C, p. 428, factual)

23.   A family history of depression increases your risk more strongly
      if you are:

      A. female.
      B. male.
      C. left-handed.
      D. right-handed.
      (A, p. 428, factual)

24.   Your risk of depression is increased if you:

      A. have relatives with a mild depression.
      B. have relatives with severe depression.
      C. have relatives with depression which began after the
         age of 30.
      D. are a male.
      (B, p. 428, factual)

25.   Depression is more common in females than males in:

      A. the United States only.
      B. Western Europe only.
      C. Asia only.
      D. all cultures for which there are data.
      (D, p. 428, factual)

26.   The sex difference in depression:

      A. remains unexplained.
      B. is likely due to hormones.
      C. is due to a single gene.
      D. is the result of more women than men seeking treatment.
      (A, p. 428, factual)

27.   The most severe episodes of depression generally occur:

      A. after a traumatic experience.
      B. in the summer.
      C. in women just before they give birth.
      D. when hormone levels are high.
      (A, p. 429, factual)

28.   The hormonal changes associated with giving birth most often
      affect depression by:

      A. decreasing the probability of a woman becoming depressed.
      B. temporarily decreasing the severity of an episode of
         depression.
      C. triggering or aggravating a depressive episode.
      D. causing temporary episodes of depression even in women who
         have no history of depression.
      (C, p. 429, conceptual)

29.   About one woman in a thousand enters a serious, long-lasting depression following the birth of a child.  What is generally true about these women?

A. They are predisposed to depression prior to the birth of their child.
B. They are less likely than other women to have experienced depression prior to the birth.
C. They show elevated activity levels in the left hemisphere of their brains.
D. They fail to respond to tricyclic antidepressants.
(A, p. 429, factual)

30.   Studies of normal people have found a fairly strong relationship between:

A. happy mood and increased activity in the left prefrontal cortex.
B. happy mood and decreased activity in the left prefrontal cortex.
C. happy mood and increased activity in the right occipital cortex.
D. sadness and increased activity in the left occipital cortex.
(A, p. 429, factual)

31.   Studies of normal people have found a fairly strong relationship between happy mood and _____ activity in the _____.

A. increased; right prefrontal cortex
B. decreased; right prefrontal cortex
C. increased; left prefrontal cortex
D. decreased; left prefrontal cortex
("WWW" C, p. 429, factual)

32.   Most depressed people show _____ activity in the _____ prefrontal cortex.

A. increased; left
B. decreased; left
C. decreased; right
D. increased; right and left
(B, p. 429, factual)

33.   If you ask depressed people to solve a cognitive problem, they are more likely than other people to:

A. look straight ahead.
B. look up.
C. gaze to the right.
D. gaze to the left.
(D, p. 429, factual)

34.    When attempting to solve cognitive problems, in what direction
       are most depressed people more likely than other people to gaze?

       A. left
       B. up
       C. down
       D. straight ahead
       (A, p. 429, factual)

35.    Left hemisphere damage is associated with:

       A. mania.
       B. PMS.
       C. depression.
       D. schizophrenia.
       (C, p. 429, factual)

36.    Several lines of evidence suggest that depressed people have
       lower than normal levels of activity in the:

       A. parietal lobes.
       B. occipital lobes.
       C. right hemisphere.
       D. left hemisphere.
       (D, p. 429, factual)

37.    Damage to which area of the brain is most likely to produce
       serious depression in the victim?

       A. the right hemisphere
       B. the left hemisphere
       C. the corpus callosum
       D. the brain stem
       (B, p. 429, factual)

38.    The Borna disease is characterized by:

       A. hallucinations.
       B. periods of frantic activity as well as inactivity.
       C. excessive eating.
       D. immune deficiency.
       (B, p. 429, factual)

39.    The Borna disease virus has been found in some of the people who
       suffer from:

       A. dyslexia.
       B. autism.
       C. stuttering.
       D. depression.
       (D, p. 430, factual)

40.  Which virus has been found to be related to major depression?

     A. Borna
     B. rabies
     C. herpes
     D. syphilis
     (A, p. 430, factual)

41.  Evidence suggests that the Borna virus predisposes people to:

     A. Huntington's disease.
     B. dyslexia.
     C. psychiatric difficulties.
     D. herpes.
     (C, p. 430, factual)

42.  What do the disulfiram, iproniazid, and bromides have in common?

     A. They all have different effects on men versus women.
     B. They all have different effects on adults versus children.
     C. They exert their effects by inhibiting the synthesis of
        dopamine.
     D. Their beneficial effects were discovered by accident.
     (D, p. 430, factual)

43.  Disulfiram was originally used in the manufacture of:

     A. fuel.
     B. rubber.
     C. insecticides.
     D. suntan lotion.
     (B, p. 430, factual)

44.  Iproniazid, an effective antidepressant, was originally marketed
     as a:

     A. pain reliever.
     B. depressant.
     C. cough suppressant.
     D. rocket fuel.
     (D, p. 430, factual)

45.  The original explanation of how bromides relieve the symptoms of
     epilepsy was that they:

     A. reduce sexual drive, decreasing masturbation, reducing
        seizures.
     B. decrease activity in the corpus callosum, restricting seizures
        to one hemisphere.
     C. produce more synchronized brain activity.
     D. desynchronize brain activity.
     (A, p. 430, factual)

47.   Which category of antidepressant drugs operates by preventing the presynaptic neuron from reabsorbing serotonin and catecholamines after releasing them?

A. tricyclics
B. MAOIs
C. selective serotonin reuptake inhibitors
D. atypical antidepressants
(A, p. 430, factual)

48.   An antidepressant drug operates by blocking histamine receptors, acetylcholine receptors and certain sodium channels.  This drug will be classified as a/an:

A. tricyclic.
B. MAOI.
C. selective serotonin reuptake inhibitor.
D. atypical antidepressant.
(A, pp. 430-431, factual)

49.   Which of the following is NOT a side effect of tricyclic antidepressants?

A. drowsiness
B. dry mouth
C. heart irregularities
D. frequent urinating
(D, p. 431, factual)

50.   How do tricyclic drugs work?

A. They block the release of catecholamines.
B. They prevent the presynaptic cell from reabsorbing catecholamines.
C. They directly stimulate the postsynaptic cell's catecholamine receptors.
D. They increase the rate of synthesis of catecholamines.
(B, p. 431, conceptual)

51.   Which category of antidepressant drugs operates by blocking the enzyme monoamine oxidase that metabolizes catecholamines and serotonin into inactive forms?

A. tricyclics
B. MAOIs
C. selective serotonin reuptake inhibitors
D. atypical antidepressants
(B, p. 431, factual)

52.    What enzyme is inhibited by the drugs known as MAOIs?

A. The one that synthesizes catecholamines.
B. The one that synthesizes GABA.
C. The one that breaks down catecholamines.
D. The one that breaks down GABA.
(C, p. 431, factual)

53.    What is true about both tricyclic drugs and MAOIs?

A. They block potassium channels in the membrane.
B. They decrease the rate of synthesis of catecholamines.
C. They prolong the effect of catecholamines after their release.
D. They directly stimulate catecholamine and serotonin receptors.
(C, p. 431, conceptual)

54.    Selective serotonin reuptake inhibitors operate similarly to:

A. tricyclics.
B. MAOIs.
C. Antabuse.
D. L-Dopa.
(A, p. 431, factual)

55.    How do selective serotonin reuptake inhibitors (SSRIs) differ from tricyclics?

A. SSRIs block reuptake of both catecholamines and serotonin.
B. SSRIs increase, and tricyclics decrease, action potential velocity.
C. SSRIs block the reuptake of only serotonin.
D. SRIs act on the left hemisphere while tricyclics act on the right.
(C, p. 431, factual)

56.    What do tricyclic, MAOI, and SSRI antidepressants have in common?

A. They decrease the synthesis of serotonin.
E. They decrease the amount of neurotransmitters released at synapses.
C. They prolong the activity of neurotransmitters at synapses.
D. They increase the synthesis of serotonin.
(C, p. 431, conceptual)

57.    The antidepressant Prozac is classified:

A. a tricyclic.
B. an MAOI.
C. a selective serotonin reuptake inhibitor.
D. an atypical antidepressant.
(C, p. 431, factual)

58.   What is a primary reason that fluoxetine (Prozac) has become
      increasingly popular as an antidepressant?

      A. It treats both mania and depression.
      B. It is very inexpensive compared to other antidepressant drugs.
      C. It leaves the body very quickly once someone stops taking it.
      D. It generally has fewer side effects than other popular
         antidepressant drugs.
      (D, p. 431, conceptual)

59.   Based on the antidepressant effects of fluoxetine (Prozac), we
      can infer that _____ synapses are in some way involved in
      depression.

      A. acetylcholine
      B. GABA
      C. dopamine
      D. serotonin
      ("WWW" D, p. 431, conceptual)

60.   Which of the following would be considered a selective serotonin
      reuptake inhibitor antidepressant?

      A. fluoxetine (Prozac)
      B. imipramine (Tofranil)
      C. disulfiram (Antabuse)
      D. chlorpromazine (Thorazine)
      (A, p. 431, factual)

61.   The group of drugs classified as atypical antidepressants are
      often used for individuals who:

      A. have more rapid mood swings than other depressed patients.
      B. are very young.
      C. have failed to respond to other drugs.
      D. are more intelligent than other depressed patients.
      (C, p. 431, factual)

62.   Following the administration of a tricyclic drug, excess
      neurotransmitters accumulate in the synaptic cleft, stimulating
      the autoreceptors.  The initial effect of that stimulation is to:

      A. decrease release of the neurotransmitter into the synapse.
      B. increase release of the neurotransmitter into the synapse.
      C. increase sensitivity of the receptors in the postsynaptic
         membrane.
      D. decrease sensitivity of the receptors in the postsynaptic
         membrane.
      (A, p. 431, factual)

63.   A prolonged increase in the release of a specific
      neurotransmitter leads to _____ in the postsynaptic cell.

      A. increased sensitivity to that transmitter
      B. decreased sensitivity to that transmitter
      C. increased sensitivity to other transmitters
      D. increased numbers of receptors
      (B, p. 431, factual)

64.   Antidepressant drugs initially _____ the amount of
      neurotransmitter present at the synapses and gradually _____ the
      sensitivity of the postsynaptic receptors to that transmitter.

      A. increase; increase
      B. decrease; decrease
      C. increase; decrease
      D. decrease; increase
      (C, p. 431, conceptual)

65.   One problem in understanding how antidepressant drugs affect
      behavior is that:

      A. doses that affect the synapses are not large enough to affect
         behavior.
      B. doses that affect behavior are not large enough to affect the
         synapses.
      C. the drugs alter neurotransmitter levels quickly but take days
         or weeks to alter behavior.
      D. the drugs alter behavior quickly but take days or weeks to
         alter neurotransmitter levels.
      (C, pp. 431-432, factual)

66.   What is the relationship between the time it takes antidepressant
      drugs to increase the concentrations of neurotransmitters at the
      synapses and behavioral changes?

      A. both effects occur within hours
      B. both effects occur within weeks
      C. neurotransmitters are altered within hours, behaviors within
         weeks
      D. behaviors are altered within hours, neurotransmitters within
         weeks
      (C, pp. 431-432, conceptual)

67.   Antidepressant drugs increase serotonin and catecholamine levels
      at the synapses and alleviate depression.  These two effects
      DIFFER with regard to the _____ necessary to produce them.

      A. dosage
      B. time
      C. part of the brain
      D. blood pH
      (B, p. 432, conceptual)

68. With long term use of antidepressants, there is increased production of brain-derived neurotrophin factor in the:

    A. hippocampus and cortex.
    B. suprachiasmatic nucleus and locus coeruleus.
    C. superior and inferior colliculus.
    D. hypothalamus and cerebellum.
    (A, p. 432, factual)

69. What areas of the brain are known to decrease in size during depression?

    A. hippocampus and cortex
    B. corpus callosum and anterior commissure
    C. hypothalamus and basal ganglia
    D. thalamus and hypothalamus
    (A, p. 432, factual)

70. Antidepressant drugs are effective in alleviating many symptoms in:

    A. 10% of all patients.
    B. about one-third of all patients.
    C. about two-thirds of all patients.
    D. over 90% of all patients.
    (C, p. 432, factual)

71. The main advantage of psychotherapy over drug-therapy in the treatment of depression is that psychotherapy:

    A. takes less time.
    B. is usually less expensive.
    C. is effective in about two-thirds of depressed patients, whereas drug-therapy is only effective in about one-third.
    D. is more likely to produce longer-lasting effects.
    (D, p. 432, factual)

72. Alleviating symptoms through the placebo effect is a function of:

    A. drug treatment.
    B. psychotherapy.
    C. acupuncture.
    D. mere expectation of improvement.
    (D, p. 432, factual)

73. A patient is told that he is receiving a very potent drug, known to alleviate symptoms in depressed patients when is actually receiving a sugar pill. Regardless, he still reports a decrease in symptoms three weeks later. This may be due to:

    A. a placebo effect.
    B. brainwashing during therapy.
    C. the excess glucose in his system.
    D. a rebound effect of drugs he took many months ago.
    (A, p. 432, factual)

74. The original impetus for the use of electroconvulsive shock therapy (ECT) for people with psychological disorders came from the observation that:

    A. an increase in epileptic symptoms was associated with a decrease in schizophrenic symptoms.
    B. damage to the prefrontal cortex often leads to a decrease in overall activity.
    C. levels of glucose metabolism vary as a patient switches between depression and mania.
    D. depressed people often show memory deficits not found in healthy people.
    (A, p. 432, factual)

75. When ECT proved to be ineffective for schizophrenia, it was:

    A. abandoned as a means of treatment for psychiatric disorders.
    B. abandoned until the 1950's.
    C. abandoned until just recently.
    D. used to treat other mental illnesses.
    (D, p. 432, factual)

76. Electroconvulsive shock is LEAST likely to be given to:

    A. patients who do not respond to antidepressant drugs.
    B. schizophrenic patients.
    C. depressed patients with suicidal tendencies.
    D. patients with delusions as well as depression.
    (B, p. 432, conceptual)

77. By the 1950's, ECT had a bad reputation because:

    A. it was overused and misused.
    B. it caused brain damage.
    C. it was always ineffective.
    (A, p. 432, factual)

78. The use of electroconvulsive shock declined in the 1950's because:

    A. it was outlawed.
    B. a new theory of depression arose.
    C. antidepressant drugs became available.
    D. a federal report concluded that it was almost never effective.
    (C, p. 433, factual)

79.   One difference between electroconvulsive therapy as it is used
      today and the way it was given in the 1950's is that today:

      A. the shock level is induced with insulin injections.
      B. muscle relaxants are no longer given.
      C. it is used for a wider variety of disorders.
      D. shock is often administered only to the right hemisphere.
      (D, p. 433, factual)

80.   For which type of disorder is electroconvulsive shock most likely
      to be used?

      A. schizophrenia
      B. depression with delusions
      C. seasonal affective disorder
      D. mild postpartum depression
      ("WWW" B, p. 433, conceptual)

81.   Electroconvulsive shock therapy is most likely to be used with
      patients:

      A. with seasonal affective disorder.
      B. with brief or mild episodes of depression.
      C. with bipolar disorder.
      D. who have not responded to drug therapy.
      (D, p. 433, factual)

82.   When one is dealing with a depressed patient with suicidal
      tendencies, ECT is sometimes preferred to antidepressant drugs
      because it:

      A. can be administered without the patient's consent or
         cooperation.
      B. takes effect more rapidly.
      C. produces more permanent changes in behavior than drug
         therapies.
      D. has a stronger theoretical basis behind it.
      (B, p. 433, factual)

83.   You are a psychiatrist dealing with a severely depressed patient
      and want to recommend a therapy. Your main concern is that it
      takes effect as rapidly as possible, therefore, you recommend:

      A. tricyclic drugs.
      B. electroconvulsive shock therapy.
      C. monoamine oxidase inhibitors (MAOIs).
      D. insight-oriented psychotherapy.
      (B, p. 433, factual)

84.  Which of the following statements regarding the use of ECT today
     is FALSE?

     A. Shock intensity is lower than it was in the 1950's.
     B. It is given in conjunction with muscle relaxants or
        anesthetics.
     C. It is given only after a patient has given informed consent.
     D. It is given once a day until the patient gets better.
     (D, p. 433, factual)

85.  Today, electroconvulsive shock is:

     A. given to a patient once a day until the mental symptoms
        are lifted.
     B. much more intense than when first developed and used.
     C. given to a patient who first must give informed consent.
     D. being used for a wider variety of disorders.
     (C, p. 433, factual)

86.  The risk of provoking a heart attack with ECT is:

     A. low except in children.
     B. low except in men.
     C. low except in elderly patients.
     D. relatively high which is why it requires a physician and
        anesthetics.
     (C, p. 433, factual)

87.  One advantage of electroconvulsive shock over antidepressant
     drugs is that shock treatment:

     A. produces its benefits faster.
     B. does not impair memory.
     C. produces permanent, not temporary, relief.
     D. is based on a theory, not just trial and error discoveries.
     (A, p. 433, factual)

88.  The most common side effect of electroconvulsive shock therapy
     is:

     A. memory impairment.
     B. damage to the frontal lobes.
     C. dry mouth and blurred vision.
     D. high probability of broken bones during the treatment.
     (A, p. 433, factual)

89.  The treatment for depression most often associated with memory
     impairment is:

     A. MAOIs.
     B. tricyclic drugs.
     C. electroconvulsive shock therapy.
     D. lithium.
     (C, p. 433, factual)

90.    If ECT is administered to the right hemisphere only:

A. depression is not alleviated as well as when administered to
   the left hemisphere.
B. depression is alleviated more quickly.
C. antidepressant effects occur with memory impairment.
D. antidepressant effects occur without memory impairment.
(D, p. 433, factual)

91.    Depressed people as a rule have signs of decreased activity in
       the _____ hemisphere of their cerebral cortex. When they are
       given ECT to just one hemisphere, it is given on the _____ side.

A. left; left
B. left; right
C. right; left
D. right; right
(B, p. 433, factual)

92.    One way to administer electroconvulsive shock with minimal memory
       impairment is limit application to the:

A. left hemisphere.
B. right hemisphere.
C. anterior half of the brain.
D. posterior half of the brain.
(B, p. 433, factual)

93.    One serious disadvantage of using ECT to treat depression is the:

A. high risk of brain damage.
B. slow onset of benefits.
C. high probability of relapse.
D. likelihood of substituting schizophrenia for depression.
(C, p. 433, factual)

94.    Repetitive transcranial magnetic stimulation is similar to ECT in
       that:

A. both deal with magnetic stimulation.
B. both increase the frequency of action potentials.
C. both are effective in alleviating depression and no one knows
   why.
D. neither requires patient consent.
(C, p. 433, factual)

95.    People generally have the greatest amount of REM sleep when:

A. they have just fallen asleep, regardless of the time of day.
B. they have been asleep for 4 hours already, regardless of the
   time of day.
C. body temperature is rising.
D. body temperature is falling.
(C, p. 433, factual)

96.    Compared to an average person, the circadian rhythm for body
       temperature in depressed people:

       A. rises and falls at random times.
       B. follows the same pattern and timing.
       C. is phase-delayed.
       D. is phase-advanced.
       (D, p. 433, conceptual)

97.    Depressed people enter REM sleep earlier after falling asleep
       than nondepressed people because:

       A. their body temperatures remain constant rather than
          fluctuate.
       B. they tend to go to bed earlier than most people.
       C. they have body temperature rhythms out of phase with their
          wake/sleep rhythms.
       D. they have rapid fluctuations in their sensitivity to
          norepinephrine.
       (C, p. 433, conceptual)

98.    One method of treating depression that has been shown to be
       effective in many cases is:

       A. increasing the amount of REM sleep and decreasing non-REM
          sleep.
       B. keeping the person in bed all day.
       C. sending the person to bed a little later than usual.
       D. sending the person to bed a little earlier than usual.
       (D, p. 433, factual)

99.    In certain cases it is possible to relieve depression by changing
       a person's:

       A. sleeping schedule.
       B. eating schedule.
       C. exercise schedule.
       D. self-grooming habits.
       (A, p. 433, factual)

**Bipolar Disorder**

100.   People with unipolar disorder are characterized by:

       A. obsessions and compulsions.
       B. varying between depression and mania.
       C. varying between depression and a normal mood.
       D. chemical imbalances in one half of their brains.
       (C, p. 434, factual)

101.  A restless, impulsive person whose speech rambles from one idea
      to another may fit which of these categories?

      A. autistic
      B. depressed
      C. manic
      D. narcoleptic
      (C, p. 434, factual)

102.  A more modern term for manic-depressive disorder is:

      A. unipolar disorder.
      B. bipolar disorder.
      C. dementia praecox.
      D. schizophrenic.
      (B, p. 434, factual)

103.  Someone with bipolar disorder alternates between:

      A. schizophrenia and normal.
      B. manic and normal.
      C. depressed and dementia.
      D. manic and depressed.
      (D, p. 434, factual)

104.  A cycle from depression to mania and back to depression again
      usually lasts:

      A. an unpredictable length of time.
      B. only a few days.
      C. no longer than a month.
      D. a year or more.
      ("WWW" A, p. 434, factual)

105.  About _____ of people have at least a mild case of bipolar
      disorder at some time in life.

      A. .01%
      B. 1%
      C. 10%
      D. 15%
      (B, p. 434, factual)

106.  The average age of onset of bipolar disorder is during:

      A. childhood.
      B. adolescence.
      C. the early 20's.
      D. middle age.
      (C, p. 434, factual)

107.  Which of the following characterizes total brain activity, as measured by the rate of glucose metabolism, in those suffering from mood disorders?

    A. high in both mania and depression
    B. low in both mania and depression
    C. low in mania and high in depression
    D. high in mania and low in depression
    (D, p. 434, factual)

108.  Glucose metabolism is _____ during depression and _____ during mania.

    A. high; high
    B. low; low
    C. high; low
    D. low; high
    (D, p. 434, factual)

109.  Which characteristic is associated with depression?

    A. decreased glucose metabolism
    B. increased glucose metabolism
    C. larger than normal cerebral ventricles
    D. smaller than normal cerebral ventricles
    (A, p. 434, factual)

110.  Which characteristic is associated with mania?

    A. decreased glucose metabolism
    B. increased glucose metabolism
    C. larger than normal cerebral ventricles
    D. smaller than normal cerebral ventricles
    (B, p. 434, factual)

111.  The highest correlation for bipolar disorder exists:

    A. between children and their adoptive parents.
    B. among siblings.
    C. between dizygotic twins.
    D. between monozygotic twins.
    (D, p. 434, factual)

112.  In what ways do genetics contribute to bipolar disorder?

    A. There are genes on several chromosomes, although the specific gene has not been identified yet.
    B. A recessive gene has been found to cause bipolar disorder.
    C. There has been no evidence of a genetic connection.
    D. The genes responsible are only passed from father to son.
    (A, p. 434, factual)

113.  Lithium is most commonly prescribed for which disorder?

      A. seasonal affective disorder
      B. endogenous depression
      C. reactive depression
      D. bipolar disorder
      (D, p. 434, factual)

114.  What is the most effective therapy for bipolar disorder?

      A. electroconvulsive shock
      B. monoamine oxidase inhibitors
      C. haloperidol
      D. lithium
      (D, p. 434, factual)

115.  Lithium prevents a relapse into:

      A. mania only
      B. depression only
      C. either mania or depression
      D. schizophrenia
      (C, p. 434, factual)

116.  Physicians must carefully monitor the dose of lithium they give
      to bipolar patients because:

      A. people develop a tolerance to the drug and must gradually
         increase their dosage.
      B. people develop a sensitivity to the drug and must gradually
         decrease their dosage.
      C. the amount of drug needed to achieve a good effect varies from
         one time of year to another.
      D. the most beneficial dosage is just less than the dosage that
         is toxic.
      (D, p. 434, factual)

117.  Therapeutic doses of lithium produce:

      A. very specific effects at serotonin receptor sites.
      B. complex effects on several second messenger systems.
      C. effects on one known neuronal pathway.
      D. effects which are short-lived.
      (B, p. 435, factual)

118.  Anticonvulsant drugs have been used to treat:

      A. schizophrenia.
      B. alcoholism.
      C. bipolar disorder.
      D. seasonal affective disorder.
      (C, p. 435, factual)

119. Depakote is an _____ drug which is also used to treat _____.

    A. antidepressant; mania
    B. anticonvulsant; bipolar disorder
    C. antidepressant; seasonal affective disorder
    D. anticonvulsant; schizophrenia
    (B, p. 435, factual)

**Seasonal Affective Disorder**

120. People suffering from seasonal affective disorder most likely become depressed in the:

    A. days after any holiday.
    B. fall.
    C. winter.
    D. spring.
    (C, p. 436, factual)

121. Where is seasonal affective disorder most common?

    A. in large cities
    B. in small towns and rural areas
    C. in tropical areas
    D. near the poles
    (D, p. 436, factual)

122. Concerning temperature cycles, SAD patients are to ___ as other depressed patients are to ____.

    A. phase-delayed cycles; normal cycles
    B. normal cycles; phase-advanced cycles
    C. phase-delayed cycles; phase-advanced cycles
    D. phase-advanced cycles; phase-delayed cycles
    (C, p. 436, factual)

123. What is one of the best treatments for seasonal affective disorder?

    A. bright light
    B. electroconvulsive shock therapy
    C. adrenal hormones
    D. dietary changes
    (A, p. 436, factual)

124. Which of the following relieves one type of depression (SAD)?

    A. mineral water
    B. sleeping late in the mornings
    C. vigorous back rubs
    D. artificial bright light early in the morning
    (D, p. 436, factual)

125.  For best results, people suffering from SAD should be exposed to
      artificial bright light in the:

      A. morning.
      B. afternoon.
      C. evening.
      D. middle of the night.
      (A, p. 436, factual)

126.  An advantage of bright light therapy for SAD, as compared to
      other antidepressant treatments, is that bright light therapy:

      A. is highly effective without apparent side effects.
      B. produces a permanent cure after one or two treatments.
      C. is well understood theoretically.
      D. is financially supported by several drug companies.
      (A, p. 436, factual)

**Module 15.3: Schizophrenia**

**Characteristics**

127.  A disorder characterized by deteriorating ability to function in
      everyday life and some combination of hallucinations, delusions,
      thought disorder, movement disorder and inappropriate emotional
      expressions is:

      A. bipolar disorder.
      B. hypomania.
      C. multiple personality.
      D. schizophrenia.
      (D, p. 438, factual)

128.  Someone with deterioration of everyday functioning and
      hallucinations or delusions or thought disorders would likely be
      classified as having which disorder?

      A. schizophrenia
      B. bipolar disorder
      C. attention deficit disorder
      D. Klinefelter's syndrome
      (A, p. 438, factual)

129.  Which of the following behaviors most closely meets the
      definition of schizophrenia?

      A. alternation between one personality and another
      B. outbursts of unprovoked violent behavior toward strangers
      C. deterioration of daily functioning, hallucinations, and
         thought disorders
      D. episodes of being unable to remember certain events of one's
         past
      (C, p. 438, factual)

130. Which of the following conditions has symptoms that vary most drastically from one person to another?

    A. alcoholism.
    B. schizophrenia.
    C. major depression.
    D. bipolar disorder.
    (B, p. 438, factual)

131. Which of the following is NOT a common characteristic of schizophrenia?

    A. deterioration of everyday functioning
    B. delusions
    C. impaired understanding of abstract concepts
    D. alternation between one personality and another
    (D, p. 438, factual)

132. The name formerly used for schizophrenia was:

    A. multiple personality.
    B. dementia praecox.
    C. bipolar disorder.
    D. hypomania.
    (B, p. 438, factual)

133. Schizophrenia is Greek for:

    A. multiple personality.
    B. hallucinations.
    C. split mind.
    D. premature deterioration of the mind.
    (C. p. 438, factual)

134. An example of a "negative symptom" of schizophrenia is:

    A. hallucinations.
    B. poor emotional expression.
    C. delusions.
    D. thought disorder.
    (B, p. 438, factual)

135. A schizophrenic patient whose main symptoms are lack of emotional expression, lack of social interaction, and lack of speech is suffering from:

    A. positive symptoms.
    B. negative symptoms.
    C. thought disorders.
    D. delusions.
    (B, p. 438, factual)

136.  What is the difference between positive and negative
      schizophrenic symptoms?

      A. beneficial behaviors versus harmful behaviors
      B. behaviors that are present versus behaviors that are absent
      C. behaviors that are related to abnormal brain functioning
         versus those that are not
      D. behaviors shown by one personality versus behaviors shown by
         another
      (B, p. 438, factual)

137.  What is meant when we say that a schizophrenic patient has a
      "negative symptom"?

      A. One engages in a behavior that is harmful to oneself.
      B. One engages in a behavior that is harmful to others.
      C. One engages in a behavior that is unusual for other people.
      D. One fails to engage in a behavior common in other people.
      (D, p. 438, conceptual)

138.  The psychotic cluster of positive symptoms of schizophrenia
      include:

      A. bizarre behaviors.
      B. loosely organized thoughts.
      C. delusions.
      D. inappropriate emotions.
      (C, p. 438, factual)

139.  A delusion is:

      A. a sensory experience that does not correspond to reality.
      B. an inability to understand abstract concepts.
      C. an unfounded belief.
      D. a loss of memory for part of one's past.
      (C, p. 438, factual)

140.  The belief that outer space aliens are trying to control one's
      behavior is classified a:

      A. delusion.
      B. hallucination.
      C. negative symptom.
      D. disorganized positive symptom.
      (A, p. 438, factual)

141.  PET scans have determined that hallucinations occur during
      periods of:

      A. decreased activity in the hypothalamus.
      B. increased activity in the hypothalamus.
      C. decreased activity in the hippocampus and prefrontal cortex.
      D. increased activity in the hippocampus and prefrontal cortex.
      (D, p. 438, factual)

142.  Inappropriate emotions, bizarre behaviors and thought disorders
      represent the:

      A. disorganized cluster of positive symptoms.
      B. psychotic cluster of positive symptoms.
      C. disorganized cluster of negative symptoms.
      D. psychotic cluster of negative symptoms.
      (A, pp. 438-439, factual)

143.  What is the most common thought disorder of schizophrenia?

      A. obsessive concentration on a single thought
      B. alternating between one personality and another
      C. excessive anxiety when thinking about one particular topic
      D. impaired understanding of abstract concepts
      (D, p. 439, factual)

144.  Nancy And  sen, one of the leading investigators of
      schizophrenia, considers the main problem to be:

      A. bizarre movements.
      B. hallucinations.
      C. disordered thoughts.
      D. depression.
      (C, p. 439, factual)

145.  Acute schizophrenic has:

      A. slow onset and a long-term course.
      B. sudden onset and good prospects for recovery.
      C. alternation between positive and negative symptoms.
      D. a mixture of positive and negative symptoms simultaneously.
      (B, p. 439, factual)

146.  Which schizophrenic condition has a gradual onset and a long-term
      course?

      A. chronic
      B. acute
      C. disorganized cluster
      D. psychotic cluster
      (A, p. 439, factual)

147.  Today, most people diagnosed with schizophrenia live:

      A. in institutions.
      B. half of their lives as inpatients and the other half of their
         lives as outpatients.
      C. very restricted lives.
      D. normally with the aid of drugs and outpatient treatment.
      (D, p. 439, factual)

148.  Which is NOT true about the incidence of schizophrenia?

    A. It is commonly estimated to occur in 10-15 percent of the
       population.
    B. It is reported more often in the United States than in Third
       World countries.
    C. Within the United States, it is more common in cities than
       small towns or farms.
    D. It is about equally common in women and men.
    (A, p. 439, factual)

149.  The age of onset of schizophrenia is:

    A. about the same time for men and women.
    B. usually earlier for women than for men.
    C. usually earlier for men than for women.
    D. never after the age of 30.
    ("WWW" C, p. 439, factual)

150.  Schizophrenia is generally diagnosed for the first time when a
      person is between which ages?

    A. 5 and 10
    B. 10 and 15
    C. 20 and 30
    D. 40 and 50
    (C, p. 439, conceptual)

151.  Childhood-onset schizophrenia is:

    A. quite common.
    B. associated with identifiable genetic abnormalities.
    C. just like schizophrenia in adults.
    D. usually of brief duration.
    (B, p. 440, factual)

**Genetics**

152.  The concordance rate of schizophrenia among twins is:

    A. higher in dizygotic than monozygotic twins.
    E. higher in monozygotic than dizygotic twins.
    F. equally high in monozygotic and dizygotic twins.
    G. very difficult to determine.
    (B, p. 440, factual)

153.  The concordance rate for schizophrenia is around _____ percent
      for monozygotic twins (MZ), and around _____ percent for
      dizygotic twins (DZ).

    A. 50; 15
    B. 15; 50
    C. 50; 90
    D. 90; 50
    (A, p. 440, factual)

154.  Of the following individuals, the concordance rate for
      schizophrenia is highest for:

      A. MZ twins.
      B. DZ twins.
      C. DZ twins who were raised as though they were MZ twins.
      D. DZ twins who were adopted by schizophrenics.
      (A, p. 440, factual)

155.  Which of the following statements about the genetic basis of
      schizophrenia is FALSE?

      A. Monozygotic twins have a higher concordance rate than
         dizygotic twins.
      B. Twins are more likely to resemble each other if they think
         they are monozygotic than if they actually are.
      C. Schizophrenia is more common in the biological relatives of an
         adopted schizophrenic child than in the adoptive relatives.
      D. A nonschizophrenic person with a schizophrenic twin has a
         higher than normal probability of having schizophrenic
         children.
      (B, p. 440, factual)

156.  When an adopted child develops schizophrenia, the disease is
      significantly more probable among the:

      A. adopting relatives than the biological.
      B. biological relatives than the adopting.
      C. siblings than the parents.
      D. fathers than the mothers.
      (B, p. 441, factual)

157.  If an adopted child becomes schizophrenic, schizophrenia is most
      likely to be found in:

      A. the child's adoptive mother.
      B. the child's adoptive father.
      C. the child's biological relatives.
      D. both the child's adoptive and biological relatives, equally.
      (C, p. 441, factual)

158.  If you had a "paternal half-sibling," what would be that person's
      parentage?

      A. your father's brother or sister and your mother's sister or
         brother
      B. your father's cousin and any other person
      C. your mother and a man other than your father
      D. your father and a woman other than your mother
      (D, p. 441, factual)

159.  The concordance rate for schizophrenia in paternal half-siblings
      who are adopted by different families is:

      A. lower that that for the general population.
      B. approximately the same as for the general population
      C. higher than that for the general population.
      D. even higher than that for MZ twins.
      (C, p. 441, factual)

160.  Schizophrenia is most likely:

      A. a single-gene disorder like Huntington's disease.
      B. influenced in some way by several genes.
      C. not genetic.
      D. controlled by nonchromosomal genes in the cytoplasm.
      (B, pp. 442-443, factual)

**The Neurodevelopmental Hypothesis**

161.  According to the neurodevelopmental hypothesis, schizophrenia is
      based on abnormalities in the nervous system which develop
      during:

      A. prenatal or neonatal development.
      B. childhood.
      C. adolescence.
      D. adulthood.
      (A, p. 443, factual)

162.  According to the neurodevelopmental hypothesis, schizophrenia
      develops as a result of:

      A. stressful experiences.
      B. lack of social support from family and friends.
      C. poor diet during adolescence.
      D. abnormalities in prenatal or neonatal development.
      (D, p. 443, factual)

163.  Many people with schizophrenia have a history of medical
      problems, malnutrition, and so forth:

      A. before or shortly after birth.
      B. which begin in adolescence.
      C. which begin in early adulthood.
      D. beginning shortly before their diagnosis with schizophrenia.
      (A, p. 443, factual)

164.  Which of the following is NOT often associated with the
      the life events of schizophrenics?

      A. prolonged labor
      B. poor nutrition during pregnancy
      C. above average birth weight
      D. complications during delivery
      (C, p. 443, factual)

165. During World War II, Dutch women gave birth to a high percentage of babies who later developed schizophrenia, if the women were starved during:

    A. the earliest stage of pregnancy.
    B. the third trimester of the pregnancy.
    C. the week of delivery.
    D. the first few months of breastfeeding.
    (A, p. 443, factual)

166. As compared to the general population, twice the usual probability of schizophrenia has been correlated with:

    A. Rh-negative mothers and Rh-positive baby girls.
    B. Rh-positive mothers and Rh-negative baby girls.
    C. Rh-negative mothers and Rh-positive baby boys.
    D. Rh-positive mothers and Rh-negative baby boys.
    (C, p. 443, factual)

167. What is one factor in prenatal development that has been found to be related to increased incidences of schizophrenia later in life?

    A. malnutrition during the third trimester
    B. Rh-negative mothers who have had several Rh-positive babies
    C. lack of exercise by the mother early in pregnancy
    D. episodes of maternal depression
    (B, p. 443, factual)

168. Among which group is schizophrenia more common?

    A. those born to mothers under 18
    B. those born in the Southeast
    C. those born in the early morning
    D. those born in the winter
    (D, p. 443, factual)

169. Which psychological disorder is more prevalent in people who were born in the winter than people who were born in any other season?

    A. major depression
    B. schizophrenia
    C. bipolar disorder
    D. attention deficit disorder
    (B, p. 443, factual)

170. Which of the following is sometimes taken as evidence that schizophrenia might be caused by a virus or bacteria?

    A. the age at which symptoms appear
    B. the high concordance between paternal half-siblings
    C. the season-of-birth effect
    B. the relationship between schizophrenia and stressful experiences
    (C, p. 443, factual)

171. The season-of-birth effect is sometimes taken as evidence that schizophrenia is caused by:

    A. genetics.
    B. viruses.
    C. stressful experiences.
    D. vitamin deficiencies.
    (B, p. 443, factual)

172. It is believed that a virus contracted by a pregnant woman might increase the incidence of schizophrenia in her child because:

    A. a mother's fever can adversely affect fetal brain development.
    B. increases in the resulting stress hormones in the mother affect fetal hormone levels.
    C. viruses are able to cross the placenta and affect the fetus directly.
    D. viral infections will harm the umbilical cord hampering the delivery of nutrients to the fetus.
    (A, p. 443, factual)

173. Which of the following is NOT a mild brain abnormality associated with schizophrenia?

    A. smaller prefrontal cortex
    B. smaller temporal cortex
    C. enlarged cerebral ventricles
    D. enlarged hippocampus
    (D, p. 444, factual)

174. Brain damage common to schizophrenia includes:

    A. larger than normal cerebral ventricles.
    C. a proliferation of glial cells.
    D. loss of axons between the substantia nigra and the basal ganglia.
    D. a heavier forebrain.
    (A, p. 444, factual)

175. The cerebral ventricles of a person with schizophrenia are _____ than normal; we conclude therefore that such a person has _____ neurons than normal.

    A. smaller; more
    B. smaller; fewer
    C. larger; more
    D. larger; fewer
    (D, p. 444, factual)

176. Brain anatomy is generally the most abnormal in schizophrenics with:

    A. onset after age 30.
    B. the most severe behavioral deficits.
    C. sudden onset and rapid recovery.
    D. a high ratio of positive to negative symptoms.
    (B, p. 444, factual)

177. The planum temporale is slightly _____ in the _____ temporal lobe of schizophrenics, compared to most other people.

    A. deformed; left
    B. larger; left
    C. larger; right
    D. smaller; right
    (C, p. 444, factual)

178. The areas with the most consistent signs of abnormality in schizophrenics include the:

    A. dorsolateral prefrontal cortex.
    B. medulla.
    C. occipital lobes.
    D. parietal lobes.
    ("WWW" A, p. 444, factual)

179. Which of the following is common in schizophrenia?

    A. bursts of rapid activity in cells of the hippocampus
    B. abnormal physical organization among neurons
    C. altered pH of the cerebrospinal fluid
    D. leakage of cerebrospinal fluid into the brain
    (B, p. 444, factual)

180. Cell bodies in schizophrenics' brains are especially smaller than normal in the:

    A. hippocampus and hypothalamus.
    B. thalamus and hypothalamus.
    C. hippocampus and prefrontal cortex.
    D. medulla and pons.
    (C, p. 444, factual)

181. Abnormal amounts of cell recognition molecules that guide the migration of neurons and axons during early development have been found in the brains of patients with:

    A. Huntington's disease.
    B. bipolar disorder.
    C. schizophrenia.
    D. depression.
    (C, p. 445, factual)

182. Research suggests that the brain abnormalities of schizophrenics
     develop:

     A. early and progressively get worse.
     B. early and then remain fairly steady.
     C. late in life and progressively get worse.
     D. late in life and remain fairly steady.
     (B, p. 445, factual)

183. If the brain is affected prenatally or neonatally, it could be
     that it takes many years before the symptoms of schizophrenia are
     evident because the:

     A. affected areas are among the slowest to mature.
     B. behavioral deficits often look like normal behavior in
        children.
     C. associated toxins do not have widespread effects until they
        have reached high levels.
     D. deficits are learned from imitation of other schizophrenic
        people.
     (A, p. 445, factual)

184. People with damage to the _____ have difficulty with the
     Wisconsin Card Sorting Task.

     A. hippocampus
     B. hypothalamus
     C. prefrontal cortex
     D. thalamus
     (C, p. 445, factual)

**Neurotransmitters and Drugs**

185. Prior to the 1950's few schizophrenic patients who entered a
     mental hospital ever left.  The discovery most responsible for
     alleviating that situation was the discovery of:

     A. chlorpromazine.
     B. the prefrontal lobotomy.
     C. electroconvulsive therapy.
     D. MAOIs.
     (A, p. 446, factual)

186. The prospects of relief from schizophrenic symptoms when
     chlorpromazine is administered are best if the:

     A. drug is administered early in the day.
     B. drug is administered early in the disease.
     C. drug is taken with certain foods.
     D. patient is not hallucinating at the time.
     (B, p. 446, factual)

187.  Another term for antipsychotic drugs is:

    A. benzodiazepines.
    B. neuroleptics.
    C. tricyclics.
    D. stimulants.
    (B, p. 446, factual)

188.  The two chemical families to which most antischizophrenic drugs belong are:

    A. phenothiazines and butyrophenones.
    B. tricyclics and MAOIs.
    C. nitrates and glucocorticoids.
    D. benzodiazepines and antihistamines.
    (A, p. 446, factual)

189.  What effect do neuroleptic drugs (antipsychotics) have on the nervous system?

    A. increase stimulation of dopamine synapses
    B. decrease stimulation of dopamine synapses
    C. increase stimulation of GABA synapses
    D. decrease stimulation of GABA synapses
    (B, p. 446, conceptual)

190.  Antipsychotic drugs:

    A. increase reuptake of catecholamines.
    B. increase synthesis of serotonin.
    C. prevent fluctuations of sensitivity at GABA synapses.
    D. block dopamine synapses.
    (D, p. 446, factual)

191.  The doses of various drugs that are typically prescribed for schizophrenia are closely related to the strength of what effect?

    A. elevated alpha waves on an EEG
    B. blockage of dopamine receptors
    C. delays in the onset of REM sleep
    D. increases in the rate of dopamine synthesis
    (B, p. 446, factual)

192.  According to the dopamine hypothesis, what causes schizophrenia?

    A. excessive activity at dopamine synapses
    B. deficient activity at dopamine synapses
    C. an unusual point of origin for dopamine fibers in the brain
    D. an unusual course and destination of dopamine fibers in the brain
    (A, p. 446, factual)

193. Repeated use of large doses of amphetamine or cocaine can lead to a behavioral condition similar to:

    A. schizophrenia.
    B. bipolar disorder.
    C. attention deficit disorder.
    D. depression.
    (A, p. 446, factual)

194. A substance-induced psychotic disorder differs from a schizophrenic episode in that a substance-induced psychotic disorder:

    A. has longer-lasting episodes.
    B. impairs abstract thinking.
    C. produces more severe "negative symptoms."
    D. produces visual hallucinations.
    (D, p. 446, factual)

195. A substance-induced psychotic disorder is to _____ as a schizophrenic episode is to _____.

    A. "negative symptoms"; "positive symptoms"
    B. delusions of grandeur; delusions of persecution
    C. visual hallucinations; auditory hallucinations
    D. preadolescents; postadolescents
    (C, p. 446, conceptual)

196. Someone shows symptoms resembling schizophrenia, especially the positive symptoms, but also has distinct visual hallucinations. Which of the following disorders is most likely?

    A. seasonal affective disorder
    B. bipolar disorder
    C. substance-induced psychotic disorder
    D. Korsakoff's syndrome
    (C, p. 446, conceptual)

197. Nearly all of the drugs that can produce a psychosis resembling schizophrenia:

    A. increase the stimulation of GABA synapses.
    B. increase the stimulation of dopamine synapses.
    C. decrease the stimulation of serotonin synapses.
    D. decrease the stimulation of acetylcholine synapses.
    (B, p. 446, factual)

198. Stressors exacerbate schizophrenic symptoms temporarily by:

    A. decreasing the release of dopamine in the hippocampus
    B. decreasing the release of dopamine in the prefrontal cortex.
    C. increasing the release of dopamine in the hippocampus.
    D. increasing the release of dopamine in the prefrontal cortex.
    (D, p. 446, Factual)

199.  Stress-induced impairments of behavior can be relieved by:

    A. increasing dopamine.
    B. decreasing dopamine.
    C. increasing serotonin.
    D. decreasing glutamate.
    (B, p. 446, factual)

200.  Why is blocking dopamine synapses to relieve schizophrenic
      symptoms not a strong clue about the underlying problem?

    A. it only works for about 10-15% of all patients
    B. it takes 2-3 weeks to affect a behavioral change
    C. it only works for about 2-3 weeks
    D. schizophrenics produce too much dopamine
    (B, pp. 446-447, factual)

201.  Which of the following is NOT characteristic of schizophrenics?

    A. They have lower than normal levels of glutamate.
    B. They have abnormal concentrations of some dopamine receptors.
    C. They have elevated levels of dopamine.
    D. Neurotransmitter levels are affected well before any
       behavioral changes.
    (C, p. 447, factual)

202.  An alternative to the dopamine hypothesis of schizophrenia is the
      proposal that schizophrenia may be due to a deficiency of
      activity _____ synapses.

    A. serotonin
    B. glutamate
    C. substance P
    D. acetylcholine
    (B, p. 447, factual)

203.  Phencyclidine (PCP) produces:

    A. only positive symptoms of schizophrenia.
    B. only negative symptoms of schizophrenia.
    C. increased stimulation of glutamate type NMDA receptors.
    D. Decreased stimulation of glutamate type NMDA receptors.
    (C, p. 448, factual)

204.  What is curious about the psychotic effects of phencyclidine
      (angel dust)?

    A. The hallucinations tend to be auditory.
    B. The hallucinations are more intense in females.
    C. Consuming alcohol lessens the psychotic experiences.
    D. The effects are minor or absent in preadolescents.
    (D, p. 448, conceptual)

205.  For someone who has recovered from schizophrenia, PCP:

   A. induces a long-lasting recovery.
   B. induces a long-lasting relapse.
   C. is quite ineffective in inducing behavioral changes.
   D. produces depression instead.
   (B, p. 448, factual)

206.  Researchers have found that the brains of schizophrenics release:

   A. too much glutamate.
   B. too much glutamate in the prefrontal cortex and not enough in
      the hippocampus.
   C. too little glutamate in the prefrontal cortex and too much
      glutamate in the hippocampus.
   D. lower than normal amounts of glutamate in the prefrontal
      cortex and the hippocampus.
   ("WWW" D, p. 448, factual)

207.  Measurements of the RNA molecules associated with certain genes
      indicate deficient expression of glutamate receptors in the:

   A. medulla and cerebellum.
   B. parietal lobe.
   C. temporal lobe.
   D. occipital lobe.
   (C, p. 448, factual)

208.  Measurements of the RNA molecules associated with certain genes
      indicate deficient expression of _____ receptors in the _____
      lobe.

   A. NPY; frontal
   B. substance P; parietal
   C. glutamate; occipital
   D. glutamate; temporal
   (D, p. 448,factual)

209.  The amino acid, glycine, provides a possible treatment for
      schizophrenia because it:

   A. can be chemically converted into dopamine.
   B. activates a secondary cotransmitter site of glutamate
      receptors.
   C. decreases the effectiveness of glutamate.
   D. increases the growth and division of glia cells.
   (B, p. 448, factual)

210.  Researchers have found that the amino acid, glycine:

    A. competes with the effects of glutamate and, therefore, blocks
       those synapses.
    B. can be converted into dopamine or serotonin in different brain
       areas.
    C. increases the effectiveness of other antipsychotic drugs.
    D. directly stimulates nicotinic-type acetylcholine synapses.
    (C, p. 448, factual)

211.  Cycloserine is a drug that has potential for use with
      schizophrenics because it:

    A. doesn't cross the blood-brain barrier.
    B. facilitates the growth and maturation of new neurons.
    C. improves the effectiveness of other antipsychotic drugs.
    D. decreases symptoms more quickly than any other drug on the
       market.
    (C, p. 448, factual)

212.  The dopamine system apparently responsible for the symptoms of
      schizophrenia projects from the _____ to the _____.

    A. midbrain tegmentum; limbic system
    B. limbic system; midbrain tegmentum
    C. limbic system; hippocampus
    D. midbrain tegmentum; prefrontal cortex
    (D, p. 448, factual)

213.  A serious side effect that develops in some people after
      prolonged use of neuroleptic drugs is:

    A. tardive dyskinesia.
    B. attention deficit disorder.
    C. saccadic eye movements.
    D. seasonal affective disorder.
    (A, p. 449, factual)

214.  What are the symptoms of tardive dyskinesia?

    A. tremors and other involuntary movements
    B. anterograde and retrograde amnesia
    C. outbursts of unprovoked violent behavior
    D. attacks of anxiety that prevent active behavior
    (A, p. 449, factual)

215.  Tardive dyskinesia may result from:

    A. denervation supersensitivity of dopamine synapses.
    B. denervation supersensitivity of glutamate synapses.
    C. disuse supersensitivity of dopamine synapses.
    D. denervation insensitivity of dopamine synapses.
    (A, p. 449 factual)

216.    What happens when schizophrenics stop taking neuroleptic drugs?

      A. They usually stop having auditory hallucinations.
      B. Schizophrenic symptoms return within hours, often worse than
         ever.
      C. Tardive dyskinesia may continue.
      D. Memory problems become more apparent.
      (C, p. 449, conceptual)

217.    Why do atypical antipsychotic drugs alleviate schizophrenia with
      fewer side effects than other drugs?

      A. They stimulate dopamine synapses instead of blocking them.
      B. They act at acetylcholine synapses instead of dopamine
      synapses.
      C. They block dopamine synapses for only minutes per day.
      D. They block certain dopamine synapses but not others.
      (D, p. 449, conceptual)

218.    What kind of drug alleviates schizophrenia with little risk of
      producing tardive dyskinesia?

      A. neuroleptics
      B. atypical antipsychotics
      C. monoamine oxidase inhibitors
      D. lithium
      (B, p. 449, factual)

219.    Atypical antipsychotic drugs differ from standard neuroleptics
      like chlorpromazine in terms of:

      A. the blood pH they require for effectiveness.
      B. which set of dopamine synapses they affect.
      C. how quickly they take effect.
      D. how long their effects last.
      (B, p. 449, conceptual)

220.    People who take clozapine are more vulnerable to:

      A. infections.
      B. developing side effects like tardive dyskinesia.
      C. developing Parkinson-like symptoms.
      D. malnutrition.
      (A, p. 449, factual)

**Comprehensive Final Exam Items**

1.  Currently, which of the following disorders can be detected by a blood test?

    A. Parkinson's disease
    B. phenylketonuria (PKU)
    C. epilepsy
    D. Wernicke's aphasia
    (B, Chapter 1, factual)

2.  If a neuron's sodium-potassium pump were eliminated, what would eventually happen to the cell's membrane?

    A. The membrane would gradually become less and less permeable to sodium.
    B. The membrane would gradually become faster and faster at propagating action potentials.
    C. The resting potential would gradually become more and more hyperpolarized.
    D. The resting potential would gradually shift until the cell was permanently depolarized.
    (D, Chapter 2, conceptual)

3.  A mature neuron can never have more than one

    A. dendrite
    B. neurotransmitter
    C. node of Ranvier
    D. axon
    (D, Chapters 2 and 3, factual)

4.  A mature vertebrate neuron can have more than one

    A. axon.
    B. neurotransmitter.
    C. nucleus.
    D. velocity of action potential.
    (B, Chapters 2 and 3, factual)

5.  Which aspect of an adult neuron is most likely to change over a period of weeks or months as a result of experience?

    A. which neurotransmitters it releases
    B. the shape of its dendrites
    C. its DNA
    D. the amplitude and velocity of its action potentials
    (B, Chapters 2 and 5, conceptual)

6.  The action potential depends on the flow of

    A. sodium.
    B. neurotransmitters.
    C. hormones.
    D. water.
    (A, Chapter 2, factual)

7.  The axons of a motor neuron are most likely to be in synaptic contact with which kind of cell?

    A. intrinsic neuron
    B. muscle
    C. sensory neuron
    D. another motor neuron
    (B, Chapters 2 and 3, conceptual)

8.  Two major advances occurred in the late 1800s or early 1900s: the determination that the nervous system is composed of separate cells, called neurons, and the inference that they communicate at specialized junctions called synapses. These two advances were made by:

    A. Cajal and Sherrington
    B. Dement and Squire
    C. Andreasen and Richter
    D. McGaugh and Levy
    (A, Chapters 2 & 3, factual)

9.  Suppose some drug partly blocks potassium gates, so that they cannot open as wide as usual, and potassium cannot flow freely. Which of the following would result?

    A. Action potentials would have a greater amplitude than usual.
    B. The membrane would take longer than usual to repolarize after an action potential.
    C. The cell would produce extra action potentials even when there was no stimulus.
    D. Action potentials would travel more slowly than usual down the axon.
    (B, Chapter 2, conceptual)

10. The "all-or-none law" applies to

    A. hormones.
    B. axons.
    C. antidepressant effects.
    D. glia cells.
    (B, Chapter 2, conceptual)

11. Which of the following is IMPOSSIBLE in the adult mammalian nervous system?

    A. As a stimulus gets stronger, a sensory neuron reacts by producing larger action potentials.
    B. Axons and dendrites grow new branches in an adult mammal.
    C. New neurons form in an adult mammal.
    D. A presynaptic terminal releases two neurotransmitters at the same time.
    (A, Chapters 2, 3, 5; conceptual)

12.   What is meant by the term "absolute refractory period"?

   A. the time required for a neurotransmitter to cross the synapse
   B. a critical stage in early development when experiences or hormones produce organizing effects
   C. a time during which a neuron is incapable of producing an action potential
   D. a point at which all of the body's homeostatic processes are at equilibrium
   (C, Chapter 2, factual)

13.   What do glucose and amino acids have in common with each other?

   A. The brain metabolizes both as sources of energy.
   B. Both accumulate to high concentrations in the cerebrospinal fluid of depressed patients.
   C. Both cross the blood-brain barrier via an active transport.
   D. Both can be converted by the brain into acetylcholine.
   (C, Chapter 2, conceptual)

14.   Because the artificial sweetener "NutraSweet" contains a large amount of phenylalanine,

   A. it is helpful to people with phenylketonuria (PKU).
   B. it decreases the brain's production of serotonin.
   C. it can act as an antidepressant.
   D. it decreases aggressive behavior.
   (B, Chapters 1, 3, 12, 15; conceptual)

15.   Which of the following had its existence and main properties inferred from observations of behavior?

   A. synapses
   B. neurons
   C. action potentials
   D. central sulcus
   (A, Chapter 3, conceptual)

16.   A hypothetical drug would INCREASE temporal summation if it

   A. prolonged the refractory period of neurons.
   B. slowed the return of a membrane to its resting state after an action potential.
   C. facilitated the flow of potassium ions across the membrane.
   D. facilitated the enzyme acetylcholinesterase.
   (B, Chapters 2 and 3, conceptual)

17.   Which of the following is NOT a neurotransmitter?

   A. serotonin
   B. dopamine
   C. glucose
   D. GABA
   (C, Chapter 3, factual)

**Comprehensive Final Exam Items**

18.  Ionotropic and metabotropic are two types of

     A. glia cell.
     B. memory.
     C. hormone.
     D. synapse.
     (D, Chapter 3, factual)

19.  One similarity between cocaine and antidepressant drugs is that
     both of them
     A. mimic the effects of neurotransmitters at certain excitatory
        synapses.
     B. increase the activity of the sodium-potassium pump.
     C. produce their main behavioral effects within one hour after
        someone takes the drug.
     D. inhibit the reuptake of certain neurotransmitters.
     (D, Chapters 3 and 15; conceptual)

20.  The reuptake of dopamine and/or serotonin is inhibited by both

     A. cocaine and antidepressants.
     B. LSD and antiepileptic drugs.
     C. marijuana and antipsychotic drugs.
     D. heroin and tranquilizers.
     (A, Chapters 3 and 15; conceptual)

21.  Addictive drugs and sexual arousal both increase activity at

     A. glutamate synapses.
     B. acetylcholine synapses.
     C. dopamine synapses.
     D. GABA synapses.
     (D, Chapters 3 and 11, conceptual)

22.  Amphetamine and cocaine INCREASE activity at synapses sensitive
     to the neurotransmitter that is DEFICIENT in people with

     A. schizophrenia
     B. Parkinson's disease.
     C. Williams syndrome
     D. myasthenia gravis
     (C, Chapters 3 and 8; conceptual)

23.  Hallucinogens, such as LSD, are chemically similar to

     A. neurotransmitters
     B. vitamins
     C. DNA
     D. glucose
     (A, Chapter 3, factual)

24.  The study of opiate and marijuana receptors led to the discovery of:

   A. previously unknown areas of the cortex that are rich in these receptors.
   B. previously unknown hormones that prevent opiates and marijuana from reaching their receptors.
   C. previously unknown neuron types that reproduce in response to opiates and marijuana.
   D. previously unknown brain peptides that stimulate those same receptors.
   (D, Chapters 3 and 7; conceptual)

25.  Caffeine increases arousal and wakefulness by

   A. stimulating endorphin receptors.
   B. stimulating GABA receptors.
   C. blocking acetylcholine receptors.
   D. blocking adenosine receptors.
   (D, Chapters 3 and 9; conceptual)

26.  One reason why a drug can produce different effects, including different side effects, in different people is that

   A. the neurotransmitters used in a given brain area differ from one person to another.
   B. people differ substantially in the relative sizes of various brain areas.
   C. the proportion of different receptor types varies among people.
   D. some people produce hormones that chemically neutralize certain neurotransmitters.
   (C, Chapters 3 and various others, conceptual)

27.  A major difference between hormones and neurotransmitters is that

   A. hormones exert their effects more rapidly.
   B. hormones alter ion channels whereas neurotransmitters alter metabolism.
   C. the chemicals used as hormones are unlike those used as neurotransmitters.
   D. hormones act at many sites whereas neurotransmitters act locally.
   (D, Chapter 3 and others, conceptual)

28.  Many of the brain's neurotransmitters are also used as

   A. genes.
   B. RNA molecules.
   C. fuel.
   D. hormones.
   (D, Chapters 3, 10, and others; conceptual)

29. Which of the following pairs of terms are OPPOSITES of each other?

    A. sagittal - distal
    B. dorsal - ventral
    C. anterior - proximal
    D. lateral - inferior
    (D, Chapter 4, factual)

30. Which of the following pairs have functions that are related to each other but generally produce opposite results?

    A. precentral gyrus and postcentral gyrus.
    B. sympathetic nervous system and parasympathetic nervous system.
    C. ventromedial path and dorsolateral path.
    D. superior colliculus and inferior colliculus.
    (B, Chapters 4 and 12; factual)

31. The hypothalamus is most directly related to

    A. language production and comprehension
    B. recall of memory
    C. control of rapid, aimed movements
    D. eating, drinking, and other motivated behaviors
    (D, Chaps 4 and 10; factual)

32. The thalamus, hypothalamus, hippocampus, and basal ganglia are all parts of the

    A. spinal cord.
    B. hindbrain.
    C. midbrain.
    D. forebrain.
    (D, Chapter 4, factual)

33. The ventricles of the brain contain

    A. neurons.
    B. glia.
    C. liquid.
    D. air.
    (C, Chapter 4, factual)

34. What is the term for the fluid-filled cavities in the brain?

    A. Pacinian corpuscles
    B. colliculi
    C. ventricles
    D. ossicles
    (C, Chapter 4, factual)

35.  The main direct source of input to the cerebral cortex is the

     A. cerebellum.
     B. medulla.
     C. thalamus.
     D. hypothalamus.
     (C, Chapter 4, factual)

36.  If we find a number of neurons in the cerebral cortex that all
     have similar properties (such as being sensitive to the same
     pattern of light or touch in the same part of the hand), we
     should expect to find that these cells:

     A. closely resemble one another in size and shape.
     B. are located in the same column within the cortex.
     C. are located in the same lamina of the cortex.
     D. have few or no connections with one another.
     (B, Chapters 4 and 6; conceptual)

37.  People are most likely to neglect the left side of the body after
     damage to the

     A. right parietal cortex.
     B. left occipital cortex.
     C. cerebellar nuclei.
     D. locus coeruleus.
     (A, Chapter 4, factual)

38.  The "binding problem" is the issue of how we

     A. convert sensory information into a pattern that produces
        movement.
     B. perceive visual, auditory, and other aspects of a stimulus as
        a single object.
     C. transfer information between the left and right hemispheres.
     D. transfer information between Wernicke's area and Broca's area.
     (B, Chapters 4 and 6, conceptual)

39.  MRI, PET, and fMRI are methods of

     A. measuring the release of neurotransmitters.
     B. controlling the release of hormones.
     C. decreasing the symptoms of depression.
     D. examining the brains of living people.
     (D, various, factual)

40.  Which of the following is NOT a method of studying the human
     brain?

     A. PET
     B. LTP
     C. MRI
     D. fMRI
     (B, various including Chap 13, factual)

41. Which of the following has NOT been shown to depend on the hypothalamus?

    A. control of eating and drinking
    B. control of sexual motivation
    C. control of muscles
    D. circadian sleep-wakefulness cycles
    (C, various, conceptual)

42. Between birth and maturity, what DECREASES in the human brain?

    A. number of neurons
    B. myelination
    C. activity in the prefrontal cortex
    D. dependence on glucose
    (A, Chapter 5, factual)

43. Of the following, which is MORE NUMEROUS in infants than in adults?

    A. neurotransmitters
    B. columns in the cortex
    C. convolutions in the cortex
    D. neurons
    (D, Chapter 5, factual)

44. Nerve growth factor tends to prevent

    A. ischemia
    B. schizophrenia
    C. anorexia
    D. apoptosis
    (D, Chapter 5, factual)

45. When researchers try to prevent neurons from dying (after stroke, in Parkinson's disease, and so forth) or try to get neurons to increase their branching, they are likely to try which kind of chemical?

    A. neurotrophins
    B. tranquilizers
    C. hallucinogens
    D. carbohydrates
    (A, Chapter 5 and various, conceptual)

46. Suppose a researcher examines the brain of several young individuals, all about the same age, and finds several brain areas with dead or dying cells. There was no reason to believe these individuals had any disease or trauma. What is one possible explanation for the dying cells?

    A. amblyopia
    B. apoptosis
    C. diaschisis
    D. neurohypophysis
    (B, Chapter 5, conceptual)

47. Magnetoencephalography and electroencephalography are methods of measuring:

    A. current activity in various brain areas.
    B. current structure of the brain.
    C. evolution of the brain.
    D. release of neurotransmitters.
    (A, Chapters 5 and 9, conceptual)

48. Prolonged practice of a stringed instrument beginning at an early age leads to:

    A. increased growth of the somatosensory cortex in the left hemisphere.
    B. increased growth of the somatosensory cortex in the right hemisphere.
    C. increased myelin development in the corpus callosum.
    D. wider branching of dendrites in the dorsolateral prefrontal cortex.
    (B, Chapter 5, conceptual)

49. A stereotaxic instrument is a method of

    A. inserting an electrode into a spot in the interior of the brain.
    B. helping blind people find their way around.
    C. measuring the amount of blood flow to various brain areas at a given time.
    D. stimulating damaged nerves to regrow and make connections.
    (A, Chapter 5, factual)

50. Which of the following is NOT a cause of brain damage?

    A. brain ischemia
    B. brain hemorrhage
    C. lesion with a stereotaxic instrument
    D. treatment with neurotrophins
    (D, Chapter 5, conceptual)

51. The phenomenon of fetal alcohol syndrome tends to support the generalization that

    A. the brain is more vulnerable to damage early in life than later.
    B. most psychological disorders depend about equally on genetic and environmental influences.
    C. the human brain has different neurotransmitters from other species' brains.
    D. deprivation of one sensory system leads to overdevelopment of others.
    (A, Chapter 5, conceptual)

52. Reorganization of connections in the somatosensory cortex is responsible for the phenomenon of

    A. photographic memory.
    B. phantom limbs.
    C. narcolepsy.
    D. infant amnesia
    (C, Chapter 5, conceptual)

53. After amputation of the left arm, the person feels a "phantom limb" at times. What is the current explanation?

    A. Axons representing the face or other areas have invaded the cortical area responsible for touch on that arm.
    B. The receptors on the stump have become hypersensitive and continue sending the same messages as before the damage.
    C. Emotional distress stimulates the memory of previous sensations.
    D. A pattern of activity across neurons in unaffected parts of the cortex sets up a field that is interpreted as if it were the amputated arm.
    (A, Chapter 5, conceptual)

54. The phenomenon of "phantom limbs" supports the generalization that:

    A. impairment of the emotional areas of the brain leads to poor decision making.
    B. brain connections remain plastic throughout life.
    C. most psychological disorders depend on both a genetic predisposition and a stressful environment.
    D. across species, intelligence depends on the brain-to-body ratio.
    (B, Chapter 5, conceptual)

55.   From the total brain mass of a mammalian species, we can most
      accurately predict:

      A. the animal's total body mass.
      B. the mass of almost any major structure within its brain.
      C. the animal's performance on a standardized test of animal
         intelligence.
      D. the amount of genetic similarity between that animal and
         humans.
      (B, Chapter 5, conceptual)

56.   The law of specific nerve energies pertains to

      A. the types of transmitters released by a given neuron.
      B. how we interpret the activity of sensory neurons.
      C. the difference between the resting potential and an action
         potential.
      D. the amplitude and velocity of an action potential.
      (B, Chapter 6, conceptual)

57.   The fovea is part of the sense organ for

      A. vestibular sensation.
      B. vision.
      C. pheromone detection.
      D. hearing.
      (B, Chapters 6 and 7, factual)

58.   Vision is to retina as hearing is to

      A. vomeronasal organ.
      B. cornea.
      C. cochlea.
      D. Pacinian corpuscle.
      (C, Chapters 6 and 7, conceptual)

59.   Which of the following deals with color vision?

      A. Bell-Magendie law
      B. Kennard principle
      C. Dale's principle
      D. Young-Helmholtz (trichromatic) theory
      (D, Chapter 6, factual)

60.   Because color vision requires a comparison of responses between
      one neuron and another, it is an example of

      A. proliferation.
      B. migration.
      C. labeled-line coding.
      D. across-fiber pattern coding.
      (D, Chapters 6 and 7, conceptual)

61. Blindsight resembles implicit memory in that both show it is
possible to have

    A. knowledge that did not enter through any sensory organ.
    B. more complex behaviors in infants than in adults.
    C. complex behavior without awareness of its causes.
    D. advantageous outcomes of brain damage.
    (C, Chapters 6 and 13, conceptual)

62. In the vertebrate visual system, lateral inhibition depends on

    A. horizontal cells.
    B. Purkinje cells.
    C. Kenyon cells.
    D. Schwann cells.
    (A, Chapter 6, factual)

63. Lateral inhibition depends directly on which elementary feature
of neurons?

    A. the refractory period
    B. myelin sheaths
    C. inhibitory synapses
    D. the sodium-potassium pump
    (C, Chapters 2 and 6, conceptual)

64. If you wanted to find the receptive field of a neuron in the
primary visual cortex (area V1), what would you do?

    A. Trace its axons to find where they go.
    B. Trace the axons arriving at the neuron to see where they
       originated.
    C. Shine light in various parts of the visual field and see which
       areas excite or inhibit this neuron.
    D. Apply glutamate to various parts of the neuron's surface and
       see which areas depolarize the membrane.
    (C, Chapter 6, conceptual)

65. Where would one find the neurons that Hubel and Wiesel designated
as simple, complex, and hypercomplex cells?

    A. frontal cortex
    B. parietal cortex
    C. occipital cortex
    D. temporal cortex
    (C, Chapter 6, factual)

66. If you look at one of your eyes in the mirror and then shift focus to the other eye, you don't see your eyes move. One major reason is that

    A. the distance is too short and the movement is too fast.
    B. you blink during and after any eye movement.
    C. fatigue of the eye muscles distracts your attention.
    D. the visual cortex decreases activity during eye movements.
    (D, Chapter 6, conceptual)

67. Various aspects of a visual stimulus are processed in distant areas of the cortex, yet we perceive the object as unified. This phenomenon is one example of

    A. the nature-nurture issue.
    B. the Kennard principle.
    C. the Young-Helmholtz theory.
    D. the binding problem.
    (D, Chapters 4 and 6, conceptual)

68. The trichromatic theory and the opponent process theory of color vision are analogous to the place theory and frequency theory of pitch perception, because in both cases

    A. two theories account for part of the information, but neither one accounts for all.
    B. the more recent theory is wrong and the earlier theory is more correct.
    C. one theory can be shown to be a special case of the other, more general theory.
    D. one theory is correct for children and the other is correct for adults.
    (A, Chapters 6 and 7, conceptual)

69. Cervical, thoracic, lumbar, and sacral are sections of the

    A. spinal cord.
    B. hypothalamus.
    C. amygdala.
    D. pituitary gland.
    (A, Chapters 4 and 7; factual)

70. Substance P is a neurotransmitter that is especially important for

    A. movement.
    B. memory.
    C. pain.
    D. hunger.
    (C, Chapter 6, factual)

71. Endorphins and substance P have opposite effects on

    A. vision.
    B. voluntary movement.
    C. sexual behavior.
    D. pain.
    (D, Chapter 7, factual)

72. Which of the following depends heavily on genetics?

    A. whether or not an amputee develops a phantom limb
    B. whether or not someone develops fetal alcohol syndrome
    C. the presence or absence of "absolute" or "perfect" pitch in adults
    D. the difference between tasters, nontasters, and supertasters
    (D, Chapter 7, factual)

73. One oddity about pheromones is that their influence on behavior

    A. is stronger before puberty.
    B. requires stimulation of three separate sense organs.
    C. develops rapidly and lasts permanently.
    D. apparently does not require conscious awareness.
    (D, Chapter 7, conceptual)

74. Which of the following has the LEAST certain importance for adult humans?

    A. the suprachiasmatic nucleus
    B. the pineal gland
    C. the vomeronasal organ
    D. the hormone leptin
    (C, Chapter 7, conceptual)

75. Of the following, which uses the smallest number of chemicals as neurotransmitters?

    A. the control of mood
    B. the nerve-muscle junction
    C. the control of feeding
    D. the control of sleep and waking
    (B, Chapters 8, 9, 10, and 15; factual)

76. Which of the following is in the frontal cortex?

    A. primary visual cortex
    B. primary motor cortex
    C. primary auditory cortex
    D. primary somatosensory cortex
    (B, Chapter 4 and 8, factual)

77. Because infants move their trunk muscles much more adeptly than their peripheral muscles, we can infer that the following part of the nervous system is slow to mature:

    A. dorsolateral tract
    B. ventromedial tract
    C. cranial nerves
    D. central sulcus
    (A, Chapter 8, conceptual)

78. The relationship between the dorsolateral tract and the ventromedial tract is analogous to the relationship between the sympathetic nervous system and the parasympathetic nervous system. In both cases:

    A. both systems are active at all times, although one may be more important than the other for a given response.
    B. activity of either system prevents activity of the other system.
    C. one is active during low states of arousal and the other during high arousal.
    D. one is responsible for learned behaviors and the other for automatic behaviors.
    (A, Chapters 8 and 9, conceptual)

79. Which of the following conditions most closely resembles the symptoms of damage to the cerebellum?

    A. bipolar disorder
    B. Wernicke's aphasia
    C. narcolepsy
    D. alcohol intoxication
    (D, Chapter 8, conceptual)

80. What effect, if any, does the cerebellum have on cognitive functions?

    A. It has no effect, except for controlling the movements that result from cognitive activities.
    B. It is important for judging the time relationship among events.
    C. It is important for judging the intensity of light or sound or the weight of an object.
    D. It is important for short-term memory but not long-term memory.
    (B, Chapter 8, conceptual)

81.    Which of the following is NOT true of the cerebellum?

A. Its neurons are arranged in a regular, repeating geometric
pattern.
B. It is one of the structures of the forebrain.
C. It is important for precise timing of behaviors.
D. It is important for certain cases of classical conditioning.
(B, Chapters 4, 8, and 13; conceptual)

82.    Which of the following disorders is usually diagnosed for the
first time after age 50?

A. phenylketonuria (PKU)
B. bipolar disorder
C. schizophrenia
D. Parkinson's disease
(D, Chapter 8, factual)

83.    Treatment with L-dopa is helpful for _____ but would probably be
harmful for _____.

A. post-traumatic stress disorder (PTSD)... myasthenia gravis
B. Parkinson's disease... schizophrenia
C. phenylketonuria (PKU)... depression
D. Huntington's disease... anorexia nervosa
(B, Chapters 8 and 15; conceptual)

84.    For which of the following is there the LEAST evidence for a
genetic basis?

A. early onset Alzheimer's disease
B. late onset Parkinson's disease
C. Williams syndrome
D. Huntington's disease
(B, Chapters 8 and others, factual)

85.    In Parkinson's disease, Alzheimer's disease, alcoholism, and
depression, genetic influences are more important for

A. late onset cases than early onset cases.
B. early onset cases than late onset cases.
C. mild cases than severe cases.
D. women than men.
(B, Chaps 8, 13, 15; conceptual)

86.    Which of the following is believed to be caused in some cases by
exposure to toxic substances?

A. anorexia nervosa
B. Huntington's disease
C. Williams syndrome
D. Parkinson's disease
(D, Chapter 8, conceptual)

87. Operations implanting tissue into a damaged brain have been frequently attempted for patients suffering from

    A. Williams syndrome
    B. Parkinson's disease
    C. Wernicke's aphasia
    D. Broca's aphasia
    (B, Chapter 8, factual)

88. One similarity among Parkinson's disease, Huntington's disease, and Alzheimer's disease is that all of them

    A. are caused by genes on the X chromosome.
    B. are caused by deficiency of dopamine.
    C. develop because of gradual loss of neurons.
    D. can be prevented by a special diet.
    (C, Chapters 8 and 13, conceptual)

89. One similarity between Huntington's disease and schizophrenia is that in both,

    A. the cause is a dominant gene that almost inevitably produces the disorder.
    B. the common symptoms include hallucinations and delusions.
    C. the brain progressively and visibly deteriorates.
    D. the usual age of onset is ages 20 to 30.
    (B, Chapters 8 and 15, conceptual)

90. For which of the following can a chromosome examination MOST accurately predict who will get the disorder?

    A. late-onset Parkinson's disease
    B. schizophrenia
    C. late-onset alcoholism
    D. Huntington's disease
    (D, Chapter 8, factual)

91. Studies of sleep-wakefulness cycles surprised experimental psychologists of the 1920-1950 era, because they had previously believed that

    A. all behaviors are influenced by heredity.
    B. human behavior is fundamentally different from that of other species.
    C. the conscious mind is separate from the unconscious mind.
    D. every animal behavior is a reaction to a stimulus.
    (D, Chapter 9, conceptual)

92. Damage to the suprachiasmatic nucleus would most severely impair which of the following?

    A. circadian rhythms
    B. working memory
    C. control of fine, peripheral movements
    D. hypovolemic thirst
    (A, Chapter 9, factual)

93. Which of the following effects of light can occur even in blind mole rats, whose eyes are covered with skin and fur?

    A. visually finding other blind mole rats
    B. resetting the wake-sleep cycle
    C. startle response to a bright light
    D. learned responses based on the location of a light
    (B, Chapter 9, factual)

94. Which of the following effects of light apparently requires the FEWEST visual receptors and the LEAST activity by the visual cortex?

    A. resetting the wake-sleep cycle
    B. color constancy
    C. shape perception
    D. visuo-motor coordination
    (A, Chapter 9, conceptual)

95. Which hormone has the greatest influence on waking and sleeping?

    A. adrenocorticotropic hormone
    B. follicle-stimulating hormone
    C. somatostatin
    D. melatonin
    (D, Chapter 9, factual)

96. What do wake-sleep cycles have in common with consolidation of memories?

    A. Both are difficult to demonstrate in nonhuman species.
    B. Both can be influenced by hormones.
    C. Both become faster under the influence of x-rays.
    D. Both depend mostly on connections between the cerebellum and the basal ganglia.
    (B, Chapters 9 and 13, conceptual)

97. Observations of people's behavior during REM sleep imply that the mechanisms of REM sleep strongly INHIBIT activity of

    A. PGO waves in the pons, geniculate, and occipital cortex.
    B. acetylcholine synapses.
    C. the ventromedial path in the spinal cord.
    D. the parietal and temporal cortexes.
    (C, Chapters 8 and 9, conceptual requiring an inference)

98. During which of the following is the ventromedial path of the spinal cord strongly suppressed?

    A. hypovolemic thirst
    B. REM sleep
    C. yawning
    D. memory consolidation
    (B, Chapters 8 and 9, conceptual requiring an inference)

99. Which of the following is an overstatement?

    A. Dreams occur in REM sleep and not in NREM sleep.
    B. The amplitude and velocity of action potentials are independent of the stimuli that evoked them.
    C. Acetylcholine is always the transmitter at the nerve-muscle junction of skeletal muscles.
    D. The cerebellum contains more neurons than the rest of the nervous system combined.
    (A, Chapters 2, 8, and 9; conceptual)

100. Which of the following is most likely to be measured with an EEG?

    A. whether someone is lying
    B. stages of sleep
    C. classical conditioning
    D. release of neurotransmitters
    (B, Chapter 9, conceptual)

101. Which of the following is most important for controlling the overall arousal of the rest of the brain?

    A. reticular formation
    B. corpus callosum
    C. superior and inferior colliculi
    D. hippocampus
    (A, Chapter 9, factual)

102. Which of the following is NOT true of the pons?

    A. It includes areas that help to regulate sleep, waking, and REM.
    B. It is next to the medulla in the hindbrain.
    C. It is the center for anxieties and learned fears.
    D. It is the point of origin of several cranial nerves.
    (C, Chapters 4, 9 and 12; conceptual)

103. Which of the following is a sleep disorder?

    A. aphagia
    B. apnea
    C. anorexia
    D. aphasia
    (B, Chapter 9, factual)

104. Which of the following is more common in obese men than in other kinds of people?

    A. seasonal affective disorder
    B. panic disorder
    C. Korsakoff's syndrome
    D. sleep apnea
    (D, Chapter 9, factual)

105. Which of the following is NOT true of acetylcholine?

    A. It is the transmitter at nerve-muscle junctions.
    B. Excesses of it are responsible for Alzheimer's disease.
    C. Its synapses are overactive in narcolepsy.
    D. Some of its synapses can also be stimulated by nicotine.
    (B, Chapters 3, 8, 9, and 13; conceptual)

106. Of the following, which varies most widely among mammalian species?

    A. which chemicals are used as neurotransmitters
    B. location of the visual cortex relative to other cortical areas
    C. number of cone types in the retina
    D. hours per day spent in REM sleep
    (D, Chapters 9 and others, conceptual)

107. Suppose you discover a new species of mammal and you find that it is a prey species active mostly at night. The best prediction is that, relative to predators and day-active species, it spends relatively _____ hours per day asleep and it has relatively ____ cones in its retina.

    A. few... few
    B. few... many
    C. many... few
    D. many... many
    (A, Chapters 6 and 9, conceptual)

108. Suppose you discover a new species of mammal and you find that it has a high proportion of cones in its retina, compared to other species, and that it spends more hours per day asleep than do most other species. Your best prediction is that this species is

    A. a prey species that is active mostly in the day.
    B. a prey species that is active mostly at night.
    C. a predator that is active mostly in the day.
    D. a predator that is active mostly at night.
    (C, Chapters 6 and 9, conceptual)

109. Several studies examined people who were deprived of REM sleep
     for a few days and then permitted to sleep without disturbance.
     The resulting sleep patterns of those people suggest that the
     need for REM sleep is to a large degree

     A. confabulated.
     B. hypovolemic.
     C. metabotropic.
     D. homeostatic.
     (D, Chapters 9 and 10, conceptual requiring inference)

110. In addition to hunger, thirst, and temperature regulation, which
     of the following behaviors is apparently also regulated by a
     homeostatic mechanism?

     A. reading
     B. Babinski reflex
     C. REM sleep
     D. auditory localization
     (C, Chapters 9 and 10, conceptual requiring inference)

111. One way in which birds differ from mammals, as a general rule, is
     that birds

     A. use different chemicals as neurotransmitters.
     B. have a higher body temperature.
     C. spend more of their day in REM sleep.
     D. have fewer cones in their retina.
     (B, Chapter 10 and various, conceptual)

112. Most of the calories that people consume are used for

     A. basal metabolism
     B. muscle movement
     C. brain activity
     D. digestion
     (A, Chapter 10, factual)

113. Maintaining biological variables within a narrow range is known
     as

     A. lateralization
     B. homeostasis
     C. prosopagnosia
     D. phrenology
     (B, Chapter 10, factual)

114. Birds' eggs and mammals' testis cells differ from most of the
     rest of the body in that they

     A. use only amino acids for energy.
     B. require a lower temperature.
     C. metabolize without oxygen.
     D. produce energy that can be detected as radio waves.
     (B, Chapter 10, factual)

115. Hunger, thirst, temperature regulation, and sexual behavior are all regulated by activity of the

    A. locus coeruleus
    B. planum temporale
    C. hypothalamus
    D. superior colliculus
    (C, Chapters 10 and 11, factual)

116. One important similarity among temperature regulation, thirst, and hunger is that each of them

    A. is more accurately regulated in humans than in other species.
    B. relies mostly on the activity of the cerebral cortex.
    C. relies on multiple physiological and behavioral mechanisms.
    D. is acquired through a process of trial-and-error learning.
    (C, Chapter 10, conceptual)

117. What is one process that modifies taste preferences?

    A. Old age increases sensitivity to weak, dilute tastes.
    B. Sodium deficiency increases preference for salty tastes.
    C. Miracle berries increase preference for sweet tastes.
    D. Adaptation to salty tastes increases preference for sour tastes.
    (B, Chapters 7 and 10, conceptual)

118. Genetically controlled differences in digestive enzymes account for a significant part of the variation among people in their preference for and consumption of

    A. water and cellulose.
    B. paprika and cinnamon.
    C. ginger and tarragon.
    D. milk products and alcohol.
    (D, Chapters 10 and 15, conceptual)

119. The consequences of consuming phenylalanine, milk products, or alcohol all depend on genetically determined differences among people in their

    A. digestive enzymes.
    B. hormones.
    C. heart rate.
    D. brain-to-body ratio.
    (A, Chapters 1, 10, and 15; conceptual)

120. Which of the following is an easily replicable finding?

    A. An injection of a brain extract from a trained animal enables a recipient to learn the same task faster.
    B. An animal that is suddenly made sodium-deficient will crave salty tastes without needing trial and error learning.
    C. Transplant of adrenal cortex tissue into the substantia nigra relieves the symptoms of Parkinson's disease.
    D. Most obese people have a deficiency of leptin.
    (B, Chapter 10, conceptual)

121. CCK limits meal size through two mechanisms:

    A. as a gene and as a nutrient
    B. as a vitamin and as a pheromone
    C. as a neuron and as a glia cell
    D. as a hormone and as a neurotransmitter
    (D, Chapter 10, conceptual)

122. Which of the following is NOT true of glucose?

    A. It is the brain's main fuel.
    B. It is used as a neurotransmitter.
    C. Insulin and glucagon regulate its entry to the cells.
    D. In order to metabolize it, we need thiamine.
    (B, Chapters 2 and 10, factual)

123. What is the similarity between insulin, glucagon, and thiamine?

    A. They all influence the body's use of glucose.
    B. The brain converts each of them into other chemicals used as neurotransmitters.
    C. The liver can convert any of them into either of the others, depending on which is needed at the time.
    D. They all circulate in the lymphatic system instead of the blood.
    (A, Chapters 2 and 10, conceptual)

124. Leptin is a _____ that influences _____.

    A. gene... feeding
    B. neurotransmitter... memory
    C. hormone... feeding
    D. cell type... memory
    (C, Chapter 10, factual)

125. One similarity between the proteins huntingtin and leptin is that researchers

    A. predicted their existence based on mathematical models of the nervous system.
    B. found that small amounts of them cause psychological disorders, but large amounts relieve them.
    C. knew how to synthesize these proteins before they had any idea what behavior was associated with them.
    D. discovered the genes responsible for the proteins before they discovered the proteins themselves.
    (D, Chapters 8 and 10, factual)

126. Which of these animal models eventually proved to have disappointingly little relevance to the human condition?

    A. the rats that consolidate their memories more effectively when they are emotionally aroused
    B. the genetic strain of mouse that becomes obese because of its lack of leptin
    C. the rats that respond more drastically to stressful events that they cannot predict or control
    D. the rats that lose most of their learned fear or anxiety after damage to the amygdala
    (B, Chapters 10 and various, conceptual)

127. Which of the following is SELDOM an effective treatment for the human condition listed next to it?

    A. bright lights - seasonal affective disorder
    B. L-dopa - Parkinson's disease
    C. leptin - obesity
    D. lithium - bipolar disorder
    (C, Chapters 8, 10, and 15; conceptual)

128. What do ACTH, TSH, FSH, LH, and CCK have in common?

    A. They are hormones.
    B. They are imaging techniques for the brain.
    C. They are psychological disorders.
    D. They are gene combinations.
    (A, Chapters 10, 11, and 12; factual)

129. Which of the following occurs mostly during an early stage of development?

    A. changes in the branching patterns of dendrites
    B. production of new glia cells
    C. activating effects of hormones
    D. organizing effects of hormones
    (D, Chapter 11, conceptual)

130. Which two body parts develop from the same prenatal structure?

    A. thalamus and cerebral ventricles
    B. pancreas and adrenal glands
    C. penis and clitoris
    D. brain and heart
    (C, Chapter 11, conceptual)

131. Which of the following surprising statements is NOT correct?

    A. A very large amount of estradiol at an early developmental stage can masculinize a mammal's development.
    B. The pheromones from an infant rat tend to decrease maternal care.
    C. An animal that is deficient in sodium shows an immediate decrease in its preference for salty tastes.
    D. Someone with no conscious awareness of vision can accurately localize some points of light.
    (C, Chapters 6, 10, and 11; conceptual)

132. Which of the following surprising statements IS correct, on the average?

    A. Decreasing men's testosterone levels increases their probability of committing sexual offenses.
    B. Bird species with an excellent spatial memory have a smaller than normal hippocampus.
    C. People with post-traumatic stress disorder have lower than normal cortisol levels.
    D. Antidepressant drugs alter behavior faster than they exert measurable effects on synapses.
    (C, Chapter 12, factual)

133. Which of the following pairs of types of people differ measurably (on the average) in their anatomy of the hypothalamus?

    A. educated people and uneducated people
    B. people born in the summer and people born in the winter
    C. vegetarians and nonvegetarians
    D. homosexual men and heterosexual men
    (D, Chapter 11, factual)

134. Which of the following depend on dopamine stimulation at different kinds of dopamine receptors?

    A. sexual arousal and orgasm
    B. black/white vision and color vision
    C. contraction of extensor muscles and flexor muscles
    D. REM sleep and NREM sleep
    (A, Chapters 11 and others, factual)

Comprehensive Final Exam Items

135. Observations on people with absence seizures suggest that it is possible for a person who is not conscious to have _____, but probably not possible for such a person to have _____.

    A. muscle movements ... emotions
    B. emotions ... muscle movements
    C. left-hemisphere activity ... right-hemisphere activity
    D. right-hemisphere activity ... left-hemisphere activity
    (A, Chapter 12, conceptual)

136. The James-Lange theory pertains to the relationship between

    A. REM sleep and dreams.
    B. the basal ganglia and movement.
    C. hunger and thirst.
    D. emotions and behaviors.
    (D, Chapter 12, factual)

137. Which of the following brain areas or systems is correctly paired with its behavioral function?

    A. limbic system - vision
    B. sympathetic nervous system - fight or flight behaviors
    C. corpus callosum - eating, drinking, and temperature regulation
    D. suprachiasmatic nucleus - control of fine muscle movements
    (B, Chapters 12 and others; conceptual)

138. Which of the following types of cells is part of the immune system?

    A. amacrine cells
    B. leukocytes
    C. astrocytes
    D. Purkinje cells
    (B, Chapter 12, factual)

139. Of the following conditions--Huntington's disease, violent behavior, and fetal alcohol syndrome--the one with apparently the highest heritability is _____ and the one with the lowest heritability is probably _____.

    A. violent behavior ... Huntington's disease
    B. fetal alcohol syndrome ... violent behavior
    C. violent behavior ... fetal alcohol syndrome
    D. Huntington's disease ... fetal alcohol syndrome
    (D, Chapters 1, 5, 8, and 12; conceptual)

140. Which of the following hormonal effects is WEAKEST in humans, detectable only as a statistical trend and not as a clear result in the average individual?

    A. the effect of testosterone on violent behavior
    B. the effect of FSH on activities of the ovaries
    C. the effect of insulin on glucose entering body cells
    D. the effect of angiotensin on hypovolemic thirst
    (A, Chapters 10-12, factual)

141. If you wanted to predict which people would be most at risk for committing suicide, which of the following biological variables would be most likely to be helpful?

    A. measurements of 5-HIAA in blood, CSF, or urine
    B. measurements of accuracy of pursuit eye movements
    C. EEG recordings during a period of behavioral inactivity
    D. stereotaxic recordings from the anterior commissure
    (A, Chapter 12, conceptual)

142. People who have low levels of 5-HIAA (a serotonin metabolite) in their blood are more at risk than most other people for

    A. myasthenia gravis.
    B. violent behavior.
    C. dyslexia.
    D. Huntington's disease.
    (B, Chapter 12, conceptual)

143. Low levels of serotonin turnover have been linked, at least tentatively, to both

    A. depression and outbursts of violence.
    B. schizophrenia and impaired spatial memory.
    C. post-traumatic stress disorder and motion blindness.
    D. epilepsy and dyslexia.
    (A, Chapters 12 and 15, factual)

144. Which of the following was demonstrated in experimental animals before it was demonstrated (or looked for) in humans?

    A. Parkinson's disease
    B. Williams syndrome
    C. the relationship between violence and serotonin turnover
    D. the relationship between the hippocampus and memory
    (C, Chapters 12 and others, factual)

Comprehensive Final Exam Items

145. If you wanted to find an area of the nervous system that is
     responsible for excessive anxieties and fears, where should you
     concentrate your research?

     A. ventromedial path
     B. lateral interpositus nucleus
     C. amygdala
     D. suprachiasmatic nucleus
     (C, Chapter 12, conceptual)

146. Enhancement of the startle reflex is studied as a way of
     measuring

     A. fear and anxiety.
     B. surprise and anger.
     C. spatial memory.
     D. working memory.
     (A, Chapter 12, factual)

147. People have trouble recognizing faces after damage to the _____;
     they have trouble interpreting the meaning of a fearful
     expression after damage to the _____.

     A. parietal cortex ... hippocampus
     B. parietal cortex ... amygdala
     C. inferior temporal cortex ... hippocampus
     D. inferior temporal cortex ... amygdala
     (D, Chapters 6 and 12, conceptual)

148. Which of the following is NOT true of cholecystokinin (CCK)?

     A. Stimulation of CCK synapses in the amygdala enhances the
        startle reflex.
     B. CCK acts as a sex hormone to increase the response to sexual
        stimulation.
     C. CCK acts as a hormone in the digestive system to close the
        muscle that separates the stomach from the intestines.
     D. Stimulation of CCK synapses in the hypothalamus decreases
        appetite.
     (B, Chapters 10 and 12, conceptual)

149. Benzodiazepines are most often used in treating which of these
     disorders?

     A. Borna disease
     B. obesity
     C. anxiety
     D. alcoholism
     (C, Chapter 12, factual)

150. Which of the following is NOT true of the neurotransmitter GABA?

    A. Its effects are almost always inhibitory to the postsynaptic cell.
    B. It acts on more than one type of receptor.
    C. Long-term potentiation (LTP) occurs by an increase in the effectiveness of GABA synapses.
    D. Benzodiazepine tranquilizers increase its effects.
    (C, Chapters 3 and 12, conceptual)

151. Which of the following is a common distinction between two types of memory?

    A. flexor-extensor
    B. explicit-implicit
    C. activating-organizing
    D. central-peripheral
    (B, Chapter 13, conceptual)

152. The neurological patient H.M. became famous because of his severe limitations on

    A. controlling his anger and fear.
    B. storing new factual memories.
    C. understanding complex sentence structures.
    D. limiting the size of his meals.
    (B, Chapter 13, conceptual)

153. Studies on the patient H. M. have most strongly supported the following generalization:

    A. development of behavior depends on a combination of genes and experiences.
    B. the gradual regrowth of neurons and connections can restore normal behavior after brain damage.
    C. people with an impairment of emotions tend to make bad decisions.
    D. it is possible to lose one kind of memory without impairing another.
    (D, Chapter 13, conceptual)

154. The hippocampus is

    A. a brain area important for hearing.
    B. a brain area important for movement control.
    C. a brain area important for memory.
    D. the location of Hippo University.
    (C, Chapter 13, factual)

155. The delayed matching to sample task and delayed nonmatching to sample task are ways of measuring

    A. vision.
    B. emotion.
    C. timing.
    D. memory.
    (D, Chapter 13, factual)

156. Which of the following is a common way of measuring spatial memory?

    A. Wada test
    B. Tower of Hanoi puzzle
    C. Morris search task
    D. Wisconsin Card Sorting Task
    (C, Chapters 13-15, factual)

157. Several species of jays differ in the size of their hippocampus. Their hippocampus size correlates positively with their

    A. aggressiveness.
    B. spatial memory.
    C. color vision.
    D. muscle coordination.
    (B, Chapter 13, conceptual)

158. Which of the following is NOT true about the hippocampus?

    A. High levels of stress hormones can damage it.
    B. It contains nuclei that control eating, drinking, sex, and temperature regulation.
    C. Damage to it impairs certain aspects of memory.
    D. It is part of the mammalian forebrain.
    (B, Chapters 10 through 13, conceptual)

159. Thiamine deficiency leads to Korsakoff's syndrome because thiamine is necessary for

    A. protecting against toxins.
    B. metabolizing glucose.
    C. digesting proteins.
    D. myelinating axons.
    (B, Chapters 2 and 13, conceptual)

160. Which of the following is caused by the lack of a particular vitamin in the diet?

    A. Korsakoff's syndrome
    B. Huntington's disease
    C. Williams syndrome
    D. intersexuality
    (A, Chapter 13, conceptual)

161. Two disorders that would be possible to prevent by changing people's diet are

    A. Korsakoff's syndrome and fetal alcohol syndrome.
    B. Williams syndrome and narcolepsy.
    C. post-traumatic stress disorder and dyslexia.
    D. myasthenia gravis and Huntington's disease.
    (A, Chapters 5 and 13, conceptual)

162. Which disease is marked by large numbers of plaques, tangles, and amyloid deposits in the brain?

    A. Alzheimer's disease
    B. Broca's aphasia
    C. Williams syndrome
    D. myasthenia gravis
    (A, Chapter 13, factual)

163. One conclusion that follows from the study of amnesic patients is that

    A. intelligence depends on the ratio of brain to body.
    B. it is possible to lose one kind of memory without losing others.
    C. all kinds of sensory information converge onto a single central processor in the brain.
    D. each memory is stored in its own individual neuron.
    (B, Chapter 13, conceptual)

164. A "Hebbian" synapse is one that

    A. has receptors for more than one neurotransmitter.
    B. sends information in both directions.
    C. increases in effectiveness after previous experience.
    D. enables convergence of information from more than one sense organ.
    (C, Chapter 13, factual)

165. Long-term potentiation (LTP) is a possible single-cell mechanism for

    A. auditory localization
    B. speech perception.
    C. emotional arousal.
    D. learning and memory.
    (D, Chapter 13, factual)

166. A drug that blocked glutamate synapses would also interfere with

    A. PNS.
    B. LTP.
    C. MDMA.
    D. CSF.
    (B, Chapter 13, factual)

167. The NMDA receptor ordinarily responds to _____ and plays a key role in the process of

    A. serotonin ... antidepressant drugs.
    B. GABA ... emotions.
    C. acetylcholine ... sleep and wakefulness.
    D. glutamate ... long-term potentiation.
    (D, Chapter 13, factual)

168. Which of the following CNS structures is composed entirely of axons?

    A. spinal cord
    B. hippocampus
    C. corpus callosum
    D. medulla
    (C, Chapter 14, factual)

169. The optic chiasm, corpus callosum, and medulla have in common with each other the fact that each of them

    A. is composed entirely of dendrites.
    B. provides transfer of information between the left and right halves of the CNS.
    C. is proportionately larger in men than in women.
    D. generates rhythmic waves of activity that control time perception.
    (B, Chapters 6, 8, and 14; conceptual)

170. Most people find it difficult to draw a C with one hand while simultaneously drawing a U with the other. Their ability to perform this task would actually IMPROVE after damage to which structure?

    A. corpus callosum
    B. Broca's area
    C. hippocampus
    D. Wernicke's area
    (A, Chapter 14, conceptual)

171. Which kind of people show behaviors that could be interpreted as indicating two separate consciousnesses within the same skull?

    A. patients with Williams syndrome
    B. people with schizophrenia
    C. depressed people
    D. split-brain people
    (D, Chapters 14 and 15, conceptual)

172. If someone can name objects seen in the right visual field but
    not objects in the left visual field, what part of the brain is
    most likely damaged?

    A. corpus callosum
    B. Broca's area
    C. Wernicke's area
    D. precentral gyrus
    (A, Chapter 14, conceptual)

173. Which kind of person follows literally the Biblical injunction,
    "Do not let your left hand know what your right hand is doing"?

    A. someone with narcolepsy
    B. someone with schizophrenia
    C. someone with damage to the corpus callosum
    D. someone with damage to the locus coeruleus
    (C, Chapter 14, conceptual)

174. Comparisons across animal species have so far been LEAST
    successful at determining the relationship between their brain
    structures and their

    A. intelligence.
    B. spatial memory.
    C. vision.
    D. hearing.
    (A, Chapter 14, conceptual)

175. People with Williams syndrome demonstrate that it is possible to
    have

    A. elaborate dreams despite lack of REM sleep.
    B. strong emotions despite unconsciousness.
    C. good language use despite mental retardation.
    D. explicit memory despite lack of implicit memory.
    (C, Chapter 14, conceptual)

176. The studies of deaf people who did not begin learning sign
    language (or any other language) until adolescence indicate that

    A. people must learn some language in early childhood or they
       will be forever at a deficit.
    B. deaf people are better able to learn sign language than
       hearing people are, regardless of their age and previous
       language background.
    C. anyone can learn any language equally well, regardless of age
       and previous language background.
    D. sign language depends on the right hemisphere instead of the
       left hemisphere.
    (A, Chapter 14, conceptual)

177. Specific loss of language is known as

    A. apnea
    B. agnosia
    C. adipsia
    D. aphasia
    (D, Chapter 14, factual)

178. Of the following, which is usually the result of a stroke?

    A. Williams syndrome
    B. Huntington's disease
    C. Broca's aphasia
    D. Korsakoff's syndrome
    (C, Chapter 14, factual)

179. Studies of people with dyslexia support this generalization:

    A. Corrective lenses can prevent or alleviate reading problems.
    B. Reading difficulties stem largely from conflict between the
       left and right eyes.
    C. Reading ability is highly correlated with brain to body ratio.
    D. Reading ability is closely related to attentional skills.
    (D, Chapter 14, conceptual)

180. Already achieved for Huntington's disease, but still sought for
     alcoholism, is

    A. a drug that can relieve the symptoms.
    B. a drug that can prevent further deterioration.
    C. a drug that can actually cure the underlying problem.
    D. a highly accurate presymptomatic test.
    (D, Chapters 8 and 15, conceptual)

181. What does the enzyme MAO do?

    A. It increases protein synthesis.
    B. It breaks down catecholamine neurotransmitters.
    C. It metabolizes alcohol into acetaldehyde.
    D. It enables glucose to enter cells.
    (B, Chapter 15, factual)

182. People with which of these disorders have sleep abnormalities,
     including a tendency to awaken early and a tendency to enter REM
     sleep soon after falling asleep?

    A. depression
    B. Williams syndrome
    C. myasthenia gravis
    D. fetal alcohol syndrome
    (A, Chapter 15, conceptual)

183. Which of these disorders frequently has been treated successfully with the use of bright lights?

    A. seasonal affective disorder
    B. sleep apnea
    C. mysasthenia gravis
    D. Broca's aphasia
    (A, Chapter 15, factual)

184. Which of the following is generally first diagnosed in young adults (age 30 or less)?

    A. myasthenia gravis
    B. Alzheimer's disease
    C. Parkinson's disease
    D. schizophrenia
    (D, Chapter 15, factual)

185. For therapeutic purposes, physicians attempt to raise dopamine levels for people with _____ but lower them for people with _____.

    A. mania... depression
    B. Huntington's disease... Alzheimer's disease
    C. Broca's aphasia... Wernicke's aphasia
    D. Parkinson's disease... schizophrenia
    (D, Chapters 8 and 15, conceptual)

186. Which of the following is true for both antidepressant and antipsychotic drugs?

    A. The side effects are temporary but the benefits are long lasting.
    B. They affect behavior in small doses but they affect the synapses only in large doses.
    C. They affect the synapses within hours but they affect behavior only after weeks.
    D. They increase activity at GABA synapses and decrease activity at glutamate synapses.
    (C, Chapter 15, conceptual)

187. For both depression and schizophrenia, the order of events has been

    A. first an understanding of the cause, then a search for effective treatments.
    B. first accidental discovery of drug treatments, then a search for underlying causes.
    C. almost simultaneous discovery of both the underlying causes and the effective drug treatments.
    D. first a theoretical understanding of the symptoms, then a logical deduction of what the causes and treatments must be.
    (B, Chapter 15, conceptual)

188. Which of the following would be a rude insult, equivalent to calling someone "crazy"?

    A. You're full of neurons!
    B. You've got convolutions on your brain!
    C. You're dopey on too much dopamine!
    D. You've got fluid-filled holes in your head!
    (C, Chapter 15 and others, conceptual)

189. Which of the following pairs are NOT chemically similar to each other?

    A. dopamine and norepinephrine
    B. testosterone and estradiol
    C. benzodiazepines and antidepressant drugs
    D. LSD and serotonin
    (C, various, factual)

190. Which of the following has NOT been shown to be associated with some kind of brain damage?

    A. Alzheimer's disease
    B. Huntington's disease
    C. schizophrenia
    D. sleeptalking
    (D, various, conceptual)

191. What do all of the following have in common: schizophrenia, Huntington's disease, Alzheimer's disease, Parkinson's disease, Korsakoff's syndrome?

    A. Likely to be caused by a dietary deficiency.
    B. Likely to be caused by a virus.
    C. Associated with brain damage or abnormality.
    D. Associated with more rapid than normal circadian rhythms.
    (C, various, conceptual)

192. What do all of the following have in common: early-onset Alzheimer's disease, early-onset Parkinson's disease, Huntington's disease, Williams syndrome?

    A. All are associated with more rapid than usual circadian rhythms.
    B. All are caused by exposure to viruses or toxins.
    C. All can be prevented or relieved by a change of diet.
    D. All are strongly based on genetic influences.
    (D, various, conceptual)

193.  What do all of the following have in common: sexual orientation,
      alcoholism, depression, schizophrenia?

      A. All are based strongly on genetic influences.
      B. All show genetic predispositions, but cannot be explained
         entirely in genetic terms.
      C. All are based mostly on children's learning to imitate their
         parents.
      D. All can be explained largely in terms of hormonal influences
         in adulthood.
      (B, Chapters 11 and 15, conceptual)

194.  Which of the following is probably NOT caused by a single gene?

      A. Huntington's disease
      B. schizophrenia
      C. Williams syndrome
      D. phenylketonuria (PKU)
      (B, Chapters 1, 8, 14, and 15; factual)

195.  Which of the following conditions is NOT generally associated
      with the biological marker listed with it?

      A. alcoholism - tendency to "hold one's liquor well" without
         feeling intoxicated
      B. depression - tendency to awaken earlier than usual, and
         earlier than desired.
      C. suicide - lower than normal levels of 5-HIAA in the blood
      D. schizophrenia - tendency to hyperventilate
      (D, Chapters 12 and 15, conceptual)

196.  Which of the following disorders is NOT paired correctly with a
      drug that is commonly used to treat it?

      A. Parkinson's disease - L-dopa
      B. depression - tricyclic drugs
      C. attention-deficit disorder - tranquilizers
      D. schizophrenia - antipsychotic drugs
      (C, Chapters 3 and 15, conceptual)

197.  Antidepressant drugs, antipsychotic drugs, tranquilizers,
      hallucinogens, and practically all other drugs that affect
      behavior are known to act on

      A. axons.
      B. myelin sheaths.
      C. synapses.
      D. glia cells.
      (C, various, conceptual)

198. According to one hypothesis, schizophrenia is related to deficient glutamate activity. However, giving large amounts of extra glutamate would be dangerous, because it could lead to

    A. understimulation and shrinkage of neurons.
    B. overstimulation and death of neurons.
    C. increased impulsiveness and alcoholism.
    D. increased appetite and obesity.
    (B, Chapter 5, conceptual)

199. Which of the following disorders is believed to be sometimes caused by (or aggravated by) abnormalities of the prenatal environment?

    A. fetal alcohol syndrome and schizophrenia
    B. fetal alcohol syndrome and Parkinson's disease
    C. Korsakoff's syndrome and Huntington's disease
    D. Korsakoff's syndrome and Williams syndrome
    (A, Chapters 5 and 15, conceptual)

200. Of the following generalizations, which one is still considered to be correct?

    A. Once the mammalian nervous system is mature, it can form no new neurons.
    B. A given neuron releases one and only one neurotransmitter from its terminal.
    C. The size, amplitude, and velocity of an action potential are independent of the strength of the initiating stimulus.
    D. All parts of the sensory cortex converge their information onto a single central processor.
    (C, Chapters 2, 3, 4, 5; conceptual)

201. Of the following statements, which one is nonsense?

    A. The size, amplitude, and velocity of an action potential are independent of the strength of the initiating stimulus.
    B. Given any mammalian species, if you know the volume of the Entire brain, you can predict the size of most of its component areas.
    C. Almost every behavior has a heritability greater than zero.
    D. We only use about 10 percent of our brain.
    (D, Chapters 1, 2, 5; conceptual)

202. Of the following generalizations, which one is most widely considered correct?

    A. New neurons can form in certain areas of the adult mammalian nervous system.
    B. A given neuron releases one and only one neurotransmitter from its terminals.
    C. Only humans can learn the meaning of a spoken word.
    D. Classical conditioning requires the growth or strengthening of axons from one area of the cerebral cortex to another.
    (A, Chapters 3, 5, 13, 14; conceptual)

203.  Which of the following statements is backed by solid evidence?

A. Some people are left-hemisphere people and some are right hemisphere people.
B. Some people are supertasters, some are normal tasters, and some are nontasters.
C. Some people are born with musical talent, including a different structure of the auditory cortex.
D. Some people are born with different neurotransmitters than other people.
(B, various, conceptual)

204.  Which of the following researchers is NOT correctly paired with his or her area of research?

A. Roger Sperry - endorphin synapses
B. Donald Hebb - mechanisms of learning and memory
C. Rita Levi-Montalcini - nerve growth factor
D. David Hubel and Torsten Wiesel - visual cortex
(A, various, factual)

205.  The most interesting topic in the world is

A. biological psychology.
B. something else.
C. Hint: (A) is the correct answer.
D. If I were you, I'd choose answer (A)
(A, various, giveaway)